Natural History
OF NEW ZEALAND

Natural History
OF NEW ZEALAND

NIC BISHOP

ARTWORK BY CHRIS GASKIN

Hodder & Stoughton
AUCKLAND LONDON SYDNEY TORONTO

ACKNOWLEDGEMENTS

This book would not have been possible without the help of many people. For discussion and comment on various parts of the text I would like to thank Athol Anderson, Doug Campbell, John Darby, Charles Daugherty, Nicola Grimmond, Tony Harris, Gerard Hutching, John Jillet, Peter Johnson, Graeme Loh, Alan Mark, Don Merton, Ian Millar, Keith Probert, David Saul and Graeme Taylor. I appreciate the many hours that Audrey Bishop and my wife Vivien spent reading the manuscript and suggesting valuable improvements.

I acknowledge with thanks the assistance of Newmans Coachlines.

My appreciation is also due to the people who helped with finding or photographing many of the subjects which appear in this book: Bevan and Lorrayne Alexander, Paul Barrett (Wellington Zoological Gardens), Roger Bartlett, Geoff Baylis, Ben Bell, Charles Daugherty, Wayne Eggleton (Department of Conservation), Richard Easingwood (North Campus EM Unit, University of Otago), Darryl Eason (Department of Conservation), Alison Evans (Dunedin Botanic Gardens), Dennis Fordham, Bernard Goetz, Tony Harris, Bob and Janice Jones, Chris Lalas, Joan Lemmon, Lincoln McKenzie, Otago SPCA, Portobello Marine Labs and John and Jessica Pybus. The electronic expertise of Owen Bishop and Ian Woodhead made the photography of insects in flight a reality. I would especially like to thank Ron and Gay Munro for their kind hospitality during the memorable times I have spent exploring their wetlands.

The author wishes to thank Shell New Zealand Limited for providing assistance to develop the equipment for high-speed photography of flying insects.

The publisher gratefully acknowledges the assistance of Tasman Forestry Limited and Fletcher Challenge Limited in the production of this book.

CONTRIBUTORS

Owen Bishop wrote the chapters titled 'Farmland' and 'Cities and Settlements'.

Keith Probert wrote the chapter titled 'The Sea'.

Gerard Hutching wrote pages 186 and 187, titled 'The environmental movement'.

Nic Bishop wrote all remaining text, but wishes to thank Owen Bishop for researching material for chapters titled 'The Inland Waters' and 'The Coast'.

Chris Gaskin prepared all the illustrations.

Photographic contributors, whose works have also been individually acknowledged as they appear in the book, are: page 37 DSIR Land Resources; 34 George Chance; 160 Ken Grange (New Zealand Oceanographic Institute); 21 Hocken Library; 56 J. Kendrick (Department of Conservation); 53 Geoff Moon; 18, 53, 175, 184 Rod Morris; 24, 154 Otago University; 111 John Pybus; 26, 186 Gordon Roberts; 158, 159 Dick Singleton (New Zealand Oceanographic Institute); 166, 168, 171, 173, 182 Graeme Taylor; 171 Rowley Taylor; 153, 155, 161, 172, 181 Kim Westerskov.
All unacknowledged photographs are by Nic Bishop.

First published 1992. Reprinted 1992
ISBN 0 340 548029

Book design and layout by Nic Bishop and Barbara Nielsen.
Production services by Graeme Leather.
Typeset by Typocrafters Ltd, Auckland.
Printed and bound by Kyodo Printing Co. Ltd, Singapore, for Hodder & Stoughton Ltd, 44–46 View Road, Glenfield, Auckland, New Zealand.

Photographs on pages 1: Chatham Island forget-me-not; 2: Red admiral butterfly and hebe; 7: Northland green gecko.

CONTENTS

FOREWORD

New Zealanders are fortunate to live on islands of great beauty and abundant wildlife. Land, sea and sky are important to every one of us. So too are the distinctive images of our flora and fauna. They have become symbols of our nation, from the beauty of an unfurling fern frond on a shaded valley floor to the colourful kea soaring among the mountain peaks.

New Zealand's natural history is unique. Fletcher Challenge and Tasman Forestry are proud to provide sponsorship for a book that celebrates this natural heritage. As companies involved in the use and development of physical resources, we are pleased to support a work that will also play a valuable part in the on-going debate about our environment. We all need to accept that sound research and constructive discussion are essential to achieve sensible environmental outcomes. With contributions by experts in their fields, this publication will be an authoritative resource for that discussion.

Good environmental management requires a contribution and commitment from everyone involved, from governments to business, from industry to the community and to individual people at home and at work. Sometimes global solutions will be needed for the environmental problems facing the world, but more often it is the individual's ability to act in a responsible manner that will bring about change.

The signing in 1989 of the landmark agreement The Tasman Accord by leading environment and conservation groups and Tasman Forestry Limited ensured the protection of several important areas of New Zealand's remaining native forest. The Tasman Accord can stand as a model for others.

We trust that the publication of this book will contribute to a better understanding of our natural heritage and enhance the quality of environmental debate.

Hugh Fletcher
Chief Executive Officer
Fletcher Challenge Limited

Bryce Heard
Managing Director
Tasman Forestry Limited

INTRODUCTION

When spending time outdoors, whether in a forest or on a beach, it is hard not to be inquisitive about the natural world. On noticing a new plant or animal, curiosity usually first prompts the question, 'What is its name?' But there soon follows a deeper level of enquiry: 'Why is it found here?' 'How does it cope with the problems of survival?' and 'How does it fit into the community of plants and animals around it?' This book answers these latter questions. It does not attempt to name all the different plants and animals found in each habitat. There are many excellent guide books already published that do this. Rather, it focuses on the processes and principles of natural history. The reader will learn how New Zealand's unusual natural history is thought to have come about, how plants and animals interact with one another in a community, and how organisms are adapted to their environment. Each major habitat is discussed in turn, in a way that will help the reader make sense of the diverse living world that is a forest, a beach or a wetland.

Condensing the natural history of New Zealand into fewer than 200 pages has compelled a selective approach. This has been done carefully to maintain a balance that is faithful to both the variety of life forms and the diversity of New Zealand natural communities. If this has also meant being to-the-point and sometimes simplifying complex issues, then perhaps this is welcome. Lengthy academic debates and conflicting points of view, interesting though these may be to the specialist, have been avoided for both brevity and clarity. Readers who wish to delve deeper into ecological or evolutionary theory should consult more technical texts. The widespread use of scientific jargon has also been avoided. The few technical terms it has been necessary to use are explained as they appear in the text, or in the glossary on pages 190–192. The scientific name for an organism has been given in the text if that organism has been discussed at some length, or if there is ambiguity over the common name. Should they wish, readers can also locate scientific names by consulting the index, where they are listed alongside common names.

This book also discusses the challenge of conservation. Such discussion is entirely apt in a natural history book, for the present growing interest in the natural world stems from the very realisation that it is under threat. Equally, it is true that if we are to find an enduring solution to the problems of conservation, it will only be through a better understanding of natural history.

NIC BISHOP

CHAPTER 1

THE PAST

Two hundred million years ago, world geography was vastly different from how it is today. The southern continents of South America, Africa, Australia and Antarctica were not spread separately around the globe as they are now. Instead, they were locked together in a single supercontinent we call Gondwana.

The site of New Zealand lay largely submerged off the eastern fringe of Gondwana, beneath seas scattered with active volcanic islands. For millions of years, this was how things had remained. But beneath the surface of this sea, sediments were slowly gathering. Erosion from nearby parts of Gondwana, now corresponding to Australia and Antarctica, washed silts and muds to the coast, where they settled on the seabed. Layer upon layer they accumulated, amassing in deposits many kilometres thick. At such depths, intense heat and pressure forged the soft silts and muds into hard rock, laying down the foundations for a future land. Then about 130 million years ago, they became caught in a series of earth movements that lifted them above the waves. The ancestral New Zealand land had been born.

Mount Ngauruhoe in winter

The first New Zealand

When it was raised from the sea about 130 million years ago ancestral New Zealand was a formidable landmass. It stretched from New Caledonia in the north to the Campbell Islands in the south and as far as the Chatham Islands in the east. At first it was attached to Gondwana and so inherited plants and animals from the supercontinent. At the time the region probably enjoyed a temperate climate, not unlike that of today. Lush forests of conifers (including ancestors of today's podocarps and kauri), tree ferns and horsetails stood over an understorey of ferns and mosses. Even Antarctica was mantled in greenery. These forests were undoubtedly rich with animal life, including earthworms, insects, spiders, snails and amphibians. It was, however, the time when reptiles ruled the Earth, for this was the age of the dinosaurs. They were not the only type of reptile. There were other groups, including those which later evolved to become today's lizards, turtles and crocodiles. Other animal groups, quite inconspicuous at the time, were to evolve to become the birds and modern mammals.

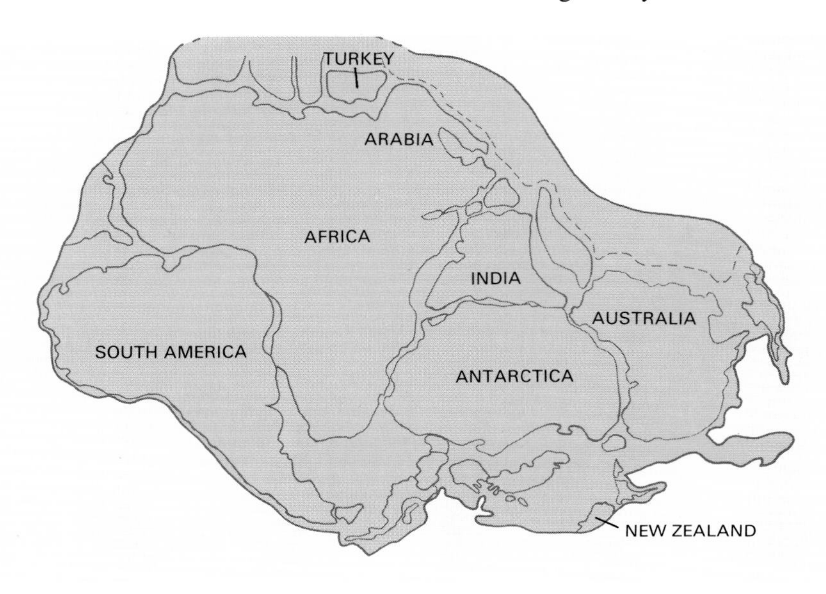

Gondwana One hundred and thirty million years ago the Southern Hemisphere was dominated by a single supercontinent called Gondwana. Australia, Antarctica, Africa and South America were joined in this supercontinent, as were some parts of the present-day Northern Hemisphere continents, including India, Arabia and Turkey. All this was changing. Earth movements had raised the young New Zealand landmass, then attached to the south-eastern fringe of Gondwana. Elsewhere, changes in the Earth's crustal system were initiating the break-up of Gondwana into the continents we are familiar with today.

Birth of the island continent

New Zealand's connection with Gondwana was not to last. Almost as soon as it was raised from the sea, earth movements started that would ultimately fragment the huge continent. Gondwana started to rift into separate continents. South America and Africa were first to break ties, giving birth to the South Atlantic Ocean and the Indian Ocean. Similar rifts opened between Australia and New Zealand, so that by 100–80 million years ago an infant Tasman Sea had crept between them.

These earth movements were happening at a critical time in the history of life, for as the continents were drifting apart, three major living groups were spreading across the globe. These were the flowering plants, the birds and the mammals. For those members that needed dry land upon which to disperse, time was running out. The appearance of new seas started to block their dispersal routes, and for New Zealand, which was beginning to detach itself completely from the other continents, this was particularly the case.

The exact origins of the flowering plants, or angiosperms, is something of a mystery. However, we know from fossil records that during the mid Cretaceous period 100 million years ago, they were undergoing a massive evolutionary radiation that would make them the most diverse of land plants. As the flowering plants distributed across Gondwana, some spread into New Zealand before it lost its land connections. The best known of these early immigrants are the southern beech trees (*Nothofagus*), which today cover large tracts of New Zealand with forest. *Nothofagus* seeds are not carried by birds and die in seawater, so they must have reached New Zealand while it was connected to Gondwana. Other early arrivals probably included some of the older families of flowering plants, among them Winteraceae, Lauraceae, Piperaceae and Proteaceae, which are today represented by horopito, tawa, kawakawa and rewarewa.

The birds evolved from reptiles and started to assert mastery of the air at about the same time as the flowering plants were spreading on land. Aided by flight, they did not find the seas that started to separate the continents insurmountable. One group, however, may have reverted to flightlessness. These were the ratites, which had become distributed, albeit by foot, across Gondwana by the time it was breaking up. They have now become isolated on the various southern continents. The ratites that once walked into New Zealand were the ancestors of the moa and possibly the kiwi. Other modern-day ratites include the rhea of South America, the ostrich of Africa, and the cassowary of Australia.

The mammals were less fortunate in their dispersal across the dividing Gondwana. They diversified and spread later than the flowering plants and birds. Marsupial mammals probably first appeared in the Americas and then colonised Antarctica and Australia. But by the time they approached New Zealand, it was too late. Earth movements about 80 million years ago had finally pulled New Zealand from Gondwana, and seas now barred the way for land migrants. Because of this critical timing the island continent of New Zealand was not dominated by mammals — until humans spread across the globe 80 million years later.

TREE OF LIFE

Life on Earth is of great antiquity. Microfossils, resembling bacteria, have been discovered in some of the oldest rocks, formed 3500 million years ago, when the planet was about 1000 million years old.

Plants and animals appeared much later, mainly within the last 1000 million years. At first they were single-celled organisms, and these were followed by multicellular forms. Simple seaweeds and sponge-like creatures may have evolved by 800 million years ago, although the few fossils discovered from these distant times are often of organisms that are hard to compare with any living today.

By 550 million years ago evolution had produced a multiplicity of different animal forms in the primitive seas, many of them ancestral to present-day living groups. Because of the sparseness of the fossil record, the exact order and timing in which these early groups appeared remains unclear. However, among them were the echinoderms, which today include starfish and sea urchins, and the molluscs, which include snails and shellfish. Other groups present at this time were the foundation from which more complex animal groups arose. Ancestors of the annelid, or segmented worms, gave rise to the arthropods, which include the insects and crustaceans. Simple chordates led to backboned animals: the fish, amphibians, reptiles, birds and mammals.

The colonisation of land, beginning about 400 million years ago, brought with it a surge of evolution as successive groups found novel ways of exploiting the new environment. Ferns, conifers and then flowering plants appeared as each evolved solutions to the problems posed by life on dry land. In a similar way, amphibians were followed by reptiles, birds and mammals.

Humans are newcomers on the tree of life. Our species, *Homo sapiens*, can claim less than a million years as its own. If we put this into a more familiar context by condensing the history of life into a 24-hour period, then we would have appeared within the final 25 seconds.

The tree of life indicates a chronological order in which some better-known plant and animal groups may have appeared, but it does not imply that each group is more successful than those before it. Even the earliest groups to appear have their modern representatives, and are often as successful and plentiful now as they have ever been. The sheer diversity today of such groups as bacteria and insects emphasises the point. All the organisms in the diagram opposite have been illustrated using modern representatives, with the exception of the drawing of the early land plant.

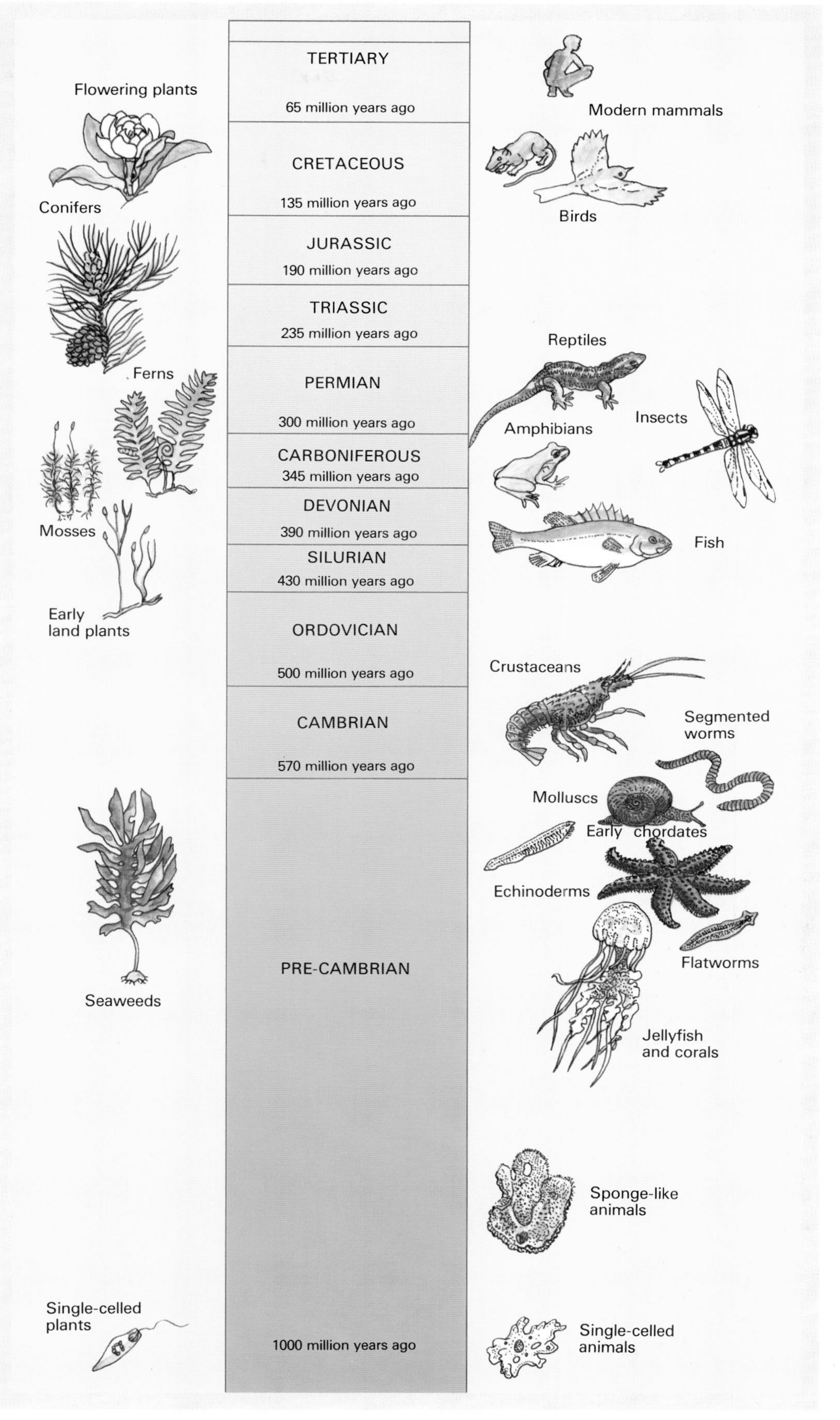

A glimpse of New Zealand's first flora and fauna

We may never know the full variety of life that once existed on the ancient continent of Gondwana. The passage of time has erased many of its life forms. New Zealand, however, because of its early separation and subsequent isolation, has retained one of the best assemblages of Gondwana life to be found.

The mixed rainforest of New Zealand, with its coniferous podocarp trees, evergreen broadleaved trees, and understorey of tree ferns, ground ferns and mosses, is probably the closest living example of the type of forest that clothed moist temperate regions of Gondwana about 80 million years ago. Some of New Zealand's major forest trees and shrubs have an ancestry that dates from this time, including the podocarps, kauri, horopito, hutu, and the beeches.

While many of New Zealand's first animal inhabitants have become extinct, including the dinosaurs, a number of modern-day representatives of Gondwanan fauna have survived. Among these are the tuatara and native frog. The forest floor abounds with

DESCENDANTS OF ANCIENT TIMES

Tuatara (*Sphenodon*)

A link with the past Tuatara (*Sphenodon*) are the most famous of New Zealand's 'archaic' animals. They belong to a very early order of reptiles, the Sphenodontida, which appeared about 230 million years ago, at the time the dinosaurs also were evolving. With the exception of tuatara, the Sphenodontida have been extinct for 60–70 million years.

Reptiles and amphibians evolved from primitive terrestrial vertebrates. Tuatara still have some primitive characteristics, such as the fish-like motion of their body when walking. Like many amphibians, tuatara also lack a penis. Fish and most amphibians reproduce in water where the sperm can easily swim to fertilise the eggs. On dry land, internal fertilisation is clearly a far more efficient process, and this is achieved in other reptiles by means of a penis. Mating tuatara, using methods akin to some amphibians, press their genital openings together so that sperm can pass from the male to the female oviduct.

A 'worm' that walks Within the damp leaf litter of New Zealand's forests lives a curious caterpillar-like creature called a peripatus. It is a hunter, feeding on insects and other small invertebrates, which it traps by spitting a sticky fluid from glands near its mouth.

The peripatus may look an unremarkable creature, yet few animals have caused more excitement to biologists. Fossils bearing a resemblance to it have been found in rocks over 500 million years old. More than this, the peripatus has a very unusual combination of characteristics, which make it the closest thing to an evolutionary link between two major divisions of the animal kingdom, the annelid worms and the arthropods. Its body has the thin, unjointed cuticle of a worm, yet the clawed feet and air-conducting tracheae of an insect. When first discovered it was hailed as a direct intermediate between worms and insects, proving the evolution of one from the other. Today it is considered to be more of an evolutionary side-branch, evolving from annelid worms at about the same time as insects. For this reason it is often placed in a phylum of its own, the Onychophora.

Peripatus

animals inherited from Gondwana times. Among them are the earthworms, some of which grow over one metre long, the moss-dwelling pelorid bugs, and the giants of the insect world, the wetas. Gondwana affinites can be found amongst many members of other groups, including the centipedes, millipedes, harvestmen, spiders, springtails, weevils, slugs and snails. Most famous of the snails are the large carnivorous snails of the Rhytididae family, some of which have shells over 9 centimetres wide. This is one of the oldest families of carnivorous land snails, whose lineage extends back some 200 million years or more.

The term 'living fossil' is often used to describe these organisms, though in the literal sense it is misleading. There are no 100 per cent primitive plants or animals. All evolve with time. Many, in fact, show a combination of primitive and more recent specialist features, which has enabled them to remain successful within their niches today. No plant or animal in New Zealand is the same as it was 80 million years ago.

Frogs that cannot croak Frogs are notoriously poor at crossing ocean barriers because they are very sensitive to salt water. The ancestors of New Zealand's three native frog species (*Leiopelma*) are therefore thought to have arrived in New Zealand before it split from Gondwana. They are considered the most primitive of all living frogs. Fossil specimens bearing similarities to them have been found in rocks about 140 million years old. Among their primitive features are tail-waggling muscles, but no tail, and fish-like vertebrae. They also lack vocal sacs and do not croak, unlike the more vociferous frogs recently introduced from Australia.

Despite their 'primitiveness', native frogs have a surprisingly specialised method of reproducing. Most frogs, although essentially land animals, must return to water to lay their eggs, which develop into free-swimming tadpoles. *Leiopelma*, however, partly avoid this need for water. The adults even lack fully webbed feet for swimming. They deposit their eggs on moist ground or in wet seepages, and the young go through part of their tadpole stage while still enclosed in the egg membrane. When the eggs of Hamilton's frog (*Leiopelma hamiltoni*) hatch, the young are virtually tailed froglets. These crawl onto the back of the adult male, who has faithfully stood guard over them, and stay on his moist body while they complete their development.

Hamilton's frog (*Leiopelma hamiltoni*)

Ancient podocarps The podocarps, which include the five giants of the forest, the totara, rimu, kahikatea, matai and miro, belong to an ancient gymnosperm family known as the Podocarpaceae. Gymnosperms reproduce via cones, or cone-like structures, and evolved before the angiosperms, which reproduce via flowers. Members of the Podocarpaceae first appeared early in the Jurassic period (190–135 million years ago) and rose to dominance on Gondwana in the Cretaceous period (135–65 million years ago) when the dinosaurs were at their zenith.

A live miro sprig, almost identical to a possible ancestor fossilised about 35 million years ago

Adrift in the Pacific

Island paradise, or island prison?

By detaching itself from the continent of Gondwana 80 million years ago and drifting into the Pacific, New Zealand has been likened to an ark, carrying a cargo of ancient plants and animals to the present day. Certainly, as New Zealand drifted away, it isolated itself somewhat from the main world stage of evolution. Its primitive Gondwanan flora and fauna were not so overwhelmed by the dramatic expansion of the flowering plants and mammals as they were on the main landmasses of the world. As a result, some of the older life forms of Gondwana, which vanished elsewhere, were able to survive in New Zealand. However, it would be simplistic to think of New Zealand as some sort of lost paradise, whose plants and animals remained undisturbed and unchanged through time. Rather, by breaking its ties with the rest of the world, New Zealand had set its own evolutionary course. Its destiny was no less subject to change and evolution. Its passage through time was to be a stormy one, subject to dramatic changes of both climate and landscape. Moreover, its passengers had to adapt to the changes or perish. There was no escape. New Zealand was as much an island prison as an island paradise.

Migrants from across the sea

When New Zealand pulled itself away from the ancient continent of Gondwana about 80 million years ago, land-distributed plants and animals were barred entry to the country. However, new plant and animal colonists could still arrive by sea and air, and do so, even to this day.

Ancestors of the short-tailed bat, rock wren, rifleman, kokako and saddleback were early winged immigrants, some, perhaps, flying across the Tasman Sea soon after it started to open. All have been in New Zealand for so long that they now have no close relatives anywhere else in the world. As it continued to drift from Gondwana, New Zealand was carried first east and then north across the Pacific, so that by the late Paleocene epoch, 58 million years ago, the Tasman Sea had opened to its present width and, by the end of the Eocene epoch, 37 million years ago, New Zealand came to occupy a latitude of about 45–40°S. Then, during a period of warm world climates about 25 million years ago, New Zealand enjoyed almost tropical times. Colonists migrated from warmer latitudes. Coral reefs appeared off the northern coastline, while coconut palms lined many shores. Many of these warmth-loving organisms later vanished as climates cooled, but some of the arrivals, such as the cabbage tree, remain today.

The return to more temperate conditions in New Zealand was caused by the movements of another Gondwana continent, Antarctica. Similar crustal movements to those that had pushed New Zealand north had separated Antarctica from Australia and pushed it south towards the pole. As the Antarctic continent slowly drifted into cooler latitudes an icecap started to extend across its surface, eventually to extinguish its rich flora and fauna.

The splitting of Antarctica from Australia had a major effect on southern weather patterns and ocean currents, which were now able to circle the isolated polar continent. Significantly for New Zealand, these changes brought not only a more temperate climate, but also the birth of the Roaring Forties that started to blow

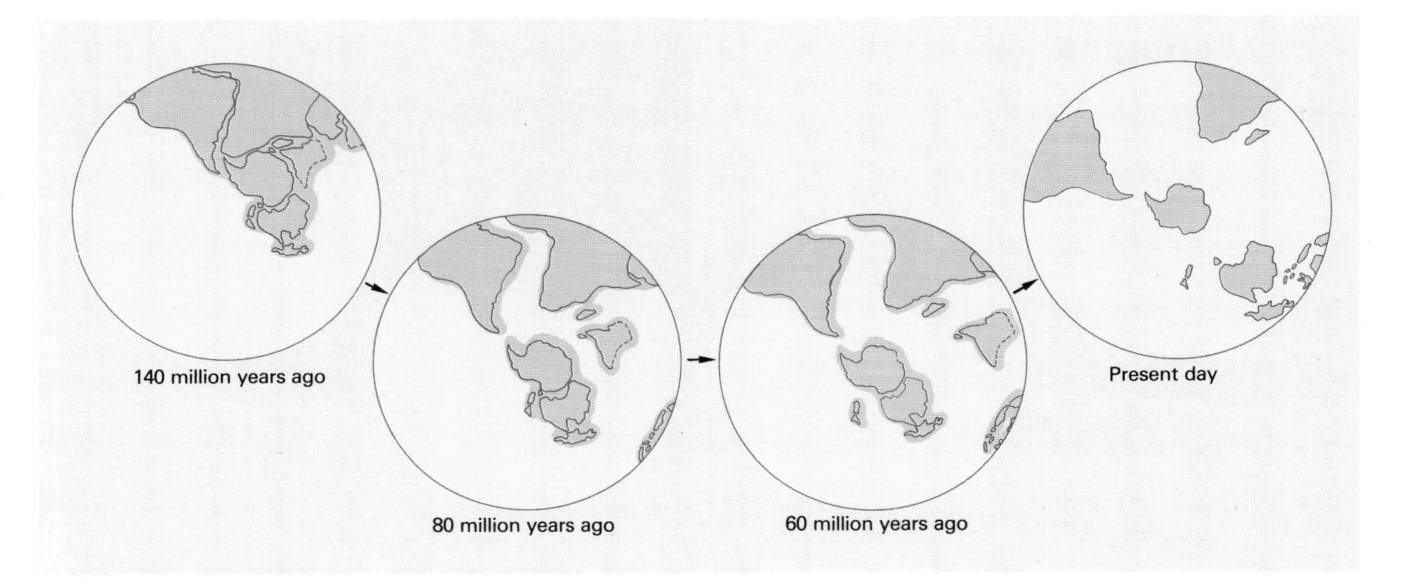

Birth of the continents
The break-up of Gondwana, which started about 130 million years ago, saw the Southern Hemisphere continents drift to their present-day positions. First to part from Gondwana were South America and Africa. India also pulled away, later to drift into and join the Asian Continent. New Zealand parted from Gondwana about 80 million years ago, as the Tasman Sea opened up. Antarctica and Australia were the last to break ties. Starting about 55 million years ago, Australia drifted north into steadily warming climates, while Antarctica moved south to ultimately become entombed by ice.

about 20 million years ago, and remain a dominant feature of the climate today. These westerly winds brought with them a whole new wave of migrants, borne by the wind from Australia. Plants with airborne seeds have been particularly favoured, as have winged insects and birds. Birds that reached New Zealand early on include ancestors of the takahe and kakapo, both of which became flightless. Very recent arrivals include the waxeye, spur-winged plover, welcome swallow and Australian coot.

THE SWEEPSTAKE DISPERSAL WINNERS

Since New Zealand's isolation from Gondwana, new immigrant plants and animals have had to contend with crossing an ocean barrier to get here. Populating an island from across the seas involves a good measure of luck, such as a storm blowing in the right direction, or the landfall of a raft of floating vegetation carrying a cargo of small animals. For this reason it is called sweepstake dispersal.

Winners of sweepstake dispersal share certain characteristics that help them carry out their journey. For this reason the types of plants and animals found on islands do not represent the normal cross-section found elsewhere. High on the list of sweepstake winners are plants with wind-distributed seeds, either with spore-like seeds, for example ferns and orchids, or those with a 'parachute' of fluffy hairs, for example willowherbs and members of the daisy family. Other winners are plants with bird-distributed seeds. These can have either hooked seeds, like the bidibidis, which are carried on feathers, or edible berried seeds, like the coprosmas, which are eaten and carried in the digestive tract of birds.

Among animals, flying birds and insects are sweepstake winners. Also included are bats. Ancestors of New Zealand's short-tailed bat and long-tailed bat both flew here after it split from Gondwana. Lowest on the list of winners are large land animals. During the 80 million years of New Zealand's isolation the only land vertebrates thought to have arrived are the ancestors of the skinks, and possibly the geckos. (Alternative evidence suggests geckos may have reached New Zealand before it broke with Gondwana.) Both these lizards are sufficiently hardy to allow island hopping on drifting rafts of vegetation.

While crossing the ocean to reach New Zealand represents one hurdle, becoming established successfully on arrival is another. An immigrant may find conditions in the new land too hot or too cold for survival, or perhaps too shady or exposed. Plants with specialised flowers may not find the specialised insects to pollinate them. Animals with a specialised diet may not find the food plants they like. New Zealand's cross-section of plants and animals is therefore very different from that of other countries, because it combines an unusual ancestral stock, including the tuatara and podocarp trees, which are left over from the time New Zealand was attached to Gondwana, and an extremely select assortment of more recent 'sweepstake winners'.

The few plants and animals that do win the sweepstakes, however, often find a land filled with opportunity. The chances are that the predators and competitors they had to deal with in their homeland are no longer present. Their new-found environment may present new opportunities that stimulate them to evolve and diversify into a number of different species adapted to these opportunities.

This process, when a small ancestral group diversifies and evolves into a number of different species, is called adaptive radiation. For example, there was possibly one species of gecko which originally colonised New Zealand, and perhaps two species of skink. These have now evolved over 40 species, each adapted to its own particular niche. Some, for example, are restricted to forest while others frequent open ground, some are larger than others and so are able to eat different foods, and some are active by day while others are active by night.

The same process has taken place among some plant groups. New Zealand's hebes, celmisias and coprosmas are represented by an unusually high number of species compared with other countries. Each group probably diversified from far fewer ancestral species, taking advantage of new habitats as they were created during past changes of climate and topography. All now have members in habitats from coastal cliffs to alpine herbfields.

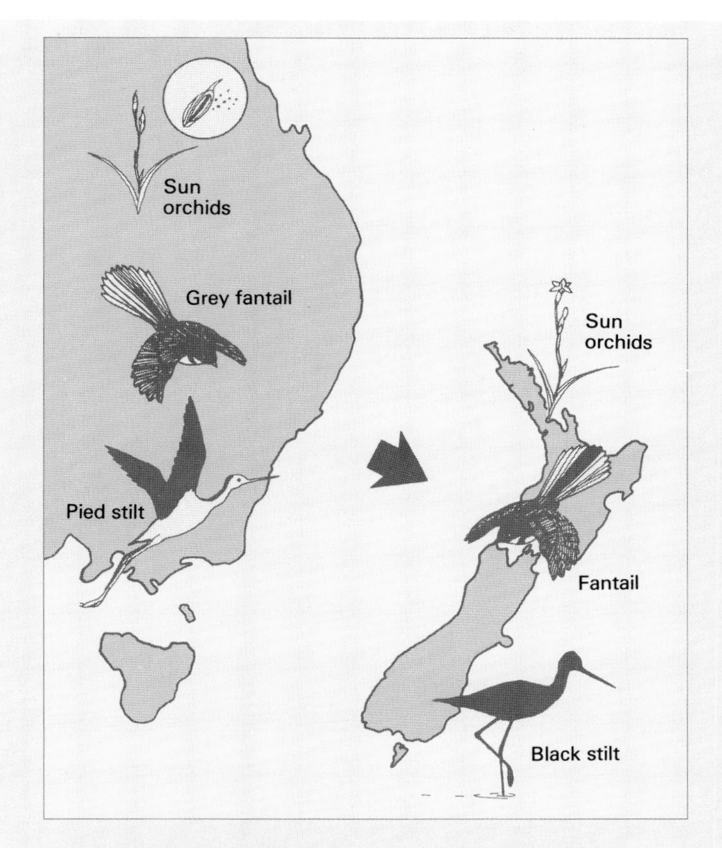

Trans-Tasman dispersal
Many sweepstake dispersal winners have flown or been blown to New Zealand from Australia, aided by the prevailing westerly winds. Trans-Tasman ties are easiest to trace for living things that have colonised New Zealand in the recent past, and so have not had time to become too dissimilar from their Australian relatives. Many native orchids, which have wind-borne seeds, have close relatives in Australia. Close ties also exist for many native birds, such as the tomtit, harrier and kingfisher, which have probably arrived since the onset of the Ice Age. New Zealand's fantails, for example, are subspecies of the Australian grey fantail (*Rhipidura fuliginosa*). The black stilt (*Himantopus novaezelandiae*) evolved from ancestors of the Australian pied stilt (*Himantopus himantopus*). Interestingly, the pied stilt has repeated the journey and although now visibly distinct from the black stilt, both birds can still interbreed.

Building the modern landscape

The changing shape of New Zealand
The familiar outline of New Zealand today will exist for only a brief episode in geological time. The forces of plate tectonics and the relentless action of erosion have seen the country's configuration change continually through the ages. Thirty-five million years ago, the land had been worn down virtually to sea-level. Then earthforces lifted it once more, culminating in the creation of the Southern Alps during the last 2–3 million years. These processes are still at work, as frequent earthquakes testify. The New Zealand landscape is changing as fast now as it ever has.

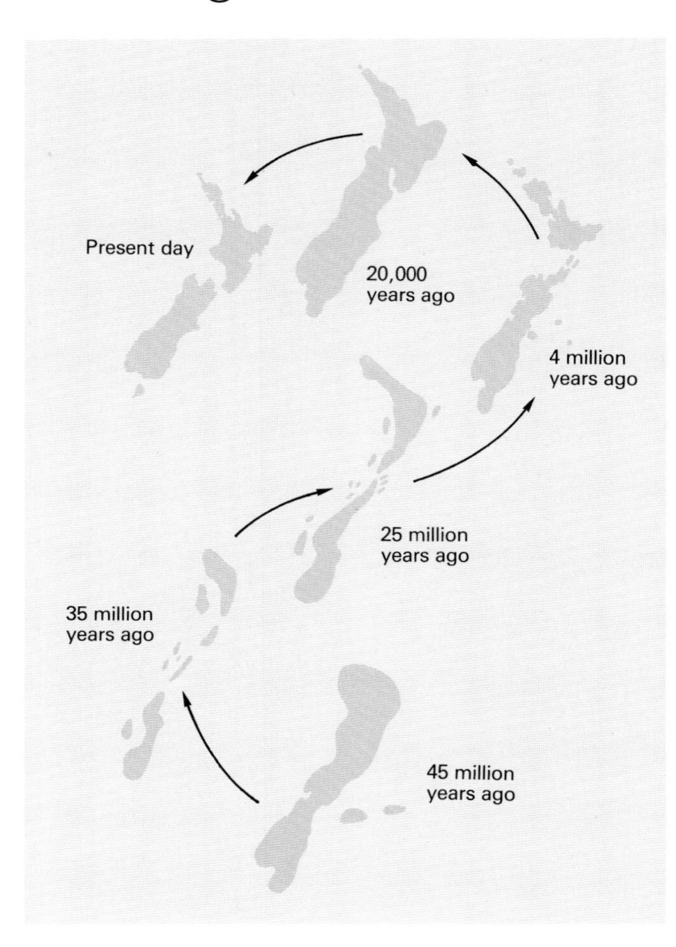

The New Zealand of 35 million years ago was a vastly different land to the one that first separated from Gondwana. Erosion had reduced it to an archipelago of low-lying islands, often covered with swamp forest and peaty bogs. The once vast island continent which had been raised from the sea almost 100 million years before was on the verge of disappearing again beneath its waves.

Reprieve came at the eleventh hour. Changes in the arrangement of the Earth's crustal system meant that New Zealand came to lie across the boundary between two crustal plates, called the Indian-Australian Plate and the Pacific Plate. As these two plates slid past and over each other, the land was shattered and lifted into mountains once more. At first the pace of mountain building was slow, but 2–3 million years ago earthforces started to thrust up the modern geography of New Zealand. As the mountains rose they created new habitats and these were filled by native plants that evolved to suit the changed environments, as well as the occasional migrant brought by the westerly winds.

However, no sooner had the alps started to rise than they came under the erosive attack of moving glaciers. At the start of the Pleistocene epoch, 2.4 million years ago, falling world temperatures initiated the Ice Age. Storms from the west and south buried the young alps with snow. Glaciers clawed out whole mountainsides, and icy fingers reached towards the lowlands. Grassland, shrubland and herbfield, which are today typical of alpine and subalpine regions, spread out across the lowlands, while forest existed in sheltered pockets. Many plants and animals retreated to refuge areas, which offered the mildest climates. Some of these refuge areas were created when falling sea levels exposed areas of former seabed, particularly in parts of coastal north-west Nelson and Southland. Extensive podocarp forests probably only existed north of Auckland, though even this was not warm enough for some plant species, which were forced into extinction.

The Ice Age was not a period of continuous glaciation. Cold glacial periods were interspersed with warm interglacial periods, when the climate was similar to the present day. Between these extremes, life migrated back and forth between lowlands and the mountains. Species became isolated, and then intermingled again as they moved across the landscape. These huge transitions brought the force of change to bear upon life, and from it rose the evolution of many new species, such as seen in the rich diversity of alpine plants today.

About 12,000 years ago the ice sheets retreated once more, heralding the present period of warmer weather. As the temperatures rose, forest began to repossess the land. The podocarps and other plants, whose seeds are distributed by birds or wind, established themselves rapidly in the wake of retreating ice. By 8000 years ago, podocarp forest covered much of New Zealand.
The beeches, which now dominate large forest areas, were very much slower to assert themselves. Their seeds are not carried far by the wind, and not carried by birds at all. They therefore had to contend with the slow task of spreading into areas where podocarp forest had already established itself. A change to seasonally cooler, drier climates a few thousand years ago is thought to have given beeches a competitive edge, though they are still making little headway into regions such as the South Island's West Coast.

The Ice Age had changed the face of New Zealand. Not only had the glaciers left their imprint upon the landscape, the climatic extremes had transformed the natural history. Some species evolved new forms, while many others became extinct. How many disappeared we do not know, but fossil records from before the Ice Age suggest a 'lost flora' no longer in existence. It seems remarkable that some of New Zealand's older inhabitants, such as the tuatara, kiwi and moa, had survived, but they were soon to face an even greater ecological trauma — the coming of humans.

ICE AGES

Throughout most of its history, the Earth has enjoyed a warmer and more equable climate than at present. However, these mild conditions have been punctuated at different times by Ice Ages. Geological evidence has been discovered for an early Ice Age during the Precambrian, more than 570 million years ago. A particularly prolonged Ice Age, spanning about 100 million years, ended at the close of the Permian, 235 million years ago. The Ice Age referred to in this book began about 2.4 million years ago, during the Pleistocene.

The glacial advance of an Ice Age occurs when summer temperatures are not warm enough to melt the snow and ice that accumulate during winter. As a result, large ice sheets develop in polar and mountain regions, spreading across the surrounding lands.

What triggers the initial cooling that heralds an Ice Age is the subject of much debate. Among the suggestions are changes in solar energy, variations in the Earth's orbit, changes in the Earth's angle of inclination to the sun, continental drift, and various combinations of these and other factors. Equally controversial is whether the recent Pleistocene Ice Age has finished. The Pleistocene Ice Age has been marked by a series of cold glacial periods, and warm interglacials when the ice receded. It is quite possible that we are in the middle of an interglacial, and that within the next few thousand years, cooling temperatures will usher in another glacial advance.

New habitats
The flora and fauna of New Zealand have faced enormous changes of habitat during past upheavals of climate and topography. Thirty-five million years ago, low-lying islands probably supported extensive swamp forests (left). By 1 million years ago, active mountain building had created new alpine habitats, while cooling world temperatures had launched the country into the Ice Age, which would sorely test the survival of lowland species (below).

CHANGE AND ISOLATION — CATALYSTS OF EVOLUTION

Even though we may not be aware of it within the short span of our lives, the physical world is forever changing. Climates get cooler or warmer and mountains are built or destroyed. These changes continually pose problems for living organisms, to which they adapt by the process of evolution.

While change can be considered a motive force for evolution, it is isolation which primarily leads to the divergence of species. When a species is separated into two populations that can no longer interbreed, both evolve in different directions according to the different environmental changes they face. In time the two populations become so distinct from each other that if they were allowed to mix again they would no longer be able to interbreed. At this point they have become two separate species.

Change and isolation in combination have had a powerful influence at different times in New Zealand's biological past. They came to bear about 30 million years ago, when the land had been eroded to scattered islands, and communities of plants and animals became separated from one another. Among the consequences were perhaps the divergence of the moas into a number of distinct types and the evolution of certain groups of present-day land snails.

The same forces came to bear during the Ice Age.

During cold glacial periods, alpine vegetation spread across large areas of lowland, while whole communities of warmth-loving plants and animals were isolated in areas where conditions were mildest. During warmer interglacial periods the tables were turned. Warmth-loving plants and animals spread back across the lowlands, while the alpine species retreated into the cool mountains, where they became isolated on separate ranges. The change and isolation caused some organisms to become restricted in distribution, or even extinct. Others, from alpine celmisias to lowland geckos, evolved numerous localised species and subspecies in different parts of New Zealand. The greatest concentrations of these occur in the southern and northern ends of the South Island and the north of the North Island, which are thought to have provided major refuge areas during the Ice Age.

Keas The cool climate of the Ice Age put New Zealand's flora and fauna under extraordinary evolution pressure. Some species became extinct while others evolved new forms to cope with the changes. The kea, a parrot of the cool high country, developed from ancestors that once inhabited warm lowlands.

Flightless birds

Few creatures arouse more curiosity than New Zealand's flightless birds. The very words seem a contradiction in terms. Just how did such animals come to be?

New Zealand's most famous flightless birds are the kiwis and the extinct moas. Both belong to a primitive group of birds known as ratites, which are thought to have become flightless on the ancient supercontinent of Gondwana. Why ratites lost the power of flight is a mystery lost in the mists of time. Perhaps as ground-dwelling animals in cooler parts of Gondwana their warm-bloodedness and insulating coat of feathers gave them an evolutionary advantage compared with the then dominant dinosaurs.

Without the means of aerial dispersal, ratites spread across the supercontinent on foot before it broke up. Today, members of the group isolated on various Gondwana fragments include the African ostrich, the South American rhea, and the Australian cassowary and emu. If the ancestors of moas and kiwis walked into New Zealand, as is assumed, this must have happened before it too broke from Gondwana. Recent studies, however, suggest kiwis are of more recent origin than moas, their lineage dating back perhaps only 40 million years. If this is so, how the kiwi's ancestors reached New Zealand is a puzzle, for the country was well and truly isolated by then.

ROD MORRIS

A flightless parrot Without mammalian predators to contend with in the forests of old, the ancestors of the kakapo (*Strigops habroptilus*) safely gave up flight for a ground-dwelling life. However, they were not completely spared from carnivores. Now-extinct species of hawk and eagle once hunted them from the air. But the kakapo was artful at hiding from their searching eyes. It evolved its cryptic moss-green plumage and the instinct to freeze when danger threatened. It also took to feeding under cover of darkness. Sadly, none of these tactics is of any use against the predatory mammals that humans have now introduced — mammals hunt by scent and often at night.

Some scientists consider that the kiwi may have originally flown to New Zealand. Certainly, other flightless birds — the takahe, kakapo and weka — flew to New Zealand after it had separated from Gondwana. Once here, though, they abandoned their powers of flight. It may seem strange that, having evolved the elaborate apparatus necessary for flight, birds should ever want to do away with it. But flight puts a great demand on a bird's energy requirement, influencing both the amount and type of food that it must eat. In compensation, flight provides a tremendous means of escaping predators. Originally these were the dinosaurs and later the mammals. Flight also enables birds to utilise with ease relatively inaccessible food sources, such as flying insects and fruit in the forest canopy. If, however, there are no predators on the ground to fly away from, and there is plenty of food in easy reach, then it is an easier option to do away with wings.

This was exactly the situation that birds found when they first arrived in New Zealand. Because it had separated from Gondwana before mammals could arrive, there were no ground-dwelling mammalian predators or herbivores for them to contend with. As a consequence some birds abandoned flight completely and took up life on the forest floor — in effect, taking on the normal role of mammals. Many others, such as the kokako, saddleback, extinct bush wren and extinct native thrush, retained partial flight but often foraged near the forest floor.

Feathered browsers

Perhaps the greatest advantage of flightlessness is that it has enabled birds to take on the role of herbivores, a position occupied on other continents by mammals such as sheep, horses and kangaroos. Green plant matter is low in nutritive value, so herbivores must eat considerable amounts. This means needing to have large digestive tracts to process all the material and hence being heavy bodied. Only birds that no longer need to fly can evolve the large body size and sedentary lifestyle to make best use of such a low-energy diet.

The takahe (*Porphyrio mantelli*) is the largest of New Zealand's flightless herbivorous birds alive today. At one time takahe were widespread, but now they are restricted to parts of Fiordland. Here they inhabit the bush edge, and browse among alpine tussocks and celmisias, using their large beak and powerful build to pluck out the most nutritive younger growth.

Perhaps even more curious than the takahe is the kakapo (*Strigops habroptilus*), a member of the parrot family. To anyone who has marvelled at the bright and noisy gatherings of parrots in Australia, nothing would be more unexpected than this bird. Unlike its gregarious relatives, the kakapo has evolved a solitary, nocturnal ground-dwelling existence and its body size has

Losing flight The increased body weight that accompanies the evolution of a vegetarian diet is striking when the takahe (*Porphyrio mantelli*) (far left) is compared with the pukeko (*Porphyrio porphyrio*) (left), a closely related bird, which has been in New Zealand only a short time relative to the takahe. The pukeko probably resembles the ancestors of the takahe when they first arrived in New Zealand, before becoming a herbivore and losing the power of flight. The pukeko feeds on both plants and animals and is a capable flyer.

increased so that it is now the largest of all parrots. The kakapo eats foliage, roots, berries and seeds from a wide range of plants, sometimes climbing trees to get its food.

The kakapo, like the takahe, has become reduced to a very small population. Nevertheless, it has fared better than other flightless birds that once inhabited New Zealand. Before the arrival of humans led to their extinction, New Zealand abounded with flightless species. Among them was a large goose (*Cnemiornis*) and a rail-like bird, the adzebill, which both stood about one metre high. Moas, however, were undoubtedly the most impressive. Their sheer size demanded huge quantities of herbage. Moa remains have shown that they fed on a wide range of foliage and berries, ripping leaves, twigs and fruit from shrubs and small trees. This was ground down in their digestive tract by up to 5 kilograms of gizzard stones, which the moa also swallowed. Birds, unlike mammals, do not have teeth for chewing.

Browsing was not the only mammal-type activity that flightless birds took on. The kiwi, which feeds on small insects and other invertebrates within and beneath the forest leaf litter, shares a similar diet to that of hedgehogs and shrews. It even shares similar night-adapted senses, including a good sense of smell, sensory whiskers and poor eyesight. The weka (*Gallirallus australis*) is an opportunist eater, feeding on a variety of animal and vegetable matter, as a large rat might do, including fruit, insects, eggs, chicks and lizards.

THE RATITES

Kiwis and moas belong to the ratites, an ancient group of flightless birds that dates back to the time of Gondwana.

Kiwis have a nocturnal lifestyle, foraging on the forest floor with their long beaks for insects and other invertebrates. There are three species today: the brown kiwi (*Apteryx australis*), the great spotted kiwi (*A. haastii*) and the little spotted kiwi (*A. owenii*). Moas were herbivores, browsing on vegetation. Before humans arrived there were about 12 species. These varied from the massive *Dinornis giganteus*, which stood over 2 metres tall and weighed about 200 kg, to smaller species, such as *Megalapteryx didinus*, which was about 70 cm tall and weighed around 20 kg. Different species browsed at different levels according to their height and may have preferred different habitats, such as scrub, forest or grassland.

The fatal impact

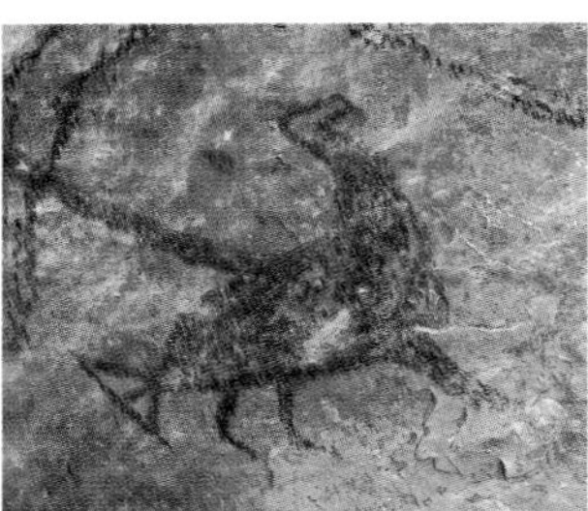

Early life Five hundred years ago, moa hunters in South Canterbury left a poignant record of early life, drawn on limestone overhangs where they once camped. Among the drawings are stylised pictures of people and a huge bird of prey in flight, probably the extinct giant eagle which preyed on the large flightless birds of the time. Other sites contain drawings of extinct moas, as well as other creatures that are hard to decipher.

The first people

Two million years ago, while New Zealand was in the grip of the Ice Age, a new creature was evolving on the African plains. At first, its numbers were limited by the same natural laws as apply to other animals, and judging by its limited physique and peculiar gait, one might have wondered how long it would survive. Then it learnt to adjust those natural laws to suit itself. It learnt to produce its own shelter, to hunt and cook new foods, to fashion tools and to trade. By about 100,000 years ago this creature had spread into Europe and Asia. Ten thousand years ago there were 10 million of them. Two thousand years ago, with the assistance of agriculture, numbers had swollen to 300 million. The human species, *Homo sapiens*, had started to exert its will upon the world.

We do not know exactly when the first humans trod the shore of New Zealand, or where they came from. Evidence suggests that people first arrived in the tenth century, from islands of the Marquesas, Cooks or Society groups. These Polynesian colonists, the ancestors of the Maori, were skilled sea people and fishermen. They had learnt to domesticate plants and animals for their needs. However, this new land abounded with large and relatively defenceless flightless birds. Its coasts and rivers teemed with fish, shellfish and seals. The first colonists, therefore, adopted a largely hunting and gathering lifestyle to reap this bounty.

Soon to be harvested were the moas. Their large size made them an ideal source of food. Archaeological investigations of early hunting encampments indicate that moas were both abundant and easy to catch. Incompletely butchered animals have been found, with some body parts discarded, as if the hunters could afford to be choosy about which portions to eat.

Other birds, too, have been found in the kitchen middens of the moa hunters, including now-extinct species of swan, flightless goose and the adzebill. Within a few hundred years of human occupation, New Zealand's large birds were rapidly disappearing. Their slow reproductive rate could not keep pace with the hunting pressure. Dogs (kuri) and polynesian rats (kiore), which the colonisers had brought with them, probably exacerbated the situation by interfering with the young, as well as with other smaller ground animals. Added to this, the birds were losing large areas of their habitat. A steadily drying climate had made forests east of the Southern Alps tinder dry, and fires lit by the hunters incinerated vast tracts of forest. Similar fires destroyed forests in parts of the central and eastern North Island.

Within 500 years of the first Polynesian arrival, the moas had all but vanished, as had the flightless goose, *Aptornis* and many other unusual birds. A giant eagle (*Harpagornis moorei*), which once preyed on these large birds, was also doomed. Many other animals, such as the tuatara, takahe and kakapo, were to become restricted in their range.

The arrival of Europeans

Despite their simple technology and the handful of plants and animals they brought to New Zealand, the coming of the Maori had far-reaching effects on the local ecology. The next colonisers, the Europeans, arrived with even greater means of change at their disposal. In the wake of Captain Cook's early visits in the 1770s came sealers and whalers. In the 30 or so years they worked the region, animal stocks were so depleted that some populations have still barely recovered. Next came the immigrants, who started arriving in earnest from the 1840s. With dreams of creating an antipodean England, they sought to replace the natural ecology with one based on their motherland. Forests were logged for timber or burnt, and then converted to farmland. Crops and pasture were sown into the ashes, along with inevitable weed species. The urge to break in the land was so great that early farmers had by law to 'improve' the land. Often this meant burning off marginal lands which subsequently reverted to scrub. In some instances poor management of high country brought erosion and severe flooding.

As part of the settlement programme, the rapidly changing landscape was populated with introduced animals, sometimes with little consideration for the native ecology. Some animals were brought for farming purposes (dogs, sheep, cattle, horses), while others were introduced for sport (deer, chamois, rabbits, pheasants), or sentiment (cats, sparrows, thrushes, blackbirds, starlings). Then there were the accidental introductions. The Norway rat and ship rat arrived as stowaways on some of the earliest ships to drop anchor. At least 175 mammal and bird species had been imported by the start of this century. Not all introductions became established. Among bizarre failures were moose, bandicoots, camels and gnu. Meanwhile, others were so successful that they became pests. Rabbits, introduced for sport, so effectively denuded the newly planted grazing pastures that stoats, ferrets and weasels were imported to try to check them.

The stoats, weasels and ferrets played havoc with the native fauna, as did the dogs, cats and rats before them. Poorly flighted or flightless native birds were almost defenceless against such predators. After millions of years of evolution in the absence of carnivorous mammals, many no longer had adequate means of

HOCKEN LIBRARY

Clearing the forest Kauri logging in Northland. Armed with technology the Europeans had a swift and premeditated impact on New Zealand.

escape, nor even the appropriate behaviour to deal with introduced predators. For instance, the flightless kakapo's habit of freezing when danger threatened simply made it all the more vulnerable. Ground-dwelling lizards and insects also suffered. One species after another declined and vanished, some almost before they were known to exist. One poignant tale is of the tiny Stephens Island wren, as told by W.R.B. Oliver:

> The history of this species, so far as human contact is concerned, begins and ends with the exploits of a domestic cat. In 1894 the lighthouse keeper's cat brought in eleven specimens, which came into the hands of H. H. Travers . . . A few more captures were made and duly reported by the cat and then no more birds were brought in. It is evident, therefore, that the cat which discovered the species also immediately exterminated it.

The settlers themselves were hardly less to blame. Sportsmen and bird collectors eagerly shot large numbers of the now-extinct native quail and huia.

The native vegetation was equally ill equipped for the onslaught of introduced herbivores. The Australian possum, released to start a fur trade, has found New Zealand's forests like a delectable salad, compared with those of its home country. Because New Zealand trees have never experienced large, sedentary canopy herbivores, many lack the wealth of toxic compounds which Australian trees have evolved to deter excessive browsing. Palatable trees such as fuchsia, rata and five finger have been browsed to destruction in some areas. In the post-war years, booming deer numbers grazed down the forest understorey, preventing regeneration, while chamois and thar denuded alpine regions. Only with recent control efforts has some of the damaged plant life been able to recover.

The massive changes of habitat caused by Europeans have permitted some species to colonise New Zealand from across the Tasman Sea. For instance, with the expansion of farmland, the spur-winged plover, an Australian bird of pasturelands, has been able to establish itself. Some native animals have also benefited from the changes in habitat. The large-scale cultivation of pastureland has been a boon to some native grass-eating insects. The grass grub and porina caterpillar have become the bane of pastoral farmers' lives. The harrier hawk, which hunts open country, has also enjoyed the expansion of its range, not to mention a new diet of small introduced mammals.

The brief 1000 years of human occupation caused perhaps more disruption to New Zealand's natural history than the 80 million years which had preceded it. Within this short span the country's forest cover had been reduced from 80 per cent to 20 per cent, and over 50 per cent of the bird life that was unique to New Zealand had vanished. Today, many unusual species, such as the takahe, kokako and kakapo, hover at the brink of extinction, their future dependent on continual vigilance by conservation workers.

CHAPTER 2

THE MOUNTAINS

The mountain environment tests life to extremes. Freezing temperatures, intense sunlight, thin soils and brutal winds must be endured, often all within the space of a single day. Added to this, plants and animals are granted but a preciously short season in which to grow and reproduce.

These problems have far from overwhelmed life. Evolution has sought survival solutions for the hardy alpine inhabitants. Feathered tussock and musky herbfield clothe the mountain slopes. On each fine day the air fills with the flutter of tiny insects, impelled by the need to mate or feed. Even at heights where the privations would seem too heavy to bear, life prevails in pockets. Each small irregularity where the force of the wind is broken and each small seepage where water flows, is clustered with tiny plants.

Neither have the hardships denied variety to the alpine inhabitants. Differences of altitude and shelter, soil and the discrete identity of separate ranges make the mountains an enormously varied place to live, and nature has filled them with a startling diversity of life. Almost half of all native plant species are found here, many of which astound with the fragile beauty of their blooms as much as the tenacity of their growth.

Victoria Range, Westland

Surviving extremes

Coping with cold

The higher you climb a mountain, the thinner the air becomes. Air at high altitude is therefore more transparent to solar radiation than air at sea-level. Because of this it absorbs less sunlight as heat and remains cold, while letting more sunlight through to the ground, which warms rapidly. This produces extremes of temperature between sun and shade, even over short distances. The exact spot a seed germinates is therefore critical to its future. A plant growing on the sunny side of some rocks may be thriving in the warmth while its neighbour on the shady side will be struggling with several degrees of frost.

Unfortunately, plants cannot choose where their seeds will fall. They must therefore have methods to cope with the cold. They do this in two ways. One is to be tolerant of cold. The metabolic systems of alpine plants have evolved so that they can photosynthesise and grow, albeit slowly, at much lower temperatures than their lowland relatives. The other way is to make the best of the precious warmth generated whenever sunlight is absorbed by rock or foliage. This plants do by avoiding the cold wind and crouching close to the shelter of the earth. Here there is a blanket of calm air, which may be warmed several degrees by heat from the sunlit ground. The greater the altitude and the more exposed the situation, the lower the vegetation becomes, hugging as best it can the warmer microclimate that exists at ground level.

Alpine plants often add to this microclimate effect themselves. Many have dense leaf canopies that trap the warm air, rather than let it blow away in the wind.

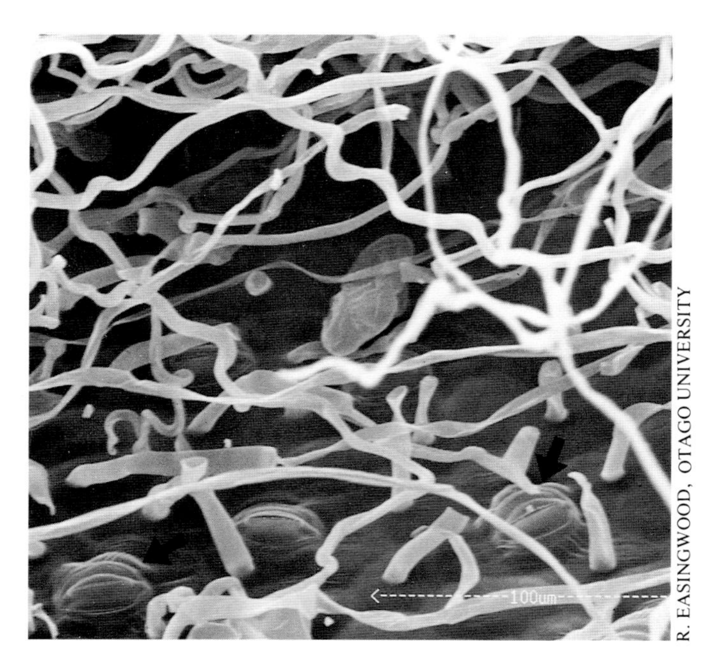

R. EASINGWOOD, OTAGO UNIVERSITY

The tomentum Magnified about 500 times, the felty layer covering the underside of a *Celmisia* leaf appears like an inside view of a densely woven carpet. This is called the tomentum, and its purpose is to minimise water loss from the stomatal pores (arrowed) seen on the leaf surface. The tangle of hairs traps a layer of dead-still air at the leaf surface so that precious water molecules are not blown away by the wind. Their only way to escape is to diffuse by a slow and tortuous path through the tomentum's maze of coiled strands.

Some plants go even further by covering their leaves with a layer of fine hair. This completely stills the air close to their surfaces, insulating the plants from extremes of temperature outside. These warmth-trapping tactics work with remarkable effect. On a sunny day, the leaves and growing tips of some alpine plants, snug within a compact canopy and blanket of felty hairs, will be as much as 10–15 degrees Celsius warmer than the surrounding air.

Winning against drying winds

Water shortage might seem a surprising problem for alpine plants to bear. After all, mountains are hardly rainless places. However, the air at high altitudes, because it is cool and thin, carries less water vapour than at sea-level. So it can be quite drying, particularly when plants are exposed to intense sunlight and strong winds. Obtaining enough water can be an even bigger problem. Mountain soils are notoriously thin and rocky, so they do not hold much moisture. Added to this, plant roots become physiologically inefficient at absorbing water when they are cold. Worst of all, if the soil freezes, it becomes impossible for them to absorb water at all. The winter months are therefore the driest ones for alpine plants. The lucky individuals are those buried by snow. They, at least, can rest the winter through in chilly dormancy, sheltered from the drying wind and sun above. For taller plants that protrude above the snowpack it is often a different matter. While their roots lie 'benumbed' in frigid soils, their exposed shoots slowly shrivel with desiccation.

Alpine plants protect themselves from water loss with much the same technique as they protect themselves from heat loss; by trapping still air near their leaves. The two things go together, because wind not only draws away warm air from the plant, it also carries away water vapour. More than that, the loss of water vapour by wind has a cooling effect of its own. This is the same effect that causes our bodies to chill faster in the wind when we are wet than when we are dry. Avoiding wind therefore has a double bonus. So, by growing close to the shelter of the ground and having a dense canopy of leaves, often insulated by tiny hairs, plants hold on to both moisture and warmth.

Alpine plants also minimise water loss by covering their leaves with an extra thick waxy waterproof coat, called the cuticle. This is what gives the leaves of the Mt Cook lily their characteristically shiny surface. Drop some water onto a leaf and you will see it sit on the surface like a ball, just as raindrops do on a waxed car bonnet. A thick cuticle might be enough to minimise water loss all on its own but for one thing — all plants must exchange air with the surrounding atmosphere.

Leaves need to absorb carbon dioxide in order to produce sugars by photosynthesis, and they do this through tiny pores called stomata. As carbon dioxide enters the plant through these pores, water vapour inevitably leaks out. The stomata are therefore a prime site for loss of water vapour, and it is no surprise that many alpine plants have gone to great lengths to afford them protection.

One way they do this is by having all their stomata on the shady underside of the leaf and then covering them with a particularly dense but porous layer of woolly hair called a tomentum. The tomentum slows water loss by making sure each molecule of water vapour has to find its way through a virtual forest of leaf hairs in order to escape to the outside air. Other plants make the escape route for water vapour tortuous by sinking their stomata into leaf pits or furrows lined with tiny hairs. The snow tussocks (*Chionochloa*), whose tall, thin leaves are particularly exposed to dry winds, use this method to protect their stomata from water loss. In fact they can go a step further. If particularly short of water, some snow tussocks curl their leaves into tight cylinders with the stomata on the inside where they become almost completely sealed off from the outside air. Such a situation may not last, for the long and thin leaves of snow tussocks are ideal for drawing dew from the air on damp nights or foggy days, allowing them to obtain a supply of moisture even if it doesn't rain!

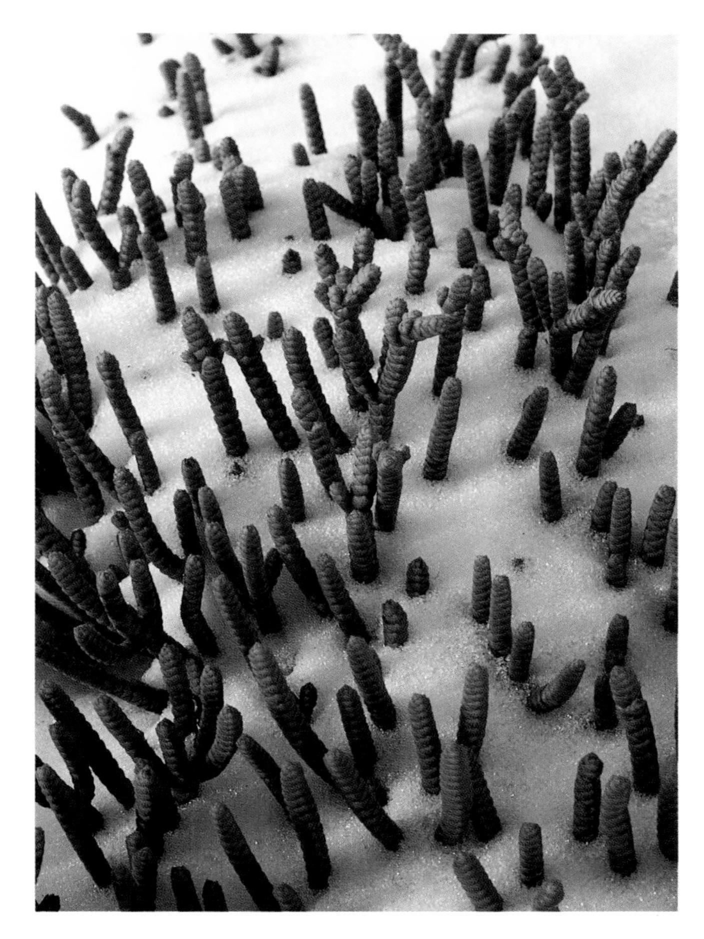

Alpine leaves Leaves are used to intercept sunlight and absorb its energy for photosynthesis. Among lowland plants they are usually broad and thin, to expose a large surface area for efficient light interception. In the alpine zone, this design is less than ideal. Broad, thin leaves lose moisture too easily to the dry air and are quickly chilled by cold winds. They are also easily torn off by gales or crushed by the weight of falling snow. Alpine leaves are designed in various ways to overcome the rigours imposed by their environment.
The whipcord hebe, whose branches are seen here sticking out of a winter snowfall (left), has virtually done away with its leaves altogether. They have been reduced to tiny overlapping green scales on each branch. The *Craspedia* (below) holds its leaves close to the shelter of the ground and covers them with a woolly coat of hairs to give insulation from extremes of temperature and moisture loss.

Economies for alpine survival

In the alpine zone the growing season is preciously short. Plants face a race against time to manufacture enough resources to compete with their neighbouring plants, produce flowers and seed for reproduction, repair the damage caused by storms and have enough left over to store as reserves to last them over the winter. The higher the altitude the shorter the summer and the more difficulties plants face trying to make ends meet. For each species there is an upper extreme beyond which it can no longer balance its energy budget, and it must give way to others that have evolved to live by more frugal means.

There are a number of ways that alpine plants can economise on resources. Their small size is one measure. Tall stems take a lot more building materials than small ones and cost more in resources to maintain. In addition, alpine plants may go several years without flowering, taking several summer seasons to save up the necessary reserves. The snow tussocks, for instance, often flower en masse every 2–3 years, with flowering events triggered by a warmer than usual summer in the preceding year.

Strict energy budgeting by plants also brings a steady changeover in the growth strategy with altitude, from shrubs to herbs. The alpine herbs, which include buttercups, gentians and ourisias, are non-woody plants that produce new, leafy flowering stems each growing season. As winter approaches they usually store their surplus food reserves in underground tissues, such as large rootstocks or special stems, and then die back, either to ground level or to a low rosette of leaves. Their growth tips, perhaps sheltered by dead leaves or tiny scales, then sleep through the winter beneath the snow, ready to send up new leaf stems again in spring. The shrubs, which have woody branches, do not have the option to die back in winter. Wood is a permanent building material, and to replace it each year would be an expense they could ill afford. Therefore they aim to make their leaves and branches last for more than one season. To do this they need to harden off their foliage

INTRODUCED MAMMALS

Many of New Zealand's alpine plants have proved to be to the liking of introduced herbivorous mammals. Soon after deer, thar and chamois were liberated in the mountains, palatable alpine herbs, tussocks and shrubs started to disappear and be replaced by less palatable species. During the post-war years, animal numbers reached plague proportions and so did the damage. Areas where the summer wildflowers grew so thickly that one could not tread between them were becoming a memory. Buttercups, ourisias and anisotomes were among the hardest hit. Then reprieve arrived, in the form of the helicopter. Intensive aerial hunting since the seventies has brought a recovery in the

Thar (*Hemitragus jemlahicus*)

GORDON ROBERTS

to a state that can withstand the winter. This means coating the leaf surfaces with a thick, waxy cuticle to reduce desiccation, as well as concentrating the cell sap to deter the formation of damaging ice crystals in their tissues.

The shrub strategy would seem to have an advantage over the herbs. With their permanent branches they are ready to resume growth as soon as warm conditions return. However, the exposed shoots of shrubs run a greater risk of damage in winter than the more sheltered growing tips of herbs. They are far more prone to freezing and desiccation, as well as the physical damage caused by strong winds and heavy snowfalls. For this reason shrubs generally lose out to herbs at higher altitudes. The new growth they produce each summer cannot balance the amount damaged each winter. Those shrubs that do survive at high altitudes often adopt non-shrub-like growth forms. These grow almost flat to the ground in mats or cushions, the best known examples being the vegetable sheep.

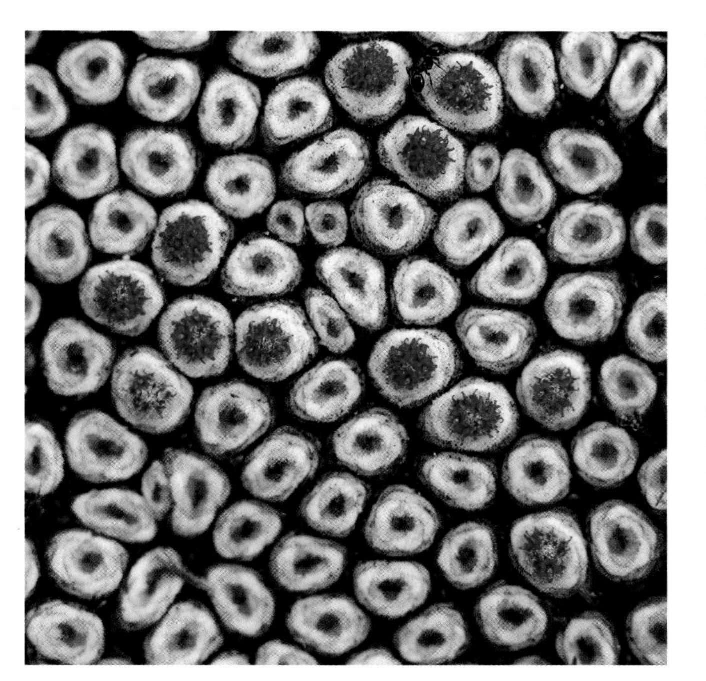

Vegetable sheep
Vegetable sheep are a peculiarly New Zealand group of shrubs. They are several species of *Raoulia* and *Haastia*, which have evolved the most extraordinary design to help them withstand the cold and arid rigours of the alpine climate. Their leaves are felted with tiny hairs and tightly clustered at the tip of each branch. The branches are then closely packed, one against the other, to form a remarkably dense canopy, firm enough to be stood on without ill-effect. The dome shape of the canopy gives it both strength and streamlining to shed the blast of the most powerful gales in summer, and the downhill shearing force caused by creeping of the snow cover in winter.

These adaptations provide a remarkable barrier to the outside environment. Even while cold, dry winds buffet the exterior, overlapping leaves and insulating hairs can trap a moist, warm microclimate around growing buds. Underneath, dead leaves and branches form a water-storing mulch, allowing the plant to recycle the proceeds of its own decay. Even the seed dispersal is remarkably apt. After flowering, downy seeds adapted for wind transport are extruded above the canopy surface into the free-flowing air, to be carried away on the breeze.

alpine vegetation almost as dramatic as its decline.

Being under attack from herbivores is nothing new for alpine plants. They have always been browsed by native animals such as grasshoppers and caterpillars, as well as some larger animals such as the takahe. The difference is that the native plants and animals have evolved a compatible equilibrium with one another during the millions of years they have coexisted. This same equilibrium is unfortunately not possible with the introduced animals that have been brought here so suddenly. Their feeding habits are sufficiently different from those of native animals that they can exterminate certain vulnerable plants. For instance, instead of cropping a little bit from each plant as takahe do, introduced mammals, often grazing in large herds, soon eat selected plants beyond the point of recovery.

Thar and chamois are the mammals most associated with mountains.

Thar (*Hemitragus jemlahicus*) Thar are native to the steep, rocky ranges of the Himalaya and were first liberated in New Zealand in 1904. They are creatures of the high country, gifted with acute senses of smell, hearing and sight which they use to identify danger. A mature bull stands about one metre high at the shoulders and can weigh up to 130 kilograms. Thar often travel in family groups, which may congregate in large herds. They tend to remain in the alpine zone throughout the year. In summer the herd establishes a daily feeding routine which takes them from the bush edge to the limits of plant growth. Here they may rest for a while, before heading back down by evening. In winter they prefer to retreat to a sunny snow-free spot of tussock or alpine scrub.

Chamois (*Rupicapra rupicapra*) Chamois were introduced to New Zealand in 1907 and 1914, being animals gifted by the Emperor Franz Josef of Austria. They are native to the European mountains, as well as those of Asia Minor. Like thar, they were first liberated at Mt Cook but have now become the more numerous of the two, being found throughout the Southern Alps. They are smaller than thar, an adult male standing about 80 centimetres at the shoulders. They do not feed so high in the mountains as thar, preferring to remain nearer the bush edge, where they can retreat to the forest during storms. Both chamois and thar negotiate cliffs with uncanny ease. Their superbly adapted hooves have a horny rim with a soft, spongy pad of hairs in the centre, which gives a non-slip grip and allows the animal to take the impact of a jump without skidding.

Red deer (*Cervus elaphus*) Since helicopter hunting, red deer have become a much rarer sight on the open tops than they were during the boom years of the fifties and sixties. Red deer are native to Europe and they have become well established in both lowland and mountain regions of New Zealand. They venture into the alpine region to browse during the summer months and cause considerable damage. Red deer tend to pick on preferred species, eating these down before moving on to other less favoured food species. An American relative of the red deer, the wapiti, was introduced to Fiordland in 1905. Of impressive stature, it is highly prized by hunters as a trophy animal. However, it is steadily disappearing as a pure population because of interbreeding with the more numerous red deer.

Hare (*Lepus europaeus*) The hare, which was introduced from Europe for sporting purposes, is now found in scrub and grassland from sea-level to the alpine zone, where it feeds on tussocks, shrubs and alpine herbs. Unlike rabbits (*Oryctolagus cuniculus*), hares are solitary creatures. They also do not burrow, but rest during the day in a grassy hollow called the form. They emerge to feed at dusk, returning to the form near dawn. Because hares tend to feed singly and do not graze individual plants heavily, they cause less damage to vegetation than other introduced mammals.

The alpine zone

Vegetation zones

To step beyond the treeline is to enter the alpine zone. The transition from tall forest to low alpine vegetation is one of the most striking boundaries in the natural world. Climb higher, however, and the plant community continues to change, visibly and predictably in response to the deteriorating environment.

The alpine zone can therefore be subdivided into a series of zones at different altitudes. The low-alpine zone starts at the bush edge. It usually begins with a narrow band of scrub, which gives way higher up to snow tussock-herbfields. Snow tussock-herbfields peter out about 500 metres above the treeline, where the high-alpine zone begins. From here on up, the vegetation becomes increasingly dwarfed and scattered among a wasteland of grey rock. This is called fellfield.

About 900 metres above the treeline is the nival zone, where snow lies all year round. The only plants here are those found rooted on rocky outcrops too steep to accumulate snow. The uppermost limit for flowering plants is reached at 2900 metres above sea-level, an altitude record shared by *Hebe haastii* and *Parahebe birleyi*. Only mosses and lichens survive higher, lichens making an appearance on New Zealand's highest point — the summit rocks of Mt Cook.

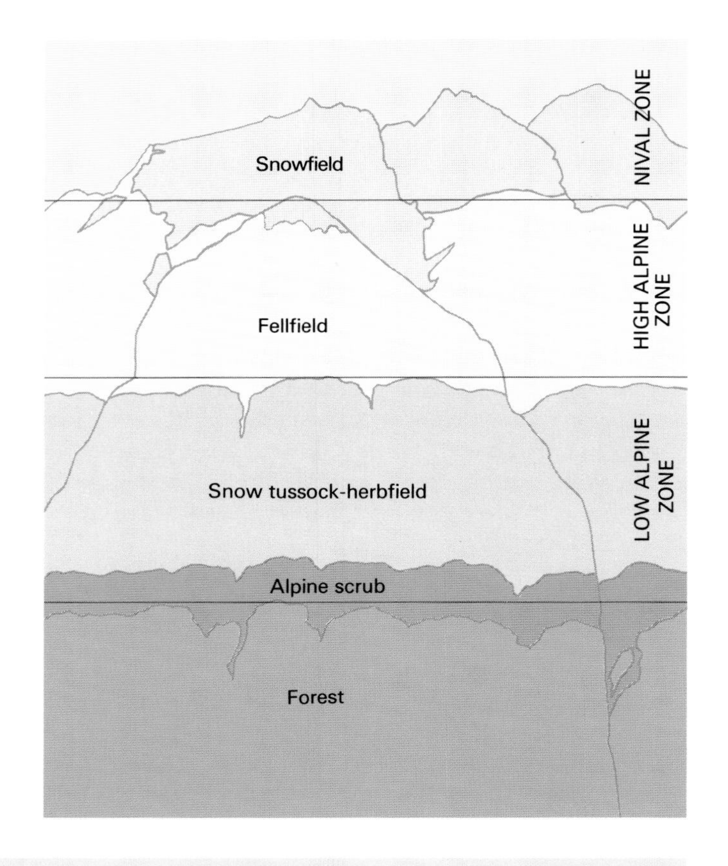

ORIGINS OF THE ALPINE FLORA

The alpine plants of New Zealand, with their extraordinary diversity, confront science with something of a riddle — where did they all come from? New Zealand's mountains are very young, true alpine habitats appearing during the last two to three million years. If the alpine flora evolved completely within New Zealand, then it has appeared in a miraculously short time; yet if we try looking for nearby overseas mountain ranges as ancestral sources for the alpines, they are few and far between.

A number of solutions to this puzzle have been put forward. One is that New Zealand once extended much further south than it does today and that alpine plants came from this cooler part of the country. However, there is no conclusive evidence for this idea. Another suggestion is that some migrated here from Antarctica, before it was finally overrun by ice. Others think it likely that alpine plants evolved from ancestors previously living in infertile or rocky habitats on the lowlands.

Some clues to whether the alpine plants have a local origin can be drawn from their evolutionary ties to plants overseas. The general rule is that the greater the evolutionary difference between two plant groups the longer they have been separated. New Zealand plants with few close relatives elsewhere are therefore those most likely to have been here the longest. The snow grasses (*Chionochloa*), edelweisses (*Leucogenes*), speargrasses (*Aciphylla*), hebes, dracophyllums and the cushion plants of *Hectorella* and *Phyllachne*, are examples of native plant groups shared with few, if any, other countries. A lot of alpine plants, however, have closer links overseas. Native willow herbs (*Epilobium*), sedges (*Carex*) and rushes (*Juncus*) are examples.

The answer then is probably that some evolved from plants that had been living in New Zealand for a considerable length of time, and that these were supplemented by more recent migrants, many arriving as the mountains were being built. These may have mountain-hopped here via the ranges of South-East Asia and Australia, carried by wind or birds.

Regardless of where or when the ancestors of New Zealand's alpine plants originated, one thing is certain. The events of the recent past have produced a flora which is now undeniably unique. The turmoil caused by the geologically recent uplifting of New Zealand's mountains, combined with the climatic extremes of the Ice Age, have caused a surge of evolution among the alpine plants to exploit the new habitats created. Today, about 95 per cent of the plant species are found nowhere else in the world. Their comparative youth is apparent in the number of different species which can still interbreed to form hybrids. These species, while having evolved quite visible differences in their outward appearance, have not yet had time to evolve the genetic boundaries which normally prevent interbreeding.

The low-alpine zone

Alpine scrub

Immediately above the bushline there is usually a narrow band of alpine scrub mixed with tall snow tussocks. To the tramper intent on the open tops beyond, it presents a waist-high hindrance of prickly bushes. But for those who care to linger, the plants here have much to offer with their diversity of form and colour. Frequently encountered are dracophyllum shrubs, with distinctive grass-like tufts of leaves sprouting from the end of thin, springy branches. Scrambling among the lower vegetation are scattered bushes of leathery-leaved gaultherias. These belong to the cosmopolitan heath family (Ericaceae), which includes the heathers and numerous other alpine shrubs worldwide. *Gaultheria crassa* is a shrub with small thick, leathery leaves and typical bell-like flowers. *Gaultheria depressa*, the snowberry, is well regarded even by the hurried tramper on account of its small, tasty white, pink or red fruits.

The *Coprosma* genus contains 100 or so native species countrywide, including a few representatives in the alpine scrub. Like many of their lowland relatives they are twiggy bushes with small leaves and red berries. Remarkably, there are even a few members of the podocarp family here, although considerably dwarfed compared with their relatives that dominate the lowland forest. The mountain toatoa (*Phyllocladus alpinus*) grows above the treeline as a shrub less than 2 metres tall. The snow totara (*Podocarpus nivalis*) is a sprawling shrub barely more than a metre high, making it a mere bonsai in comparison with its 30-metre big brother, the lowland totara (*P. totara*). Even smaller is the pigmy pine (*Lepidothamnus laxifolium*), the smallest conifer in the world. It grows no higher than a turf in some alpine areas.

Snow totara Cherry-red fruits of the snow totara (*Podocarpus nivalis*) await the pleasure of a bird. The attached green seed, if swallowed at the same time, will then be carried away and deposited to grow elsewhere.

HEBES

The most diverse shrubs in the alpine scrub are the hebes. The hebes are renowned for their remarkable symmetry of form, a characteristic that has made them popular for cultivation here and overseas. Even growing in the rigours of the alpine zone, hebes faithfully maintain a trimmed appearance, with perfectly rounded bushes and leaves precisely arranged in four symmetrical rows along their branches. Equally striking is their foliage, which varies from small, spoon-shaped leaves to minute overlapping 'scales'.

While the hebes could be admired on looks alone, they are also an extremely resourceful group of plants. There are about 100 species in New Zealand. This extraordinary number has probably come about during the mountain-building and the Ice-Age episodes of the last few million years. During this period of intense change, habitats were both created and destroyed. Many plants became extinct during the turmoil, but the resourceful hebes adapted apace with the change. They evolved numerous species that successfully occupied the new niches that appeared. Today, hebes occur throughout the full spectrum of New Zealand's landscape, from the coast, where *Hebe elliptica* grows just above the tideline, right up to 2900 metres in the Southern Alps, where *H. haastii* has the distinction of growing at the highest altitude for any flowering plant. *H. pinguifolia*, shown in the photograph, grows on drier ranges throughout the South Island.

Snow tussock-herbfields

As the shrubs climb away from the bush edge, their number declines and snow tussocks predominate, interspersed with herbaceous flowering plants, such as alpine daisies, buttercups and gentians. This vegetation type is snow tussock-herbfield, and it covers most of the low-alpine zone. The number of herbs present, however, can vary considerably, giving way almost entirely to snow tussocks on drier eastern mountain ranges.

Snow tussocks belong to the Australasian genus *Chionochloa*, which is centered in New Zealand. Fourteen species of *Chionochloa* are found in the high country, several of which are widespread. The narrow-leaved snow tussock (*C. rigida*) is the most common species in the low-alpine zone on the drier east of the Southern Alps, from the Rakaia River southwards. The smaller slim snow tussock (*C. macra*) is often found at higher altitudes, and is widespread over a large altitudinal range to the north of the Rakaia River. On the wetter western side of the Southern Alps the broad-leaved snow tussock (*C. flavescens*) dominates much of the low-alpine zone, along with the mid-ribbed snow tussock (*C. pallens*), which is more common on better-drained, more fertile soils. At higher altitude these give way to a number of much shorter relatives. The curled

FLOWERS OF THE SNOW TUSSOCK-HERBFIELD

Although snow tussocks by and large clothe alpine regions, it is the smaller herbs which draw attention with the beauty of their flowers. A summer display of alpine wildflowers rewards every bit of the effort in climbing up above the bushline. The numbers are at first almost bewildering. There are literally hundreds of species. Of these, several more prominent groups deserve special mention.

Buttercups (*Ranunculus*) Few fail to recognise the buttercups, so ubiquitous are they in temperate regions of the world. They are a very large plant group, widespread in Southern and Northern Hemispheres, the latter being the source of the introduced ones most commonly found growing as garden weeds. There are 34 species of buttercup native to New Zealand, about half of which live in the alpine region. Most conform to the normal buttercup flower colour of bright yellow. The best known, however, is the white-flowered Mt Cook lily (*R. lyallii*) illustrated here, which is not a lily but a buttercup — the world's largest.

Alpine daisies (*Celmisia*) Alpine daisies are conspicuous members of the snow tussock-herbfields. *Celmisia* is an Australasian genus, with about 60 species in New Zealand, most of which occur in the alpine zone. Sometimes as many as five species can be found growing together in a small plant community. *Celmisia* belongs to the Compositae family, which includes thousands of plants with daisy-like flowers in both Northern and Southern Hemispheres. As far as their flowers go, celmisias are a conservative group. All conform to the daisy design, with little to distinguish one species from the next. They vary much more in growth habit and the texture of their leaves. Some grow close to the ground, flowering from small tufted rosettes of leaves, while others stand up to half a metre high.

Anisotomes The anisotomes are restricted to New Zealand and the subantarctic islands. There are 15 species, 11 of which grow in the alpine zone. With their often finely divided leaves, anisotomes are recognisable members of the carrot family, Umbelliferae, which also includes parsley, fennel and celery. Crush a piece of foliage between your fingers and you will even smell that sweet carroty aroma. Unfortunately, the anisotomes, like so many of their relatives, are quite palatable, and have suffered the effects of browsing by introduced animals.

Alpine daisies

Speargrass

Mt Cook lily

Anisotomes

snow tussock (*C. crassiuscula*) is the most common species south from about Lewis Pass, while the extremely short carpet grass (*C. australis*) is found in the wetter north-western parts of the South Island. In the North Island, red tussock (*C. rubra*) dominates the volcanic peaks of Mt Taranaki (Egmont) and those of the Tongariro region, while broadleaved and mid-ribbed snow tussock prevail on the main North Island ranges.

Tussocks Snow tussocks (*Chionochloa*) are very slow growing, and some plants may be centuries old. They are the essence of the high country, their shaggy heads covering the ranges with straw-coloured tones of russet and gold.

Gentians

Speargrasses (*Aciphylla*) These rather unlikely looking members of the carrot family are almost wholly restricted to New Zealand, where 39 species occur. Any visitor to the alpine zone is soon acquainted with them, not so much for the beauty of their flowers, but for the treachery of their rosette of stiff, bayonet-like leaves. The briefest encounter with the needle-sharp tips of these leaves is enough to make one remain wary forever. Even the flower head carries an armoury of sharp bracts. Such a system makes an ideal defence against browsing animals.

One can only assume it originally evolved to rebuff the attention of hungry moas. Unfortunately for the speargrass, its weaponry does not deter the small six-legged variety of browser. In fact most weevils and caterpillars that feed on speargrasses cleverly use the plant's defence system to their own advantage. At the slightest disturbance they make themselves utterly inaccessible by dropping neatly into the centre of the plant's prickly rosette.

Gentians Towards the end of summer, gentians come into their own. Their flowers are among the last to appear in the tussock-herbfields, blooming from February to April like a sprinkling of early snow. Gentians abound in alpine regions throughout the world. Unlike their colourful overseas counterparts, New Zealand's 19 mainland species are creamy white, save for the occasional fleck of purple.

Orchids To give them due credit, orchids are far more than denizens of tropical rainforests. They are a versatile family, with about 30,000 species worldwide in habitats from forest to arctic tundra. Six species of orchid occur in the snow tussock-herbfields. The odd-leaved orchid (*Aporostylis bifolia*) and leek orchid (*Prasophyllum colensoi*) are examples found in damp snow-tussock herbfields.

Eyebrights There are 15 native species of eyebright, or euphrasia. Their innocent-looking flowers belie a rather underhand method they have evolved to get their nutrient requirements. Their roots are able to latch onto the roots of other plants, tapping them for water and nutrients. This saves the eyebright the expenditure of growing its own extensive root system. To ensure it gets a lion's share of its requirements, the eyebright has leaves densely covered with stomatal pores. These evaporate moisture rapidly, so that the eyebright can act as a wick, drawing a strong flow of water and dissolved nutrients from its host's roots.

Odd-leaved orchid

Eyebrights

Leek orchid

The high-alpine zone

Fellfield

Much of the high-alpine zone is covered with apparently barren rocky slopes. These are called fellfields, and at a glance they appear lifeless. But a closer examination reveals scatterings of green life. Pockets of thin soil provide a haven for clusters of plants. Others tuck themselves into the shelter of large boulders or on small outcrops, which offer stable homes compared with the surrounding slopes of loose rock, exposed to continual disturbance by frost, snow and wind.

The richest fellfield communities occur in moist mountain regions. In sheltered spots live enclaves of plants usually associated with the snow tussock-herbfields lower down. Elsewhere there are plants more typical of fellfields. Among these are high-alpine species of *Gentiana, Ranunculus, Celmisia* and *Hebe*. Also there are scattered low turfs of grasses and sedges, as well as cushions of *Hectorella* and *Chionohebe.*

Fellfields in drier mountain regions are more spartan in their vegetation. Several of the ubiquitous hebes make an appearance in this austere environment, as well as a few speargrasses, which resemble pincushions compared with their large relatives in the snow tussock-herbfields. The most notable residents, however, are the vegetable sheep. These large, hummocky and intensely woolly plants have evolved such a degree of imperviousness to their environment (page 27) that they seem to thrive here. *Raoulia eximia* is one of the more common vegetable sheep found in Canterbury and North Otago. *Haastia pulvinaris*, the chunkiest of the group, lives in the dry fellfields of Marlborough and south-east Nelson.

Fellfield (right) Expanses of rock and occasional small plants are typical of fellfield, such as seen here at an altitude of 1800 metres in Mt Aspiring National Park.

Edelweiss
Edelweisses (*Leucogenes*) are the best known of fellfield plants. They are often found sheltering among rocks or on outcrops. Their small leaves, felted with fine hairs and growing almost flat to the ground, are superbly adapted to the rigours of the high-alpine environment.

Cushion vegetation

On the open, flat-topped summits of the Central Otago ranges, extreme cold and persistent strong winds encourage a cushion vegetation of dwarf mat or creeping species. A mosaic of different plants grows flat to the ground, each plant finding shelter from any small surface irregularity, as well as from the other plants. The ground cover is sparse, despite the fact that the underlying soils, consisting of wind-blown loess deposited as the Ice-Age glaciers retreated, are relatively good.

THE CURIOUS SCREE PLANTS

The South Island mountains of Marlborough, Canterbury and parts of Otago are built of a rock called greywacke. Unlike schists and granites, common to ranges elsewhere, greywacke weathers very quickly. Its numerous joints and weaknesses take up water, which, when it freezes, expands and fractures the rock. Outcrops continually shed large beds of shattered scree, which are so much a feature of these central South Island mountains. Sometimes they extend from the summits to the valley floor — a slowly moving 'conveyor belt' of rocky debris.

Scree would seem the most inhospitable of alpine habitats. Apart from the problems of tumbling stones, screes experience extremes of surface temperatures, from hot, dry days to icy nights. Yet despite this, a number of specialist plants live here. At first they are difficult to spot, as they often have cryptic colours that resemble their rocky home. But a patient search will locate them hidden among the rubble. What is more surprising is that they are a very cosmopolitan group. Among them, for example, is the penwiper plant (*Notothlaspi rosulatum*) from the cabbage family, *Stellaria roughii* from the chickweed family, *Lignocarpa carnosula* from the carrot family and *Ranunculus haastii* from the buttercup family. Although they come from widely different backgrounds, each has developed similar solutions to the problems of scree life. It is a striking example of convergent evolution.

So how do these plants survive in scree? Fortunately for the plants it is usually only the surface 10–30 centimetres of scree that is mobile, and below this is a moist, sandy soil.

Scree buttercup (*Ranunculus haastii*)

Scree plants have extensive root systems anchored in this stable soil to absorb moisture. If the upper leafy portions are sheared off by moving rocks, the plant can renew itself from reserves stored in underground roots or stems. Some species in fact have their leaves and flower stalks weakly connected, so they can be broken off without uprooting the rest of the plant. The foliage of scree plants also shares certain adaptive features. Their leaves are usually a grey-blue colour, succulent, and covered with a waxy bloom, all of which afford protection from the intensely drying conditions and harmful levels of ultraviolet radiation at the scree surface. Their grey-blue colour may help by also making the plants very well camouflaged in their rocky surroundings, concealing them from the eyes of herbivores.

Flowering with the snow-melt (left) *Ranunculus sericophyllus* is common on snowbanks. Like other plants in this habitat it tolerates the unusually short growing season by having fully formed flowers ready to open as soon as the snow melts.

Snowbanks

Snowbanks have an ecology of their own. They occur in sheltered hollows, where winter snow may persist into spring and summer. Because they are sheltered, these hollows offer several advantages for plants; notably they have deep, moist soils and offer protection from winds. But against this is the disadvantage that plants must wait for the snow to melt away before they can begin their summer growth. Since the same pattern of snowmelt repeats itself each year, the snowbank community establishes itself in a sequence of species according to how long each requires for its growing season. Those at the top of the snowbank, which are first to be released from the melting snow, require the longest season; whereas those at the bottom, which are last to be exposed, are adapted to cope with a very short growing season.

One important adaptation is to have flowers ready to open soon after the snow has fully gone, to allow maximum time for flowering and seeding. Experts are the white-flowered *Caltha obtusa* and yellow-flowered *C. novae-zelandiae*, which have their flowers fully formed in the bud by the preceding autumn. After overwintering, they are ready to bloom as soon as they emerge from the snow. Sometimes the flowers even start opening beneath the melting snow.

Birds of the mountains

The harsh realities of the mountains mean that few birds make their home there. Only one native bird, the rock wren, remains in the alpine zone all year round. The others live both above and below the bush edge and can escape the cold winter months. Even the kea usually nests below the bush edge and forages in alpine or forest areas according to season.

A bird often encountered in the tussock-herbfields is the native pipit (*Anthus novaeseelandiae*), which nests on the ground in open country, from sea-level to the low-alpine zone. Although it can be mistaken for the skylark (*Alauda arvensis*), which is sometimes seen above the treeline, the pipit distinguishes itself with its gait. It has a habit of hurriedly walking or running while constantly dipping and flicking its tail. The skylark gives itself away with its song. Its constant warblings are the esssence of warm summer days and grassy meadows. The notes cascade from the sky as the bird hovers invisibly above.

A rarer encounter would be with the chukor (*Alectoris chukar*), an introduced partridge. It comes from barren rocky ranges in Asia and has found a suitably similar home on the drier eastern slopes of the Southern Alps, where it lives as high as 2000 metres. Its unmistakable 'chukar-chukar-chukar' call often punctuates the stillness of morning and evening, but the bird itself is almost impossible to locate.

As recently as the last century the visitor to the tussock tops in western parts of the South Island may have been rewarded by the sight of the kakapo (*Strigops habroptilus*), which has now all but vanished from the wild. The kakapo, a large flightless parrot, inhabits the high bush and scrub, venturing onto the tops to taste the tender summer growth of tussocks and alpine herbs. The flightless takahe (*Porphyrio mantelli*), now restricted to parts of Fiordland, was also once much more widespread. It frequents the bush edge and low-alpine zone where it browses snow tussocks and selected large-leaved alpine herbs, using its large bill to expertly pluck out the tastiest parts. It seems to know exactly which plants are most nutritious, favouring particular species such as mid-ribbed snow tussock and *Celmisia petriei.*

HIGH-COUNTRY BIRDS

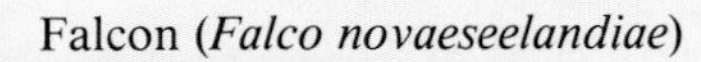

Falcon (*Falco novaeseelandiae*)

GEORGE CHANCE

Rock wren (*Xenicus gilviventris*)

Rock wren (*Xenicus gilviventris*) Rock wrens are found as high as 2400 metres in the Southern Alps. Their favourite haunt is an area of jumbled rocks, where they can be seen bobbing incessantly on their oversized legs and flitting in short flights between rocks and shrubs in search of insects. Breeding pairs weave a nest from snow tussocks and lichens, siting it in the shelter of boulders or beneath a shrub.

The rock wren is New Zealand's only true alpine bird, spending its entire life in the alpine zone. Just how it survives the winter above the treeline baffles scientists. The smaller an animal is the more difficulty it has in retaining its body heat, because its ratio of body volume (which generates heat) to body surface area (which loses heat) declines. The rock wren, weighing little more than a 50-cent piece, would seem hopelessly ill-equipped to take on the chilling months of winter.

Some ornithologists speculate that during the coldest months it shelters beneath the snow, leading a mouse-like existence living and feeding among passageways between the rocks. Others feel it is more likely it seeks a dry resting place and goes into a state of torpor, allowing its body temperature and pulse rate to fall.

Native falcon (*Falco novaeseelandiae*) The native falcon lives in dense lowland forest as well as the open tussocklands of the high country. Since European settlement it has become scarce in many areas, having often suffered the bewildering and ignominious finality of a bullet. This magnificent bird can still be found, however, particularly once one comes to recognise its distinctive 'kek-kek-kek' call. It hunts either from a favourite perch, usually a rocky outcrop with grandstand views over the surrounding landscape, or by soaring in the sky. It takes a wide variety of game, both native and introduced, including pipits, gulls, rabbits, hares, lizards, beetles and dragonflies.

To watch the falcon in its natural habitat is impressive. The decisive momentum of its stoop, sometimes at speeds of 200 kilometres per hour, is chillingly awesome, yet in courtship and nesting, falcons form a bond of endearing affection. The male woos the female with a courtship flight and afterwards nesting begins. The nest itself is little more than a simple scrape, often situated on a sheltered rocky ledge. While the female incubates the eggs and cares for the chicks, the male hunts for food. This is passed from one parent to the other at a prearranged spot away from the nest, as shown in the photograph. The food is then carried back to the nest by the female, who picks out the choicest parts to feed her charges. The nesting area is fearlessly defended from all intruders, not the least humans. If anything happens to the female, the male may continue to raise the young alone until they leave the nest.

Kea (*Nestor notabilis*)

Kea (*Nestor notabilis*) The kea is a member of the parrot family and is closely related to the kaka (*N. meridionalis*), which inhabits lowland forest. Keas nest in high altitude forest, often in rocky crevices or old trees, and during the summer spend a lot of time above the treeline feeding on berries, leaves, buds, seeds and grubs. While the female tends to the young, the male provides food for the family.

Before forming breeding pairs, juveniles join groups which roam the nearby mountains, landing to investigate whatever attracts their inquisitive nature. Such groups have a strict pecking order, members constantly asserting their rank with specific calls and postures. At this stage of life the young are distinguished by the typical yellow markings around the eye and at the base of the beak.

Despite the harshness of their environment, keas always seem to have time for a moment's entertainment. They are often seen performing aerobatics in high winds, delighting in the sheer exhilaration of the experience. Humans and their associated worldly possessions are a mainstay of the kea's delight. The colours, sizes and textures of our everyday paraphernalia come in such baffling variety as to be deemed purposeless by the kea, except for amusement.

Alpine bogs

Alpine bogs are found wherever the ground is permanently waterlogged through poor drainage. They often cover relatively flat-topped mountain regions with vast, soggy expanses, particularly in moist parts of Otago, Southland and Stewart Island. Smaller bogs, however, occur throughout the wetter mountain ranges of New Zealand. Most commonly they fill hollows that were scooped out from the underlying bedrock during the Ice Age.

Air is excluded from bogs, so organisms that live within them are starved of oxygen. In normally drained soils the leaf litter and other organic matter are broken down by soil organisms such as earthworms, fungi and bacteria. However, in oxygenless bogs, most of these decomposers cannot survive. Dead matter is therefore not broken down fully and minerals are not recycled properly. Cold temperatures add to the effect by slowing microbial decay. As a result the organic matter slowly accumulates as a spongy layer of semi-decayed vegetation called peat. The few organisms that do live in the bog cause chemical changes. These make the peaty soil acidic, and while certain minerals necessary for plant growth, including nitrogen and phosphorus, become less freely available, other minerals and compounds may become more freely available, often to the point of being toxic.

Alpine bogs
Alpine bogs and their associated plant communities occur throughout wet mountain regions where drainage is poor. This small one fills a hollow scooped from impermeable bedrock by glaciers during the Ice Age.

Plants that live in bogs must therefore contend with a shortage of oxygen and minerals, combined with a surfeit of toxic compounds. Not surprisingly, bogs are uninhabitable for most plants, yet they do provide a niche for a few specialists which can tolerate such a stressful environment. Some avoid the stress by having shallow roots which live near the relatively well-aerated surface. Others have adaptive mechanisms to help them cope with the stress. For example, bog plants often have internal spaces within their roots to allow air to circulate down from the leafy stem above. More remarkable are the adaptive features that some plants have to overcome the mineral deficiencies of bogs. Sundews and bladderworts supplement their mineral requirements by trapping and digesting insects. Bog-dwelling plants of *Gunnera* tackle the nutrient problem in another way. Normally, plants have to obtain their nitrogen from the soil, usually as nitrate or ammonium compounds, but in glands at the base of their leaves *Gunnera* hold colonies of a blue-green alga (*Nostoc*) that obtain elemental nitrogen from the air. *Gunnera* therefore alleviates the shortage of nitrogen in the bog by tapping a supply from its own *Nostoc* 'fertiliser factory'.

The types of plant found in bogs vary with altitude and the amount of drainage. Clumps of red tussocks often grow at the edges, while sedges and rushes are common further in. Amongst the grasses may grow dwarf heathy shrubs of pigmy pine, *Dracophyllum*, *Leucopogon*, and *Coprosma*. Other plants are so dwarfed that they form low-growing cushions with their stems packed tightly together to expose a dense mat of leaf tips to the sky above. Species of *Gaimardia* and *Centrolepis* grow as soft mossy cushions, and the comb sedge (*Oreobolus pectinatus*) looks like cut lawn.

The wettest parts of bogs are usually the preserve of sphagnum moss. There are over 300 species of this moss, which grows in bogs all over the world. Sphagnum has an extraordinary tolerance of waterlogged conditions. In fact it deliberately promotes its own wet and acidic environment by holding large quantities of water. It does this with millions of tiny pores in its surface that draw up water by capillary action. As the sphagnum grows upwards and outwards, it carries its favourite soggy environment with it like an enormous sponge. Eventually it can grow beyond its original water supply, spreading a green blanket across the surrounding land and smothering other plants as it goes.

INSECTIVOROUS PLANTS

Insectivorous plants have always intrigued people because they have managed to turn the tables on the normal rules of nature by trapping and digesting animals. Their curious diet, however, has evolved more as a means of obtaining mineral nutrients, such as nitrogen and phosphorus, which are deficient in bogs, rather than food. Like other plants they have green leaves and produce their own supply of sugars and other food compounds.

The schemes they use to catch their prey are both cunning and varied. Sundews (*Drosera*) have leaves covered with sticky hairs which attract insects. But any insect that touches them makes a fatal mistake. It becomes hopelessly stuck. As it struggles to free itself, other sticky leaf hairs are stimulated to curl around, holding the victim as if with tentacles. Enzymes then digest the insect and nutrients released from its body are absorbed and used by the plant. When digestion has been completed, the leaf casts its spent prey to the wind, and then waits for the next meal.

Sundew (*Drosera*) with prey

Bladderwort (*Utricularia*)

The bladderworts (*Utricularia*) have evolved an equally nefarious way to trap insects. Some of their leaves are modified into small chambers or bladders held in the muddy ooze below. These have an inward-opening trapdoor with a special tripping mechanism. When an aquatic insect or small animal comes nearby, it triggers the door to open. Water rushes into the bladder, taking the insect with it. Nutrients are then absorbed as the insect decays. Later, water is pumped from the bladder and the trap is reset.

Peat — Nature's time machine Because decay is inhibited in peat bogs, they can be remarkable natural archives of the past. Objects trapped on the surface are preserved and buried in sequence as the peat accumulates layer upon layer over the centuries.

Peat bogs have turned up remains of extinct moas and giant eagles that were victims of the muddy mire hundreds of years before. However, much useful information contained by bogs comes from pollen grains, such as the matai pollen grain (right). These resist decay and are very distinctive, so they can be identified as known plants. By sampling pollen buried at different depths in the peat, scientists have been able to reconstruct prehistoric changes of vegetation, giving insights into the past effects of climate or humankind. They tell us of the rapid spread of podocarp forest about 9000 years ago, as temperatures warmed after the Ice Age, and the later expansion of beech forest, as climates cooled a little. They also record the change from forest to bracken when the early Maori started burning the lowland forest about 1000 years ago. Alpine bogs generally only contain records going back 12,000 years because before this, Ice-Age climates prevented peat accumulation. But in some lowland areas, peat and lignite deposits contain records extending back for millions of years.

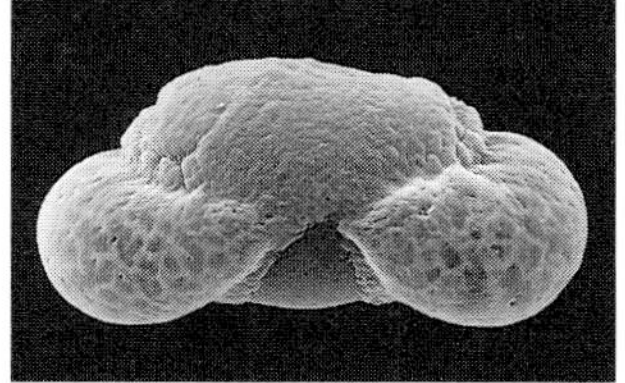

DSIR LAND RESOURCES

Alpine insects

The variety of plants in the alpine zone is more than matched by the diversity of insects that feed upon them. On a calm summer's day the mountains literally buzz with activity. At each step, there are hundreds of insects chewing through vegetation. Others fly purposefully by, searching for pollen, nectar, or a mate.

Cicadas, beetles, grasshoppers, moths and flies are all common in alpine regions. Moths are particularly numerous, with about half of New Zealand's species living above the bushline. Sometimes as many as 300 different types can be found on a single mountain range. Alpine moths are different from their lowland relatives in a number of ways. They tend to fly by day rather than by night, to make use of the warmer temperatures. Because they are day-flying they are often quite colourful, like little butterflies. Alpine moths are also noticeably more cautious on the wing than their lowland relatives. They can often be seen flying close to the ground and diving for cover in strong gusts to avoid being blown off course.

Moths, as well as flies and beetles, are important flower pollinators. Without them hundreds of alpine flowers would not be able to set seed. Moth caterpillars, however, eat plants. Many are fussy feeders, specialising in a few closely related plants or even a single species, which largely explains how the varied alpine flora can support so many different types of moth. As well as grasshoppers, moths' caterpillars are important alpine browsers. Though not so conspicuous as deer or chamois, they are so numerous that they probably consume just as much vegetation, if not more.

When winter arrives, insects are no longer evident in the mountains, although they have not necessarily died. Because New Zealand experiences a maritime climate, its alpine winters are not so intensely cold as on more continental ranges. Some insects survive as adults by crawling deep between rocks and vegetation and lying in a quiescent state, their body temperatures hovering near freezing point and their metabolic processes at a near standstill.

A MASTER OF SOLAR HEATING

Of New Zealand's 11 endemic species of butterfly the black mountain ringlet (*Percnodaimon merula*) is a true alpine inhabitant. It is most commonly found above 1200 metres in the Southern Alps, particularly on open scree areas. Like other butterflies it sips nectar, which it takes from the flowering herbs and shrubs in its habitat.

To survive in its cold habitat, the black mountain ringlet makes remarkable use of the sun's heat. Like a number of alpine insects it is darkly coloured, which helps it warm in sunlight much faster than if it were a light colour. Warmth is particularly important to a flying insect like the ringlet. In order for its flight muscles to work efficiently they need to be at a temperature of about 32 degrees Celsius, which may be more than 15 degrees higher than the air temperature. To achieve this the butterfly uses its wings like solar heating panels. It opens and carefully orients them at right-angles to the sun's rays, so intercepting maximum solar energy. Blood flowing through the dark wings is rapidly warmed, and the heat is retained in its body by the thick woolly coat of black hairs. During the day, the black mountain ringlet constantly alights on rocks, orienting itself carefully to the sun according to whether it wants to warm up or cool down. If the sun goes in and it becomes too cool for flight, the butterfly folds its wings and seeks safety by crawling into the shelter of rocks or vegetation.

The butterfly even makes use of solar heating to hatch its young. Instead of laying its eggs on plants, as most butterflies do, it deposits them on rocks. Rocks warm in the sun better than foliage and even retain heat for short periods. The only drawback is that, after hatching, the caterpillars have to search for the alpine grasses they feed on.

ISLANDS IN THE SKY

Each discrete mountain range has its intrinsic living character, with its own collection of local races or subspecies of particular organisms, whether they be wetas, cicadas or snails. This has happened by a process of genetic isolation. During the Ice Age, alpine conditions existed throughout large areas of lowland and many plants and animals evolved and adapted to these conditions. As the climate slowly warmed again these organisms retreated to the mountain tops where cool conditions prevailed. Here, breeding populations became separated from one another as if on islands, surrounded by 'seas' of inhospitable lowlands.

In time, separate populations evolved distinct local types in response to their differing local conditions. Flightless insects, in particular, have been isolated this way because they cannot travel by wing from range to range. An example is one of New Zealand's alpine wetas, *Hemideina maori*. Studies of *H. maori* populations living on different Otago ranges show that they are visibly distinct from one another, so much so that some people think they are really a series of closely related species.

Alpine weta (*Hemideina maori*)

The greenhouse effect poses a threat to some of these weta populations. Those restricted to the summits of lower ranges have run out of mountain where they can retreat to should the climate get warmer.

INSECTS THAT LOSE THEIR WINGS

In New Zealand there are over 500 species of cranefly (Family Tipulidae). Most commonly seen are the winged 'daddy-long-legs', but the cranefly pictured here is a flightless species that inhabits the alpine mountains of Otago.

Flightlessness is much more common among alpine than among lowland insects. Even some alpine moths display flightlessness among females, while the males retain wings to search for their mates. Flightlessness in alpine regions may have several explanations. Flight muscles have a high energy demand, and need to be warm in order to work effectively. Having wings is hard to justify in the alpine zone, where the climate is often too cold for them to be used. Even if an insect does manage to get airborne, strong winds usually make flying a haphazard method of transport. Worse still, the insect might get blown away from its habitat altogether. This acts as a natural selection process, since it leaves the poor or cautious flyers behind to breed. These therefore have more chance of passing their genes on to the next generation, so the population steadily trends towards flightlessness.

The art of disguise

New Zealand's 12 species of alpine grasshopper demonstrate remarkable camouflage in their various habitats. *Brachaspis nivalis* (left) resembles the colours of the greywacke rock where it lives, right down to the subtle mottled patterns on the stone's surface. *Sigaus australis* (below) wears a mix of olive greens and browns, to superbly match the leaves and twigs of its scrubby home.

By resembling their habitats, grasshoppers avoid being seen by predators. Their impeccable camouflage has evolved by natural selection. Individuals best matching their surroundings are least likely to be eaten. They therefore have more chance of surviving to pass on their successful 'camouflage genes' to the next generation. Thousands of generations of weeding out the poorly matched has produced breeding populations that resemble their surroundings perfectly.

Tussock grasslands

Tussock grasslands, Dansey's Pass

Tussock butterflies
Tussock butterflies are a common sight in the tussocklands in summer. The caterpillars of this one, *Argyrophenga antipodum*, feed on a number of grasses including silver tussock, and are found from sea-level to 2000 metres.

When Europeans first arrived in New Zealand, forest was not the only vegetation covering the plains and foothills. Extensive areas supported tussock grasslands, notably the dry regions of Marlborough, Canterbury and Otago, to the east of the Southern Alps. Short tussock grasslands, consisting of species of *Festuca* and *Poa* covered the lowlands, and these merged with tall snow tussock grasslands of *Chionochloa* about 700 metres above sea-level. Large areas on the damp Southland Plains, as well as the North Island Volcanic Plateau, were covered with tall snow tussock grasslands of red tussock (*Chionochloa rubra*).

For a long time it was thought that the eastern tussock grasslands were the natural vegetation. The regions they covered were considered too dry for the growth of forest. Then evidence came to light that there was once a forest cover. In some areas, old logs were found littering the soil surface and buried layers of charcoal were uncovered.

From these remains the history of the tussock grasslands has been put together. Conifer-broadleaved forest originally covered much of the lowlands, with beech forest on the hills. The only exceptions were some inland areas, such as the Cromwell Basin, where the climate was seasonally too cold or dry for forest. A change in the climate, starting about 2000 years ago, led to increasing drought in the east. This made the old forest susceptible to fires, probably lit by the Maori during the last 1000 years, which burnt wildly out of control. Vast forest tracts were incinerated and dry conditions, along with repeated burning, retarded regeneration of trees. The burnt areas were invaded by grasses which spread out from their normal habitats. Hard tussock (*Festuca novae-zelandiae*) and silver tussock (*Poa cita*), which previously grew on dry sites in open river valleys and forest clearings, colonised the lower slopes, as well as blue tussock (*Poa colensoi*), which grew in both alpine and lowland regions. Red tussock, which was common in boggy areas, became more widespread on moister ground. In the uplands, the alpine snow tussocks spread down from the mountains to occupy areas that were previously high-altitude forest.

Other plants also extended their range with the forest destruction. These came from open habitats and so were already tolerant of exposed dry environments. Matagouri (*Discaria toumatou*), a spiny bush normally found on dry riverflats, is one example. It has reduced leaves that largely disappear in late spring as an adaptation to summer drought. Other examples are the brooms (*Carmichaelia*) found in tussock grassland, all of which have insignificant leaves, relying instead on flattened green stems for photosynthesis. Smaller plants of tussock grasslands include bushes of *Cassinia*, *Pimelea*, and *Leucopogon*, as well as several speargrasses.

SKINKS

Apart from geckos, skinks (Scincidae family) are the only other lizards native to New Zealand. One of the unusual features of New Zealand's geckos and skinks is that, with the exception of one skink species, all give birth to live young. This is rare among lizards in other parts of the world. Most lizards lay eggs. Live birth, where it is found, usually occurs in cooler regions. Its prevalence among New Zealand lizards is thought to have evolved in adaptation to this country's cool climate, particularly during the Ice Age. The eggs, rather than being laid, are held within the body until they hatch. Since lizards seek out warm sunny spots to bask, this ensures that the eggs are kept at a favourable temperature.

There are over 25 species of skink in New Zealand. These live in open habitats, including scrub, seashores, rocky outcrops and grasslands, where they feed upon small animals and occasionally carrion. They have few of the adaptations for climbing trees and shrubs that the more forest-dwelling geckos have, such as adhesive toe pads and 'prehensile' tails. Rather they are more adapted for a ground-dwelling or burrowing life. For example, their ear drums are protectively sunk into cavities on the side of the head and they have protective eyelids.

Leiolopisma infrapunctatum

About nine species of skink are found in the South Island mountains, up to subalpine regions. Here they tolerate extremes of environment, from blistering hot summer days to chilling winter nights. They cope with such a daunting climate by maintaining a basking behaviour. In the early morning skinks locate themselves in a sunny spot. Then during the day they regulate their temperature by returning to bask if they are too cool or retreating into the shade if they are too hot.

The effect of farming

Tussock grasslands were exploited early in the European settlement of New Zealand. They offered ready-made grazing country and by the middle of the last century large sheep-runs were established. The life of the run-holders epitomised the pioneer spirit, when vast and lonely acreages of rolling tussocklands were managed on horseback, and musters lasted for weeks at a time. But while the lifestyle was romantic, the impact upon the tussock environment was often devastating.

To improve the palatability of the native grasses, they were periodically burnt to provide a flush of tender young growth that the sheep relished. This opened up the tussocks and destroyed the leaf litter. Grazing by sheep, followed by plagues of rabbits and other introduced animals, depleted the slower-growing and more palatable plants, allowing the thinned vegetation to be invaded by faster-growing and less palatable plants, particularly introduced weeds.

These are now common in many short-tussock grasslands, to the point of being dominant on favourable sites. Prevalent weeds are browntop, Chewing's fescue, catsear, hawkesbeard, sheep's sorrel and sweet vernal. In parts of inland Otago too harsh even for many weeds, the loss of tussock has left a virtual wasteland of bare ground, apart from the growth of the native mat-like scabweed, *Raoulia australis*.

In the tall-tussock grasslands at higher altitudes introduced weeds are not as prevalent, although burning and grazing have had their impact. In places tall tussocks have been replaced by faster growing and less palatable species of short tussock, such as blue tussock.

Today, tussocklands have gone from more accessible and productive areas. Topdressing with fertilisers and oversowing with introduced grasses and clovers have largely replaced them with productive grazing pastures. Sometimes they have been turned to forestry or croplands. Where tussock landscapes remain, in the inland river basins and foothills of Otago, Canterbury and Marlborough, attempts have been made in some sensitive areas to alleviate further damage by the cessation of burning, retirement from grazing and control of rabbits.

TUSSOCKLANDS —
THE VULNERABLE HABITAT

Most non-alpine tussocklands have been created by the burning off of an original forest cover. If left alone they would revert back to forest. Native trees can only invade tussocklands slowly, because they are not well adapted to establish in dry conditions. This leaves the way open for introduced trees, mainly pines but also larch, Douglas fir and others, which have already proved capable colonisers of tussocklands. Escapees from pine plantations and shelter belts have spread at an alarming rate into surrounding areas. They have advantages over native trees of being tolerant to cold and drought, having good seedling establishment and rapid growth. In years to come there is a very real prospect that inland tussockland will turn into naturalised exotic forest.

CHAPTER 3

THE FOREST

On first entering a forest, most people's impressions are of overwhelming and profligate growth. From the forest floor, tall trees rise like pillars, holding aloft a vaulted ceiling of leaves. The sheer size of many specimens speaks of immense age. A kahikatea, its crown swaying in the breeze 50 metres above, may have germinated at the time that people first reached New Zealand, about a thousand years ago. A kauri may be twice this age.

But a forest is much more than trees. The complicated architecture of trunks and branches is home to many other organisms. Lichens, mosses, ferns, orchids and many other plants are in abundance. In moist, western rainforests they smother virtually every available surface. If you look carefully you will see there are animals too. A green gecko gives itself away as it darts for cover. The thud of falling wood betrays a kaka ripping apart rotten branches in search of grubs.

None of these plants and animals simply live in the forest. They are the forest. The life of each one has a part in the complex community. A single tree will support hundreds of other organisms. Yet its life also depends on many of these organisms. It may need insects to pollinate flowers, fungi to help collect minerals from the soil and birds to distribute seeds. These are a few of the relationships on which forests are built. They are the most complex living systems on land.

Rainforest, Fiordland

Conifer-broadleaved forest

Conifer-broadleaved forest, with its mixture of evergreen trees and welter of small plants, flourishes on the moist lowlands of New Zealand. To visitors used to temperate forests elsewhere in the world it appears unexpectedly luxuriant, almost tropical. Towering coniferous trees of podocarps and sometimes kauri rise over a dense canopy of broadleaved flowering trees, which in turn grow above other canopies of smaller trees and shrubs. The whole multi-layered community is then entwined by lianes and hung with perching epiphytes, creating a verdant assemblage of plant life.

This complexity is nurtured by New Zealand's benevolent maritime climate, which is wet and mild, without seasonal extremes. Regular and generous dousings of rain allow plants to take hold almost anywhere. Shaggy coats of mosses and ferns clothe the sides of tree trunks and clusters of epiphytes grow on canopy branches. The lack of prolonged cold or dry periods also means that there is no need for proper dormancy. Most trees remain evergreen rather than shedding their leaves in the autumn 'fall' so characteristic of the oakwoods and beech forests of north temperate regions.

The podocarps

The podocarps belong to a Southern Hemisphere family of coniferous trees named the Podocarpaceae. Best known are the five giants whose presence dominates the conifer-broadleaved forest; rimu (*Dacrydium cupressinum*), kahikatea (*Dacrycarpus dacrydioides*), miro (*Prumnopitys ferruginea*), matai (*P. taxifolia*) and totara (*Podocarpus totara*). Like grand dignitaries they stand head and shoulders above the other trees. From the forest floor to the top of the crown may span 50 metres, not to mention over 800 years of life.

Which of the five is most common depends partly on the soil conditions. Totara, matai and kahikatea favour fertile soils. Where these soils are dry, totara predominates. Where they are wet, stands of kahikatea are common. Rimu, the most widespread of podocarp trees, prevails on less fertile soils, as does miro. Such individual preferences dictate the way a forest can change as one generation of trees inevitably replaces another. If the forest soil is slowly becoming less fertile, then a rimu seedling will have a favoured chance of replacing a fallen totara. If the area is becoming swampy, then a young kahikatea may grab the spot. No forest is static, though given the extraordinary lifespan of a podocarp, the pace of change seems to be so compared with our own ephemeral lives.

Rimu Kahikatea

Totara Matai Miro

So prominent are the five podocarps that rule over the conifer-broadleaved forest that it is easy to overlook the others of their family. There are, in fact, 17 different members of the Podocarpaceae in New Zealand. Among them are the dwarf pines (*Halocarpus*), and the curious celery pines (*Phyllocladus*), whose apparently broad leaves are not leaves at all, but flattened green stems. Perhaps the most unusual of all, certainly in comparison with giants such as the rimu and kahikatea, is the pygmy pine (*Lepidothamnus laxifolium*). In boggy areas, where it is not uncommon, it grows no higher than your ankles.

The podocarps belong to the conifers, a group that represented the acme of plant evolution about 200 million years ago, before the now more numerous flowering plants pushed them to one side. Instead of bearing flowers, they reproduce via the structurally more simple cones, which are pollinated by the wind. Other conifers include the native kauri and kawaka, as well as the introduced pines, spruces and firs from the Northern Hemisphere. The podocarps, however, are distinguished by not bearing their seeds in typical cones. They are often held instead on a fleshy stalk or within a succulent 'berry', which is edible. This way the podocarp seeds are distributed by fruit-eating birds.

Although the Podocarpaceae family first appeared in the Jurassic period, 190–135 million years ago, they came into their own during the Cretaceous period, 135–65 million years ago. This was at a time when the southern continents were joined together in the single supercontinent of Gondwana, and dinosaurs roamed the Earth. Today, about 100 family members still grow on these southern lands, which have now split into the continental fragments of South America, Africa, Australia, New Guinea and New Zealand. Podocarps are therefore a part of New Zealand's ancient natural heritage. Fossil records suggest that rimu and kahikatea have changed relatively little in the last 70 million years. By contrast, our own species, *Homo sapiens*, has been in existence for less than a million years.

The layered forest

Compared with the three canopy layers typical of temperate forests in the Northern Hemisphere, up to five layers can be recognised in the conifer-broadleaved forest, each with its own particular mixture of plants.

The emergent layer
The very tallest of the forest trees thrust their crowns well above the main canopy, hence the term emergent. The most common emergents are the five podocarps: rimu, kahikatea, totara, matai and miro, whose massive trunks stand 30–50 metres tall. A few of the flowering trees can also grow tall enough to be considered emergent. Northern rata can climb to these heights by attaching itself to the trunk of a host podocarp tree. Pukatea and rewarewa are forest giants rising to heights of over 30 metres.

Trees that reach these airy realms grow in an environment completely different from that of the sheltered layers below. Their leaves enjoy first shares of the sunlight, but at the same time they have to endure the greatest extremes of humidity and temperature. Their crowns must also bear the full brunt of the wind. Emergents therefore need massive trunks for support. Kahikatea and pukatea, which grow on very soft, swampy ground, gain extra support by bracing themselves with plank buttresses that spread out from the base of their trunks.

The subcanopy layer
This layer, which is about 10–15 metres above the ground, contains a wide assortment of small trees and large tree ferns. Among the trees are mahoe, whose skeleton leaves often litter the ground, and New Zealand's only native palm, the nikau. Many of the subcanopy trees specialise in colonising forest clearings, ripped open by storms or slips. Here, and along forest margins, there will be thickets of wineberry, fuchsia, lacebark, pigeonwood and putaputaweta. They are the pioneers of the forest world, able to grow and mature quickly in the flood of light, seeding themselves before they are eventually shaded out by the slower-growing trees of the main canopy.

The forest floor
The moist twilight of the forest floor provides an ideal environment for simple plants such as mosses and ferns, many of which could not survive if exposed to the full force of the sun and wind. A number of tiny flowering plants also live here. Hidden in the carpet of mosses are tiny orchids, whose intricate flowers reward a patient search. Elsewhere one may find creeping mats of red-berried *Nertera* and feathery clumps of *Astelia*, bush rice grass and hook grass.

The hardwood canopy layer The majority of trees form a dense mixed canopy about 20 metres above the ground. Most are flowering trees. The relative abundance of different types varies from Northland to Southland. In the far north, taraire and towai are prevalent. Taraire gives way to its close relative tawa near the middle of the North Island, and tawa, in turn, gives way to kamahi as the commonest tree in the South Island. Many other trees come and go in the canopy. Puriri and black maire, for example, are more common in the North Island than in the South Island. Southern rata and Westland quintinia occur in both islands, but are particularly abundant on the west coast of the South Island.

The shrub layer
This layer is the one which we, as ground dwellers, are most familiar with. At one time it would also have been the layer most familiar to the flightless moas, which avidly dined on the reachable vegetation. Perhaps for this reason many of the shrubs seem to carry some form of defence to deter browsing. Hardly needing introduction are the stinging leaves of tree nettle. Then there are those with peppery or downright foetid tastes, such as kawakawa, mountain horopito and *Coprosma foetidissima.* The leaves of tutu and rangiora are toxic. Also discouraging the attention of hungry moas would be the divaricating shrubs (page 64), whose small leaves are held within a protective mesh of criss-cross branches.

Ancient forms The forest shelters some life forms that have changed little in millions of years. One example is *Tmesipteris*, a plant often found hanging in clumps from the trunks of tree ferns. *Tmesipteris* has no roots and its leaves are barely more than simple appendages. Essentially it is a stem growing from a rhizome lodged in the trunk of a tree fern.

Tmesipteris, however, has vascular tissue. If you were to look inside a stem you would find bundles of phloem and xylem vessels, which distribute water and food along the length of the plant. This is significant to botanists since it places *Tmesipteris* among the vascular plants, which include the more advanced ferns, conifers and flowering plants. *Tmesipteris* belongs to a group of plants which are the simplest of vascular plants alive today. In many ways it resembles the earliest vascular plants, which colonised land about 400 million years ago.

The kauri

In the warm far north of the North Island the giant kauri (*Agathis australis*) joins the conifer-broadleaved forest. With a massive trunk and a 50-metre-high crown it all but takes over. Even the podocarps are dwarfed by the tree's monumental presence.

The kauri is a conifer, which is apparent immediately you see one of its typical cones, or one of its triangular woody seeds, which are not unlike those of *Pinus radiata*. The tree belongs to the Araucariaceae, a Southern Hemisphere family whose ancestry extends to the golden age of conifers some 200 million years ago. Other members of the family are found mostly in the western Pacific and South America. Among them are the Norfolk Island pine and the monkey puzzle tree of Chile.

The life of a kauri starts with the groundwards fall of a seed from a cone high in the canopy. Small wings give it a skittish descent, tossing and tumbling through the air, but sheer weight means it rarely travels far from the parent before coming to rest on the forest floor. If the seed lands somewhere not too shady and its energy-rich food stores do not become a meal for a passing animal, the young plant will germinate and slowly make its way skywards. By the age of 35 years it will start producing its own cones and seed. By the time it is 100 years old the first branches will have poked their spiky leaves above the forest canopy, about 30 metres from the ground. Then for the remaining 2000–4000 years of its life, for no one is exactly sure how long a kauri lives, the tree puts on girth. The crown loses the gracious conical form of youth and thrusts out massive branches, which hold a lofty plateau of foliage above the canopy. The trunk meanwhile takes on its famous columnar form, perhaps 20 metres in circumference with barely a taper for the first 25 metres from the ground. By the time the tree reaches old age it will have assumed its status as the 'redwood' of New Zealand. In terms of its volume of wood, the kauri is by far the biggest of all native trees. It ranks as a giant, even by world standards.

Giants of the forest The kauri (*Agathis australis*) is by far the largest of New Zealand's forest trees. The trunk of one specimen was measured to have a girth of 23.4 metres.

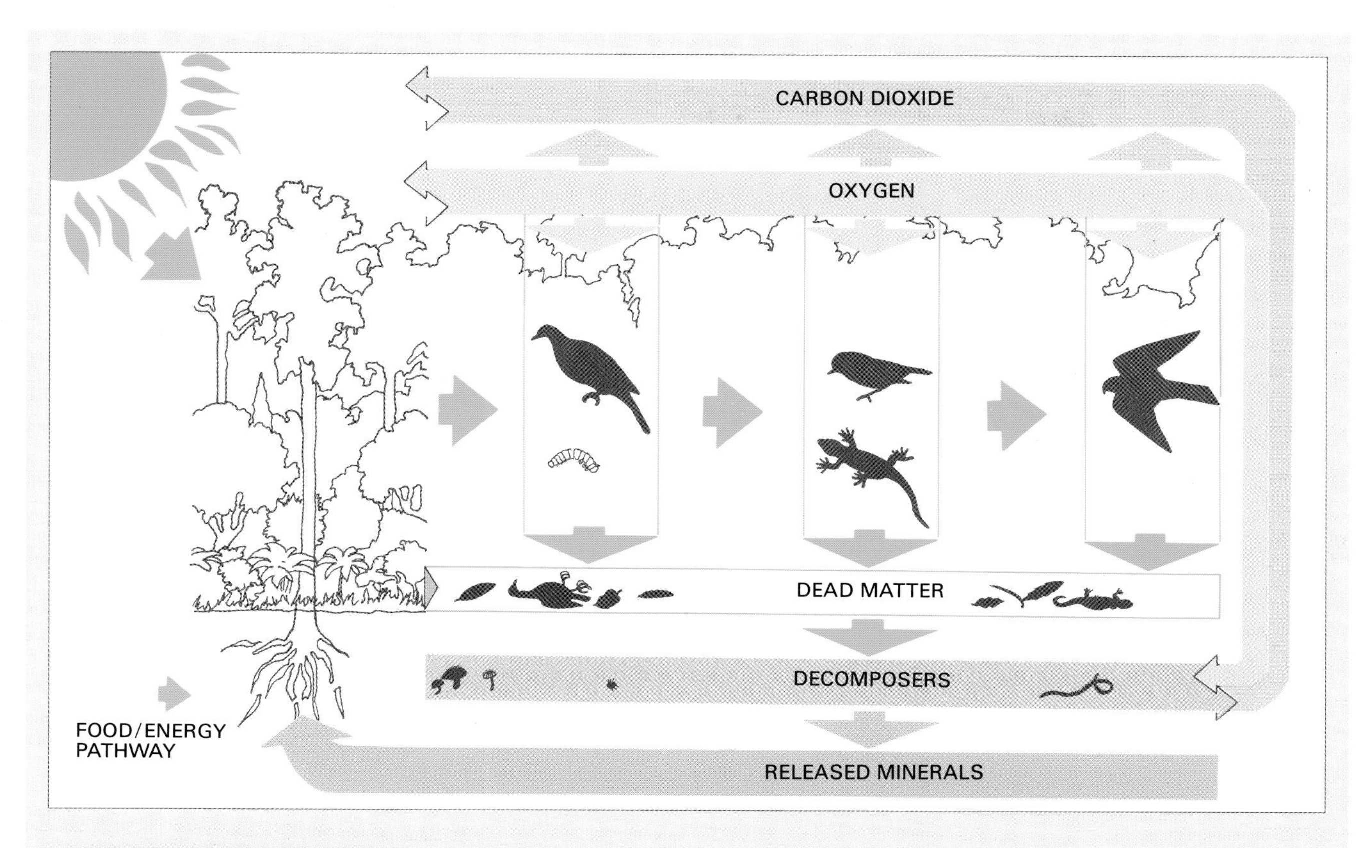

THE FOREST ECOSYSTEM

Any of the organisms living in a forest can be studied as an individual. A pigeon, a caterpillar or a totara: each is engaged in its own quest for growth and reproduction. But if you take a step back to view the forest as a whole, everything that lives in it can be regarded as being part of a much bigger living entity — a kind of superorganism. This is the forest ecosystem. Within it the chemical elements of earth and air are constantly being cycled from the environment through life and back again.

The energy that drives this cycle comes from the sun. Therefore the trees and smaller plants of the forest are crucial. They take water from the soil and carbon dioxide from the air. Then, by the process known as photosynthesis, they use the energy of sunlight to build these into simple sugars, liberating oxygen to the air as a waste product.

These sugars are used for one of two purposes. Some are 'burnt' again to release energy, which the plant can use to fuel its living processes. Oxygen from the air is used to break the sugar molecules down, unlocking the solar energy stored in them. In essence, this is the reverse of photosynthesis, and carbon dioxide is returned to the air. Other sugar molecules, however, are invested in growth. They are combined with minerals that the plant absorbs from the earth and converted into the many organic constituents of wood and leaves.

Plants grow throughout their lives. Each year, new leaves are unfurled and stems are lengthened as their owners seek to obtain more sunlight than their neighbours. Older plants increasingly invest their resources in flowers and fruit, ensuring they leave as many offspring as possible in the next generation.

Inevitably some of this plant growth is eaten by herbivores. Animals, too, need energy and organic materials. Since they cannot produce their own requirements, they take what they need from plants. A forest tree might support hundreds of feeding caterpillars. Flocks of pigeons will descend upon its crown to feast on flowers or fruit. Some of the food they convert to energy in the same way as the plants do, by taking in oxygen and releasing carbon dioxide. Some is converted into the tissues of their growing bodies, or perhaps used to feed their young.

The herbivores may likewise be eaten by predators. A caterpillar may be seized by a robin or a gecko. In this way the solar energy stored by plants flows through the food chains of the forest. A falcon may acquire these resources third hand if it feeds on a gecko or second hand by catching a pigeon.

In the hierarchy of the food chain, the falcon is termed a top carnivore. There are no predators which especially hunt it. But when it dies it will nevertheless be consumed. All dead matter shares a similar fate. On the forest floor it is invaded by millions of decomposing bacteria. Fungi extend feeding filaments into the decaying material, while scavenging animals chew it into smaller and smaller fragments. These organisms also take in oxygen and release carbon dioxide as they tap the energy stored in the organic molecules of the decomposing food source, using it to fuel their own lives. Eventually each item that falls to the forest floor will be broken down. Everything is returned to its original components of water, carbon dioxide and minerals — available to be used again by the solar-driven recycling system of the forest.

Vines and epiphytes

High in the forest canopy, life would seem to be blessed. Leaves receive more light. Flowers are displayed for pollination by insects, and seeds are given a greater chance of dispersal by the birds or the breeze. But such a privilege has a price. To reach the canopy, a tree must invest huge resources in growing a thick trunk, to provide support against not only the force of gravity, but also the wind.

It is perhaps not surprising then that many plants have become adept hitch-hikers, using the trunks and branches of other trees to snatch a spot in the sun. There are two main groups; the vines, or lianes, which scramble upwards from the ground, and the epiphytes, which perch high up on the spreading branches of canopy trees.

Climbing plants

The vines have evolved an assortment of techniques to climb to the canopy. These include hooks, twisting stems and special roots. The infamous bush lawyers (*Rubus*) use backwards-pointing thorns to grip other vegetation like grappling hooks as they scramble up and over shrubs and small trees. This is exactly the same technique as adopted by their introduced relatives the blackberries.

The supplejack vine (*Ripogonum scandens*) relies on the twisting stem method. Its stem tip revolves anticlockwise, coiling itself round branches and thin trunks until it reaches the canopy where it branches out with leafy stems. If the vine does not find a suitable trunk it drops back down to the ground, before twisting back up for another groping search. Often the self-same procedure weaves a frustrated knotty mess on the ground to the despair of trampers.

Other twining climbers use slightly different tactics to ascend their host. The clematis vines (*Clematis*) are a common sight in scrub and along forest margins, particularly in spring when they put on bold displays of creamy white flowers. The vines ascend other plants by means of leaf stalks that are sensitive to touch. When a leaf contacts a branch, it coils, securing itself to the support. Another vine common at forest margins is the native passion flower (*Tetrapathaea tetranda*), which belongs to the well-known and predominantly tropical Passifloraceae family. The vine produces stems modified into tendrils and these 'corkscrew' around small stems and branches.

Hooks and twisting stems work well when there is lots of vegetation to cling to, or thin stems to coil around. But tackling the smooth sheer sides of a massive forest tree calls for a completely different method. This involves producing special roots which grip the host's bark. The rata vines (*Metrosideros*), whose thick woody stems dangle from the canopy, are such plants. The seedling vine starts life on the shady forest floor. When it reaches a tree trunk, it inches its way upwards, sending out short roots to latch onto the bark as it goes. Once in the sunlit canopy the vine puts out masses of foliage. At the same time, its climbing stem thickens to supply water to the burgeoning growth above, eventually becoming so large that it swings free of the host trunk and hangs like a length of hawser.

Climbing to the canopy
A climbing vine of *Metrosideros carminea* makes its way up the trunk of a forest tree by putting out special roots to grip the bark (right). Once in the canopy its leaves will flourish in the sunlight and it will flaunt its flowers to attract the attention of pollinating birds and insects (far right). But trees are not entirely defenceless against the vines and epiphytes that seek to use them as a support. A number, including totara, rimu and kauri, have constantly flaking bark to dislodge the grip of climbing vines and perching epiphytes.

Plants that grow on plants

The epiphytes, or perching plants, do not climb to the canopy. Instead they germinate on canopy branches, their seeds carried there by wind or animals. They therefore occupy a sunny spot right from the start, but face the problem of having no root connections to the ground. Survival means being thrifty with supplies of water and minerals. Astelias and collospermums hold out their pineapple-like rosette of leaves like funnels to catch rainwater. *Collospermum hastatum* channels this precious supply down ridged leaves into special holding tanks where it can be tapped at leisure by roots which grow into the leafy reservoir. Many other epiphytes have special tissues loaded with water-storage cells, like plants that live in deserts.

Gazing up at a canopy branch crowded with epiphytic plants, it is hard to imagine how such a hanging garden ever assembled. It is, in fact, quite a slow process. Lichens and mosses are usually the first to colonise a bare branch. They build up a layer of humus, providing a seed bed for larger plants such as the astelias to take hold. Pendant epiphytic *Asplenium* ferns and weeping clumps of *Lycopodium* may then root themselves in the moist base of the astelias. The steady accumulation of dead matter builds up a soggy water-holding mass and enables the plants to judiciously recycle the products of their own decay. Even animals are eventually attracted to the prospering community. Mosquitoes use the water

EPIPHYTIC ORCHIDS

Orchids epitomise the ingenuity of plants, and none more than those that spend their lives as epiphtyes, perched on canopy branches. Of the world's estimated 30,000 orchid species, about half are thought to be epiphytic. Most inhabit remote tropical rainforests, where large numbers still await classification by botanists. New Zealand has eight epiphytic orchids. Among them is the Easter orchid (*Earina autumnalis*), which is noticed more often for its fragrance than for its sprays of tiny cream flowers.

Orchids deal with the shortage of moisture in their treetop environment by absorbing water quickly while it is available and holding on to it during the drier periods. To do this they have a special layer around their roots called a velamen, which consists of dead cells pierced by tiny holes. When wet these cells fill almost instantly with water, allowing the orchid to capitalise on erratic and brief downpours. This water is then passed on to be stored in special holding cells for use till the next rainstorm.

Epiphytic orchids are also remarkably efficient in how they use water. Most plants lose water rapidly during daylight hours. This is because they must open the stomatal pores on their leaves in order to absorb carbon dioxide for photosynthesis. Unavoidably, as carbon dioxide enters the plant so water vapour leaks out. Orchids can overcome this problem by opening their stomata at night instead, when it is cool and damp. Carbon dioxide is absorbed during the hours of darkness and stored chemically in the leaf. Then during the daytime, the stomata can remain firmly closed while the carbon dioxide is released from storage to be used in photosynthesis.

tanks of collospermums as a nursery to raise their larvae. Ants, millipedes and even earthworms find their way up from the forest floor to inhabit the moist compost of rotting plant matter that the epiphytes produce.

When they die, these small creatures, as well as fallen canopy leaves and airborne particles trapped by the epiphytes, build up a source of nutrients that other plants take advantage of. In time there seems no limit to what takes root in the epiphytic community. Shrubs and even small trees sometimes establish and grow high up in the forest canopy.

Many of these larger plants have no special adaptation to epiphytic life and so fail to reach maturity. A number of trees, however, begin their lives as epiphytes in order to steal a march on the competition for light. The most spectacular of these is the northern rata (*Metrosideros robusta*), whose growth tactics have been likened to those of the strangler figs that live in tropical rainforests. Northern rata first establishes itself as an 'innocent' epiphyte, but as it gets larger it sends down roots that encircle the host trunk. Once these reach the ground, the rata's growth takes off. Its crown becomes massive and competes with the host tree for light. Eventually, the host dies, probably as much of old age as competition, and the rata takes its place, becoming a giant canopy tree in its own right.

Hitching a start
A kamahi (*Weinmannia racemosa*) seedling gains a head start in the race for the canopy by germinating on the trunk of a tree fern. Here it is spared the long battle of growing up through the dark undergrowth. From its perch it will send roots down to the forest floor. Then the kamahi will grow rapidly, engulfing its host and eventually growing into a canopy tree.

Flowers and fruit of the canopy

The canopy conducts its sex life aloof from earthbound observers. Sometimes there is a dusting of fallen rata blossom, blushing red on green moss, or the indiscreet perfume of orchid blooms, drifting with the breeze. But these are scant signs of the perennial quest for reproduction, which trees, like any other organism, undertake with purposeful subtlety.

For the trees of the forest, and most other plants, sexual reproduction requires the transfer of pollen, which contains the male sex cells, to fertilise the female ovule of another plant of the same species. Podocarps, like other conifers, cast their pollen to the whim of the wind, in the hope that some will get carried to a suitable female cone. Most, however, is simply blown away and lost. So podocarps, like all wind-pollinated plants, have to shed millions of pollen grains to ensure a chance of success, much to the discomfort of those humans who get hay fever.

The wind is therefore a fickle go-between. It also works best for tall trees such as the podocarps, whose crowns protrude into the breezy topmost regions of the canopy. Lower down, where the air barely stirs, most plants rely on animals to do their ferrying, by enticing them with flowers. The intricate structure of a flower is not intended for our pleasure. Its bright colours or tempting perfumes are designed to advertise a feast of nectar or pollen to passing pollinators such as insects, birds, bats or lizards. In return for putting on a meal, the flower obtains a vital service from its guests. As the diners move through the canopy, indulging here and there on the floral banquet, they inadvertently carry pollen grains on their bodies from one bloom to the next.

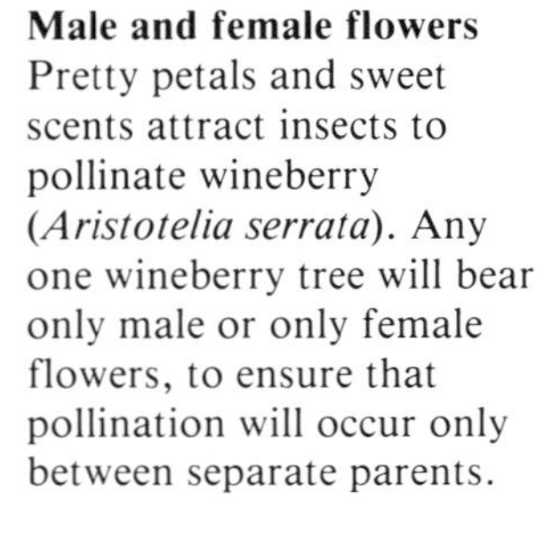

Male and female flowers
Pretty petals and sweet scents attract insects to pollinate wineberry (*Aristotelia serrata*). Any one wineberry tree will bear only male or only female flowers, to ensure that pollination will occur only between separate parents.

Wind pollination
Podocarps shed their pollen into the wind from male cones.

A tree will only achieve sexual reproduction if one of these animals successfully carries the pollen to receptive flowers on another tree of the same species. If a flower fertilises itself or another flower on the same plant, which would be a lot simpler, the important mixing of genes does not occur. Fortunately, plants have perfected a number of ways to avoid this. One way is for the male and female parts of flowers on the same tree to mature at different times. Another is for plants to have the ability to recognise their own pollen and inhibit it from fertilising their ovules. The most popular method among native trees, however, is the simplest and safest. That is to have male and female flowers on completely separate male and female plants, like the wineberry in the photograph.

There remains the problem that a pollinating animal may take the pollen to the wrong type of tree. Pollen from a wineberry deposited on a rata flower is pollen lost. One way to boost the probability of successful fertilisation is for all the trees of a single species to flower en masse, literally swamping the system with their flowers for a short period. The massed flowering of southern rata trees which occurs every few years is one example of this. Another way to increase the chance of pollen being carried to the correct tree is to produce flowers of such distinctive design, colour or scent that they are especially recognised and visited by their pollinators. Such purpose-built flowers are common in tropical rainforests, where some are so intricate that they can only be pollinated by one sort of insect.
In New Zealand, however, complex flowers are the exception rather than the rule. Native plants are serviced by an unusually unspecialised set of pollinating insects, such as flies, moths, beetles and tiny thrips, which are indiscriminate pollinators. The trees therefore have very simple flowers to suit the simple predilections of their visitors, and these often bear the colour which attracts the widest range of insects — white. Even some plants which have colonised New Zealand in the past have simplified their flower structure, adopting the 'open house' policy to suit all comers.

DISPERSING THE NEXT GENERATION

A tree must distribute its seeds, since those that fall on the ground below can rarely compete with the parent. Plants that reach the breezy realms of the canopy can make good use of the wind to do this. The climbing clematis equips its seeds with downy hairs to take them aloft on the breeze.

The wind, however, becomes less effective the more sheltered the tree is in the canopy or the heavier its seeds are. Most trees and shrubs therefore exploit animals as couriers. The kahikatea packages each seed with a tempting edible berry. When the seed is mature, the fruit turns bright red, a colour very visible to birds. If eaten, the seed, which resists digestion, passes through the bird and is excreted intact, with luck, some distance away.

Providing a tasty fruit uses resources the tree could otherwise invest in growth. It is a cost which the tree pays in order to get its seeds distributed. It is not surprising, then, that some plants try to obtain the same service on the cheap, by producing fruit of low food value or by mimicking the appearance of tasty berries. For instance, the open capsules of *Pittosporum* display what appears to be a very exciting meal, whereas they offer nothing more than hard seeds coated with a sticky golden glue which attach to any animal inquisitive enough to investigate.

Small ground plants can use the general traffic of animals that wander to and fro on their everyday business. The forest-dwelling hook grasses (*Uncinia*) and the bidibidis (*Acaena*) of grassy clearings have hooked seeds to hitch on to passing animals. The tiny seeds of a hook grass have attached themselves to the feathers of a kiwi.

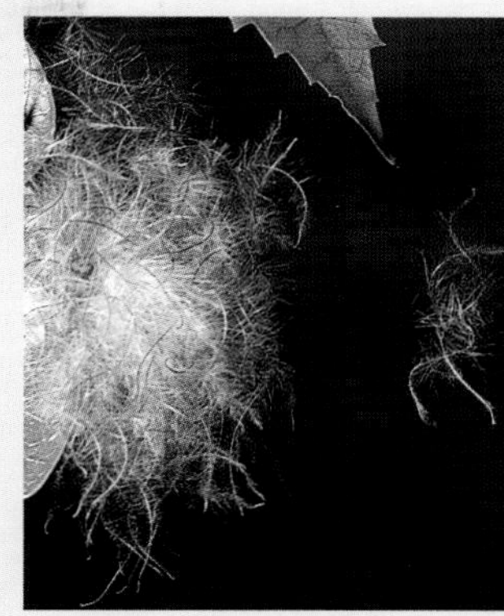

Clematis

Kahikatea

Pittosporum

Hook grass

SEED STRATEGIES

The seeds of miro are more than a hundred times larger than those of northern rata, yet both will grow into trees of similar sizes. So what is the reason for the difference?

For plants, there is a trade-off between producing a small number of large seeds, like the miro, and a large number of small seeds, like the rata. A large seed with lots of food reserves has a greater chance of surviving than a small one. But smaller seeds have the advantage that more can be produced, increasing the numerical chance that some will land in a spot suitable to grow. Large seeds are often produced by trees such as miro, whose seedlings are intended to germinate on the shady forest floor. Having a large food store enables the seedlings to get by while they grow above the immediate shade of the ferns and mosses, and, if needs be, to survive in poorly lit conditions until a falling tree opens up a well-lit gap for them to grow into. Northern rata, by contrast, establishes itself in the sun-drenched canopy as an epiphyte. Shortage of light is therefore not a difficulty. A much bigger problem is overcoming the odds against lodging a seed on a suitable branch. So rata produces thousands of tiny seeds that blow like grains of pepper through the canopy, gathering in nooks and crannies among the branches.

The high-seed-numbers strategy is also used by the so-called pioneer trees such as wineberry, fuchsia and ribbonwood, which specialise in colonising well-lit clearings in the forest, opened when slips or storms topple a few canopy trees. Once again, shortage of light is not a problem. But it is important to be on the site quickly to grab a sunny spot before everything is shaded out again. So it is prudent to improve the chances of this by shedding large numbers of widely distributed seeds.

Miro seeds (left) and rata seeds (right)

Canopy birds — the nectar and fruit eaters

Red for birds Bright red blooms and heavy nectar production are typical of bird-pollinated flowers. Northern rata (*Metrosideros robusta*) (above) holds out its red stamens like tiny pin cushions, dusting its visitors with pollen to be carried to other flowers.

The pigeon The native pigeon (*Hemiphaga novae-seelandiae*) (right) is primarily a fruit eater, although it also feeds on flowers and leaves. To satisfy its varied diet it travels widely through the forest each year, sampling the seasonal menu as various trees come into flower or fruit. In early summer it may sate its appetite on kahikatea or rimu fruit, and later feast on a canopy spread with succulent tawa 'plums', and cherry-red berries of miro. When winter arrives and food is scarce it ranges further afield, perhaps searching out kowhai leaves, supplejack berries or winter-fruiting puriri. In spring it may fly into the subalpine silver beech forests to eat the bright orange fruiting bodies of the beech strawberry fungus, before returning to the lowlands to begin its year-long menu again.

Without the constant activity of birds, the forest would be not only austere and silent, it would cease to exist as we know it. Those birds that feed on nectar and fruit do more than satisfy their appetites as they flit from tree-crown to tree-crown through the canopy. At the same time they are pollinating flowers and distributing seeds.

Trees have probably availed themselves of this service ever since birds first took wing. Some have evolved flowers specifically designed for bird pollination, and most produce edible fruit so their seeds will be swallowed and scattered by birds. The birds, meanwhile, have evolved ways to exploit this food source. They have acquired specially designed beaks, tongues or feeding habits to suit a diet of nectar or fruit. No partnership, of course, is knowingly undertaken between the bird and the plant. Each is satisfying its own needs for food or reproduction, but in a way that happens to be mutually convenient. Over millions of years the relationship has developed into an outstanding example of co-evolution. The life of one is now so profoundly dependent on the other that either partner would have difficulty surviving alone.

Among flower-pollinating birds the most important belong to the honeyeater family, Meliphagidae, which includes the tui, bellbird and the now rare stitchbird. All have long, brush-tipped tongues especially designed to lap up the nectar provided by flowers. Trees that rely on bird pollination provide flowers particularly suited to these winged visitors. Their blooms are usually held in clusters on stout branches to give birds ready access. Each flower also produces nectar in amounts that best ensure its chance of being pollinated. This is just enough to provide a worthwhile reward for a visiting bird, yet sufficiently limited to ensure the bird is always kept moving to find more, thereby carrying pollen from flower to flower.

To advertise themselves to the keen colour vision of birds, the flowers are usually red, orange or yellow to stand out against the green of the canopy. Examples of such flowering trees are kowhai, rata, puriri, rewarewa and fuchsia. A specimen in full bloom in the forest becomes a mecca for feathered feeders. Despite the apparent commotion, there is usually a strict hierarchy among the various visitors. The tuis agitatedly assert themselves over the lower-ranking bellbirds. Even the robust kaka may be banished by the chiding of a few belligerent tuis.

The honeyeaters feed on more than nectar. They are omnivorous and eat insects. They also feast on berries of the forest, so they are vital to the distribution of many seeds, particularly from the many smaller-berried plants of the understorey. The pigeon (*Hemiphaga novaeseelandiae*), however, is the most specialised of the seed-distributing birds. Being the largest canopy-fruit

eater it is vital to the distribution of seeds that have large berries, particularly those of miro, tawa and taraire. In fact, tawa seeds germinate better once their fruit coat has been digested by a pigeon.

Pigeons are equally important in the way that they disperse seeds. After gorging themselves on fruit from laden trees, they like to retire to a favourite perch to digest their meal. This will be in a massive and ancient canopy tree, whose lofty branches offer a splendid sunny spot for an afternoon snooze. Below on the forest floor, seeds excreted by the pigeon germinate and wait, ideally placed for the day the aged tree falls and tears a gaping hole in the canopy that they can grow into.

FOREST PARROTS

Parrots are primarily tropical birds, and their short, powerful beaks are ideally suited to crack open the hard casing of seeds for food. They therefore often function more as seed thieves than seed dispersers. New Zealand's lowland forests contain four native species: three are parakeets (*Cyanoramphus*) and the third is the kaka (*Nestor meridionalis*). These have adopted tastes more catholic than many of their tropical relatives in order to get by in this country's less bountiful temperate forests. As well as seeds, they eat fruit, nectar and leaves. They also extract grubs from old tree trunks with their powerful beaks.

Parakeets often fly in small groups, travelling widely across the forest canopy and flocking to abundant food sources. The kaka is a more solitary feeder. It has a brush-tipped tongue for licking up nectar, which it feeds on during the flowering season. As a winter alternative, it has learnt to dig grooves into the bark of southern rata and other trees and lick up the sugary sap that seeps from the wound, returning at intervals to collect more.

Native parrots spend most of their time high in the canopy, even nesting discreetly within tree holes, so they are rarely noticed by earthbound observers. Sadly the truth is also that they have become increasingly scarce. Habitat destruction and introduced animals have taken a toll on their numbers.

Kaka (*Nestor meridionalis*)

ROD MORRIS

THE KOKAKO

Where or when the ancestors of the kokako (*Callaeas cinerea*) originated no one knows. They, along with their relatives the huia and saddleback, have been living in isolation in New Zealand's forests for so many millions of years that they bear no close relationship to birds elsewhere. Therefore the three have been placed in a family of their own, the Callaeidae, commonly known as the New Zealand wattlebirds on account of the fleshy wattles that hang near the corners of their beaks.

None of the wattlebirds has fared well since humans reached New Zealand. Introduced predators, competitors and habitat destruction have all had a part in their downfall. The huia became extinct last century and the saddleback now survives only on offshore islands. The kokako alone still lives on the mainland of New Zealand, though even its future is not assured. The South Island kokako, which has orange wattles, may already be extinct, while the blue-wattled North Island kokako lives only in a few forests.

The kokako is an unusual bird. Unlike the other omnivorous birds that often range widely in search of food, the kokako remains within a territory all the year round. This it proclaims to its neighbours with the most beautifully haunting call, often sung from the top of a tall tree which offers grandstand views of the surrounding forest. The kokako has lost some of its powers of flight and usually travels in short glides between trees, running and hopping among the branches with unusually strong and agile legs. To obtain an adequate diet from within its territory it has developed very wide tastes. It eats some 60–70 different foods, sampled from the canopy right down to the forest floor. Fruit is the dietary mainstay, whether from giant totara and rimu trees, or shrubs of mingimingi and five finger. When fruit is in short supply it may browse the leaves of epiphytes and vines, search for insects, or feast on flowers and buds.

GEOFF MOON

The forest at night

At dusk, when the sun sinks below the western horizon, the forest switches to night-shift. The chorus of cicadas falls silent, and birds of the daytime cease their song. New noises start to fill the air. The shrill cry of a kiwi pierces the darkness. A rasping sound betrays a weta nearby. To wander with a torch is to discover a new world. Long-legged harvestmen come out to patrol tree trunks. Millipedes and centipedes rustle through the leaf litter. Surprisingly, the forest community is as active now as it was during the day.

There are several reasons why animals come out at night. Many of the more 'primitive' creatures are prone to drying out, so prefer the cool dampness of the night. Among these are soft-bodied invertebrates, such as slugs and snails, and arthropods which lack fully waterproofed cuticles, such as the millipedes. Another reason for coming out after dark is that it enables different animals to share the same food source without competing with one another. By feeding at night, the short-tailed bat avoids competing with day-feeding birds for a diet of nectar, fruit and insects. Thus the forest food web works 24 hours a day. The flowers of a tree may be visited by bats, birds, lizards, flies and moths, each coming and going at different times of the day and night.

The cover of darkness also offers some protection from predators. By flying at night, moths avoid insectivorous birds that hunt by day. Their safety, however, is not guaranteed. A cobweb is an equally fatal trap by night or by day, and many spiders prefer to weave their webs after dark. There are also some predators, such as moreporks, kiwis and bats, that have evolved sophisticated night senses to enable them to hunt after dark.

A human can easily get lost in the forest at night, even with a torch. But nocturnal animals find their way with ease. They are able to do so because they live in a sensory world far removed from our own, navigating through the darkness using highly evolved senses of touch, smell or sound, as illustrated by some of the following examples.

Avoiding competition
(below) By feeding at night, the nocturnal gecko (*Hoplodactylus granulatus*) avoids competing for the same foods as day-active species of gecko. It also has different camouflage requirements. It bears sombre greys and browns to conceal itself in its daytime hideout, where it sleeps hidden among dead leaves and branches, whereas geckos that feed in the canopy by day are coloured with greens to match their leafy hunting ground.

Avoiding desiccation
(right) Creatures like this native leaf-veined slug, whose body dries out easily, travel by night to avoid the desiccating conditions of day.

Nocturnal birds

The kiwi (*Apteryx*) and the morepork (*Ninox novaeseelandiae*) hunt at night, though both have different ways to 'see' after dark. The kiwi does so with some very unbirdlike characteristics. It has acquired catlike sensory hairs around the base of its bill to give a tactile sense of its immediate surroundings. It has also partly lost the powers of sight, and cultivated the sense of smell instead, which is usually very poor in birds. Furthermore, in a unique development among birds, the kiwi has its nostrils at the tip of its long beak. The beak therefore makes an excellent sensory probe, which the kiwi constantly taps here and there on the ground as it wanders along, sniffing for food beneath the leaf litter. If something suitable is detected, such as a buried insect grub, it plunges its beak deep into the soil to pluck out the item.

It has been suggested that kiwis also use their sense of smell to keep in contact with one another. They may leave signs of their territorial rights or sexual receptivity in the form of smelly faecal markers or other deposits, in a manner which is more common to nocturnal mammals. Whether this is so awaits further research. Sound, however, is certainly used as a medium for communication, as anyone who has listened to kiwis will testify. During the hours of darkness they maintain a noisy dialogue of whistles, mews, hisses and gruff grunts.

Unlike the kiwi, the morepork flies, so its sensory requirements are very different. Far from abandoning sight, it relies on vision to navigate safely through the forest canopy. Both of its eyes face forwards, giving good binocular vision to judge the distance of objects as it travels through the air. The morepork's vision is also many times more sensitive than our own. In fact its eyes are so large and specialised that they can no longer swivel. Instead the morepork has to turn its head, which can turn at an extraordinary angle. Nevertheless, despite the sensitivity of its eyes, the morepork still requires light in order to see. For this reason it is most active during the twilight hours or when the moon is out.

While sight helps the morepork fly, sound is probably more important for it to locate prey. Owls have evolved a very refined hearing system. From a perch they scan the surrounding forest for telltale noises, partly using their discs of facial feathers to funnel the sounds. Owls have ears widely placed on either side of their broad head, and one ear opening is slightly larger than the other. If the rustling of an animal on the forest floor comes to attention, the slight difference of sound perceived in each ear gives the owl a directional fix on the source. Then when it takes off for the kill, special soft feathers muffle the sound of its beating wings, so it can swoop silently on the unsuspecting prey.

'Seeing' with scent Kiwis (*Apteryx*) (left) rely heavily on scent and touch-sensitive hairs to find their way at night.

Owls The morepork (*Ninox novaeseelandiae*) (below) has large sensitive eyes that can see in dim light. It also has acute hearing.

J.L. KENDRICK DOC

Short-tailed bat
The short-tailed bat (*Mystacina tuberculata*) is unique to New Zealand and is now very rare.

Bats

Bats have evolved the most elaborate navigation system of all night-flying animals. As well as being able to see by light, they 'see' with sound, using the principle of echo-location or sonar. As a bat flies through the forest canopy it emits bursts of ultrasound. Its sensitive ears pick up and time the return of the echoes which bounce off nearby objects and from this it judges their distances. The slightest changes of pitch, timing and volume detected in each ear are used to build up an extraordinarily accurate 'picture' of the surroundings. It is so good that bats can competently snatch night-flying insects on the wing.

New Zealand has three species of bat: the long-tailed bat (*Chalinolobus tuberculatus*) and two species of short-tailed bat (*Mystacina*). The long-tailed bat has close relatives in Australia, so its ancestors probably blew across the Tasman Sea and established in New Zealand within the last few million years. The long-tailed species is so named because of its V-shaped tail membrane, which it uses rather like a net to scoop up flying insects as it hunts in forest glades or over streams. It is by far the commonest bat and it is even at home in exotic forests and farmland.

The purely forest-dwelling short-tailed bats, however, have become increasingly scarce since humans arrived in New Zealand. One of the two species may already be extinct, and the other is now found only in a few forest areas. Short-tailed bats take wing after dusk to search for an unusually wide variety of food. They may visit flowers to lap up nectar or feast on forest berries. Equally they may hunt for insects, snapping them from the air or on the ground.

Many scientists consider *Mystacina* to be among the most unusual of all bats. They are the descendants of a very early group of bats that flew to New Zealand many millions of years ago. Research indicates their ancestors may have originated in South America and spread to New Zealand via Antarctica before it was entombed by ice. Without mammalian predators to contend with on the forest floor, they then evolved into the most terrestrial of all bats. They acquired very strong limbs and a unique way of folding their wings, allowing them to crawl up tree trunks and rummage through the leaf litter in an almost rodent-like way. Unfortunately such habits are now their undoing. Like so many native birds that have evolved partial flightlessness, short-tailed bats are exceedingly vulnerable to introduced predators.

NAVIGATING BY SCENT

Scent plays an important role in the ability of moths to travel by night. The moth-pollinated flowers of *Pittosporum* shrubs and New Zealand jasmine (*Parsonsia*) emit heady scents at dusk to advertise their presence. Similarly, moths signal to one another by scent. When a female moth is ready to mate she releases chemicals called pheromones into the night air. These are picked up by the antennae of the male moth, which are often elaborately branched into comb-like structures to sieve the air for pheromones as he flies along. Detection is extremely sensitive. Just a few molecules are all that is needed to alert the male, before he homes in on the female by following the increasing concentration of her scent.

Sometimes the scent trail does not lead to the encounter that was hoped for. *Celaenia* spiders are thought to have evolved the ability to produce convincing copies of female moth pheromones. All the spiders have to do is sit on a twig in the forest with legs outstretched, ready to grab the male moths that have been fooled by their clever mimicry.

Female moth and *pittosporum*

Forest mammals

When humans first reached New Zealand, the forest community had evolved in the absence of mammals for millions of years. The only exceptions were three native species of bat. So it was inevitable that when people liberated a succession of different mammals, a catalogue of catastrophy would unfold for the forest inhabitants.

First among the introduced predators were the Polynesian rat (kiore) and dog (kuri) released by the Maori, and later the Norway rat, ship rat, cat, dog and stoat brought by Europeans. Many ground-dwelling birds, reptiles, snails and large, flightless insects such as weevils and wetas vanished or became reduced in numbers.

The kuri is now extinct and the kiore more or less restricted to offshore islands, both displaced by the more recent mammals introduced by Europeans. Today, two of the commonest forest predators are the ship rat (*Rattus rattus*) and stoat (*Mustela erminea*). Both are capable tree climbers, so they can feed on eggs and nestlings, as well as forest floor creatures.

Apart from eating other animals, rats eat plant matter, including seeds and seedlings, so they may also affect forest regeneration. So, too, does the introduced house mouse (*Mus musculus*) that is common in forests. It is interesting to note that in Europe, from where the house mouse was brought, other species of wood mice are forest inhabitants. New Zealand's 'house' mouse has been free to extend its habitat and move into the forest in the absence of competition from its relatives.

Pigs (*Sus scrofa*) and goats (*Capra hircus*) living in forest are wild descendants of animals that have been liberated or escaped from captivity at various times since the first arrival of European explorers. Pigs are omnivorous, feeding in scrub and forest on seeds, fruits, ferns, roots, carrion, and invertebrates such as snails. Goats are vegetarian, eating shrubs and seedlings, as well as debarking trees. The way that their teeth are set allows them to graze very close to the ground, giving little chance for young plants to recover.

The impact of grazing mammals on forest plants has been as dramatic as that of the predators on forest animals. As well as goats, eight species of deer have been successfully liberated during European settlement, although one of these, the moose, has probably since died out. In combination, goats and deer have grazed down palatable shrubs and tree seedlings, in some places leaving the undergrowth virtually stripped. Meanwhile the marsupial possum (*Trichosurus vulpecula*), introduced from Australia, has made an expeditious job of devouring the canopy. Historically, native trees have not had to withstand large and specialised canopy browsers, so few have evolved ways to cope with their attentions. Although birds may sometimes eat canopy foliage, they cannot consume leaves as a primary item of diet because they are not a concentrated enough food to fulfil the very high energy demands of flight. The larger and more sedentary possum, however, is amply provided for, devouring masses of leaves and shoots, as well as berries and flowers. Its actions have caused profound changes to the forest. Palatable mistletoes have almost vanished in their wake. In large parts of the country, stands of rata and pohutukawa have been devastated, along with numerous other trees, including fuchsia, kohekohe and mamaku. Pepper tree, pigeonwood and other trees that have distasteful leaf chemicals to defend themselves with have been left.

Introduced grazers can threaten native animals just as seriously as introduced predators, by denying them the plants they need for food or shelter. The effect, however, is less easy to measure. There is, after all, no tangible evidence such as the sight of a bird clamped in the vice-like jaws of a stoat. Native populations just fail to replenish themselves and it is hard to establish the exact cause. Indeed, the cause can be quite complex. For example, with the disappearance of mistletoes, kaka in the South Island beech forest have lost one of their few sources of nectar. At the same time, competition from introduced wasps has denied them access to honeydew. It is not hard to imagine each individual effect compounding. Then all it would take is a natural occurrence, perhaps a few poor flowering and fruiting years, to tip the balance against the kaka altogether.

Deer The white-tailed deer (*Odocoileus virginianus*), a native of North America and northern South America, is one of seven species of deer now well established in New Zealand, and lives on Stewart Island and near Lake Wakatipu. As in its homeland, the white-tailed deer inhabits forests and forest margins, where it grazes understorey shrubs and saplings. It is a shy creature, often only giving itself away with the characteristic white flash of its rump as it bounds into the bushes.

Canopy browser
Mammals have evolved into efficient canopy herbivores in many of the world's forests. Koalas, sloths and some monkeys are examples that have acquired the capacious digestive tracts and steady appetites necessary to make a living by eating nutritionally poor leaves. Because New Zealand has been an isolated landmass for millions of years, its forest canopy has not had to sustain mammalian browsers — until the Australian possum (*Trichosurus vulpecula*) was introduced. For vulnerable trees the impact has been so severe that large forest tracts have been thoroughly denuded. Meanwhile the possum population has soared to over 70 million individuals.

The forest floor

On a walk through the forest it is the canopy that beckons. The antics of birds or the rare colours of forest flowers attract attention. Barely a thought is given to what happens on the ground. Yet here, within the seeemingly lifeless compost of rotting leaves, is one of the most diverse of all animal communities. A single square metre will contain thousands of small animals, from microscopic protozoa to *Powelliphanta* snails that can grow as big as your fist.

The forest floor is a sheltered habitat. The trees above keep it forever moist and dark, with little change of temperature. Such a stable environment favours many primitive groups of land animals whose bodies have not evolved the means to avoid drying out. Crawling through the depths of rotting vegetation are wingless springtails. These tiny creatures, often equipped with a hinged springing apparatus to leap around, belong to a class of arthropod known as the Collembola, which are considered to be primitive relatives of insects. The familiar millipedes are likely to have inhabited the forest litter for as long as plants have shed leaves. Preying on these is a creature of possibly even greater antiquity, the peripatus. Fossils resembling this curious half insect half worm (page 12) have been found in rocks 500 million years old.

Most of the forest-floor creatures spend their lives chewing through the huge amounts of dead leaves and branches that fall continually from the canopy above. They comprise a varied collection of different animal groups, and, remarkably, each group is also represented by scores of different species. For instance, New Zealand is thought to have around 600 species of millipede alone, compared with Britain, which has about 50. Then there are over 170 types of native earthworm and perhaps 1000 species of land snail. Added to this there are symphylans, woodlice, springtails, mites and numerous insect larvae that collectively contribute hundreds, if not thousands, more species.

Exactly how so many different creatures can be engaged in the same task of eating dead leaves and twigs is not fully understood. The finer details of litter decay remain little studied. However, it seems that many are selective about the type and size of plant material they eat, or its state of decay. Also, considering that such factors as temperature, moisture, and the pore sizes that animals can crawl through will all vary at different depths in the litter, one can begin to comprehend how each creature secures its own little niche.

Another surprising fact is that although litter-eating animals may consume huge quantities of dead matter, they usually extract little food value in the process. Most is excreted again in smaller fragments, which are then attacked by smaller animals. In this way a single leaf will be eaten repeatedly by a succession of different creatures before it is finally reduced to its chemical constituents.

The reason for this is that animals have trouble directly digesting much of the organic material contained in leaf litter, particularly cellulose and lignin, which are the main components of woody tissue. This aspect of the decay process is done chiefly by fungi

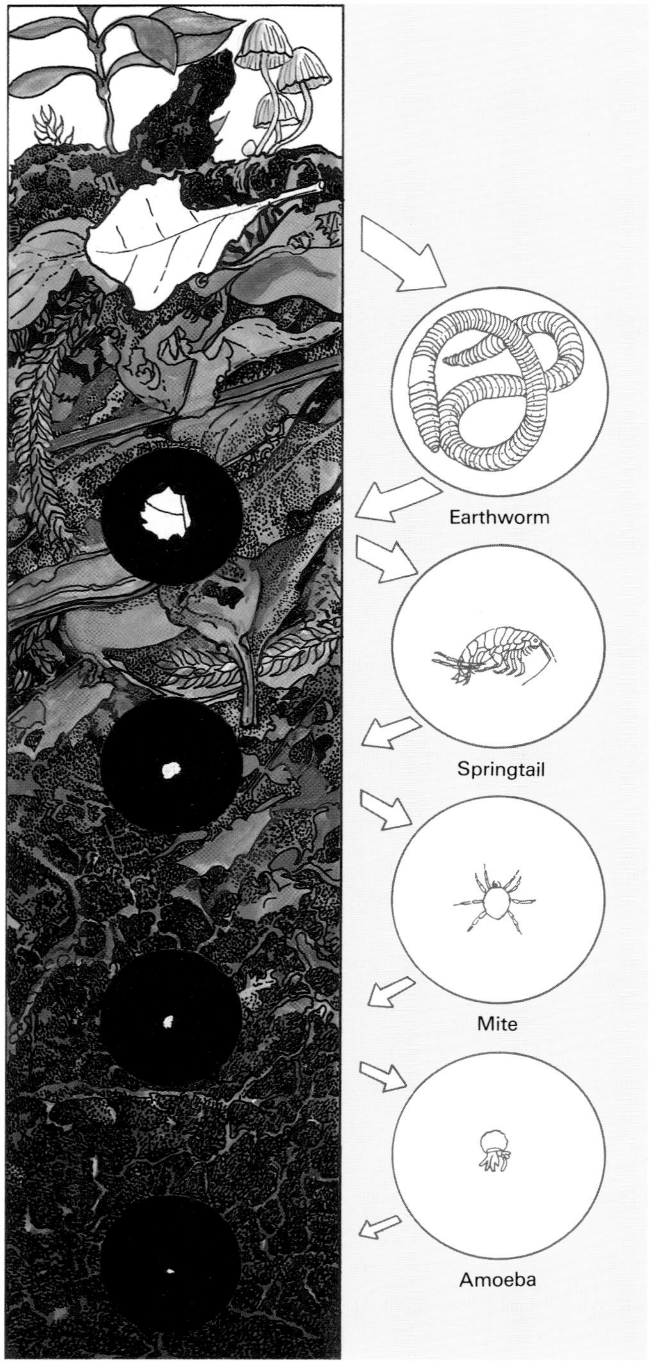

Leaf litter consumers
Although the forest floor may receive little energy directly from the sun, it receives it second hand, stored as food in the steady rain of dead matter that falls from the canopy above. This fuels the enormously mixed community of litter animals. Each organism seems to find its place in the overall scheme by eating litter of different dimensions and different stages of decay. In this way the dead material is reduced to ever-decreasing sizes and its mineral elements are released to be absorbed once more by the trees above.

Millipedes (far left)
Millipedes are vegetarian creatures and most feed on leaf litter. This one, the pill millipede, inhabits the surface layers of the litter, where it is likely to be attacked by birds and other predators. To deal with such an event it rolls neatly into a defensive ball, exposing the hard plates of its exoskeleton on the outside.

Agents of leaf decay
These tiny *Marasmius* fungi (left) have grown and fruited from a single fallen leaf.

and bacteria which can produce the necessary enzymes. The litter animals in turn often get more of their nourishment from the fungi and bacteria than the dead plant matter itself. One could logically conclude, therefore, that litter animals are more of a hindrance to decay than a help. However, by constantly chewing up and circulating the litter they make it more accessible to fungi and bacteria. Also, because the fungi and bacteria are continually being eaten, they are always kept actively growing and replenishing themselves — by breaking down more litter. So the animals help keep the whole process from stagnating.

Fungi and decay

Largely unseen but forever present, fungi are ceaselessly at work breaking down the leaf litter. The cycle of decay would not operate properly without them, for fungi can produce enzymes to dismantle virtually any of the complex substances produced by living organisms. Significantly, they can tackle cellulose and lignin, both of which are major components of plant tissues that almost all other organisms find indigestible.

Some fungi are no more than single-celled organisms, but most are filamentous, growing via long strands called hyphae that extend through the dark depths of the litter or within fallen logs. As the hyphae spread, so they secrete enzymes which digest surrounding organic matter, breaking it into simpler substances which can then be absorbed and used as food. An actively growing fungus may produce 100 metres of hyphae in a day, which branch endlessly into a cobwebby mass called the mycelium.

Sexual reproduction occurs when two compatible strains of fungal hyphae meet and fuse. A secondary mycelium is produced which then produces fruiting bodies. Often these fruiting bodies are so small as to be barely visible. However, many members of the ascomycete and basidiomycete fungi are responsible for producing the conspicuous mushrooms and toadstools encountered on the forest floor. Each of these is designed for liberating spores, whether by wind, water or passing animals, so the fungus can renew its life of decay elsewhere.

DISPERSING SPORES

Fungi disperse their spores with all the ingenuity that plants disperse their seeds. The basket fungus, *Ileodictyon cibarius*, belongs to the stinkhorn family, which uses insects to disperse their spores. When the fruiting body is ripe it expands into the distinctive basket structure which has a brown spore-carrying mucus, or gleba, smeared on the inside. The gleba smells exactly like animal dung, and flies attracted to it carry away spores that stick to their legs. Puffball fungi, such as those of *Lycoperdon*, are so named because when hit by a rain drop they launch a cloud of spores into the breeze. The birdsnest fungus, *Crucibulum laeve*, uses rain in a different way. When a raindrop splashes into one of its nests, the spore-filled eggs are shot out. Each egg is equipped with a tiny cord with a sticky end which then whips itself around nearby supports.

Top: basket fungus (*Ileodictyon cibarius*); bottom: birdsnest fungus (*Crucibulum laeve*); far right: *Lycoperdon*

Carnivorous snails
Measuring up to 10 centimetres in diameter, New Zealand's large and beautiful *Powelliphanta* snails are an impressive sight on the forest floor. They are voracious carnivores, hunting earthworms, slugs and smaller snails, which they demolish with the hundreds of tiny dagger-like teeth that cover their radula, or tongue. They belong to an extremely ancient family of snail, the Rhytididae, which prowled the forests of Gondwana over 100 million years ago, at the time of the dinosaurs.

Hunters of the forest floor

Like any community, the forest floor has its predators. Many of these remain hidden by day beneath the mulch of leaves and branches, but come out at night to patrol the forest floor. The peripatus is one example. More common are the centipedes, which use a pair of poison fangs to capture other invertebrates. Although they look similar to millipedes they are not closely related. They have one rather than two pairs of legs on each segment, and flattened bodies to crawl beneath fallen twigs and leaves. Species of different shapes hunt at different depths in the litter. The deepest layers are inhabited by thread centipedes, which have evolved to become extremely thin as well as blind in their confined and perpetually dark habitat.

The most numerous hunters of the forest floor belong to the class of arthropods known as the Arachnida, which include false scorpions, harvestmen and spiders. The false scorpions are tiny creatures, measuring only a few millimetres long, with a pair of crab-like poison claws. They crawl through the lower layers of litter, preying on small inhabitants such as mites and springtails. Harvestmen, with their typically spindly legs, are sometimes known as 'daddy-long-legs'. Some are ornately covered with bumps and spines, and have large grasping pedipalps which they use to seize dead and live prey. There are hundreds of species of spider. Those living within the litter are usually very small,

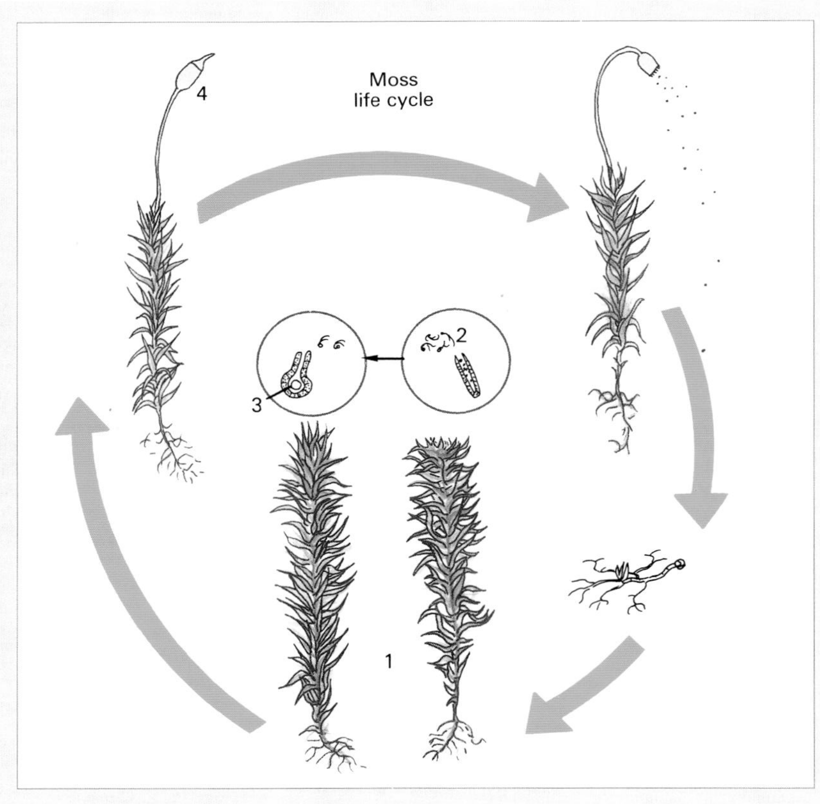

THE SEXUAL LIFE OF MOSSES AND FERNS

The life cycle of mosses and ferns makes a fascinating comparison with that of the more familiar flowering plants and conifers. Their reproduction is a two-stage affair, sexual then asexual in alternate generations. What may be more surprising is that they produce swimming sperm.

Essentially, sexual reproduction is the fusion of two cells, termed haploid cells, to produce one cell with double the amount of genetic material. These cells, termed diploid cells, must at some stage then halve their genetic content again, becoming haploid, before sexual reproduction can recur.

The familiar green moss plant (1) is the sexual generation consisting of haploid cells. This produces male sperm (2) and female eggs (3). When there is sufficient moisture, the male sperm, each with beating, whip-like flagella, are extruded onto the plant surface. They then journey through the thin film of moisture coating the moss, impelled towards the egg by chemical attractors. Once fertilised, the egg, now with double the genetic content, multiplies and grows into the diploid generation. This produces a hollow capsule held aloft on a narrow stem (4), which is still attached and dependent on the green moss for nutrition. Within the capsule, cells divide asexually to form hundreds of tiny haploid spores, which are then cast to the air to grow into new moss plants.

Ferns have evolved to better suit life on dry land. Spores, similar to those of the mosses, germinate on the moist forest floor and first grow into a thallus (1), a small green sliver, perhaps only a few millimetres in length. The surface dwellers are considerably bigger. The bush wolf spiders go in active search of prey. The tunnel web spiders prefer to wait within silk-lined lairs for an insect to pass. They lay out silk 'tripwires' that trail away from their hideouts to inform them when a victim is near and leap out to grab the unwary prey. Sometimes the plan backfires. Instead of prey, the black tunnel web spider (*Porrhothele antipodiana*) may find that the hunting wasp *Salius monachus* has lured it out. The tables are turned and with a sting the wasp immobilises the spider and carries it away as food for her larvae.

Simple plants of the forest floor

The moist and sheltered world of the forest floor provides the perfect environment for two groups of plants which are only partly adapted to life on dry land. One group is the mosses and liverworts, collectively called the bryophytes. The other is the ferns or pteridophytes. The bryophtyes are the simplest of land plants, being tied to damp places because they have few specialised structures to absorb and retain water. Most, for example, lack a waterproof coating or cuticle on their green surfaces, and although they have root-like appendages called rhizoids, these are not properly adapted to absorb and transport water. They must therefore grow close to the moist forest floor, like a soft green carpet. The bryophytes also need water for sexual reproduction. They produce sperm that must swim their way to fertilise the egg, much as their primitive forbears the aquatic algae did.

Ferns have evolved a structure considerably more sophisticated than that of the mosses and liverworts. They have strong stems supporting large leaves covered with a watertight cuticle. Roots absorb water and minerals, which are transported to the leaves by an efficient vascular system of canals. Other parts of the vascular system meanwhile conduct sugars back down to the roots. These developments allow ferns to reach a significant size without drying out, the largest being the tree ferns. Nevertheless, like the mosses, ferns produce swimming sperm during sexual reproduction, so they still require moisture to complete their life cycle.

Although mosses and ferns are considered to be primitive plants, this does not mean they are unsuccessful. They carpet the shady forest floor to the virtual exclusion of other understorey plants. There are also some mosses that flourish in habitats that are periodically very dry, such as on the tops of exposed boulders. These mosses manage by surviving in a dormant, almost completely dried-out state — something that would kill more advanced plants. When moisture falls, the moss rehydrates and resumes growth.

A few ferns, too, can colonise relatively dry places. Bracken (*Pteridium esculentum*) does so by avoiding sexual reproduction, with its need for water, and replicates itself asexually by sending out rhizomes.

Ferns Ferns, like the more advanced conifers and flowering plants, have an efficient vascular system of conducting tubes which carry water, minerals and food throughout the plant. These are apparent as veins in the leaf of the hound's tongue fern (*Phymatosorus*). The vascular system is a vital adaptation to life on dry land, allowing a plant to grow large yet keep all its parts supplied with essential requirements.

often no bigger than a fingernail. The thallus is equivalent to the haploid stage of the green moss, since it produces the male sperm (2) that must swim through a film of water to fertilise the female egg (3). Next there is a major departure from the moss situation, for the fertilised egg does not grow into a simple spore-bearing capsule and stalk; it becomes the large and familiar leafy fern (4). Thus in ferns the diploid stage, which now bears spores from under its leaves, is the dominant one. This is an evolutionary progression one might expect. Since the diploid stage is not involved in sexual reproduction, it is not tied to water. Therefore it is free to grow tall.

The situation in mosses and ferns can now be compared with that in the more advanced conifers and flowering plants, collectively called the spermatophytes. Here the plant, for example a kauri tree, is the now-massive equivalent of the tiny diploid moss capsule and stalk, and it produces the equivalent of their spores, which are male or female. The female spores are retained by the tree within the shelter of a cone, where they are fertilised by the male spores, now called pollen, which are blown to it by the wind. So the need for sexual reproduction to occur on the moist confines of the forest floor has been negated and the haploid stage reduced to a tiny entity, contained within the parent plant.

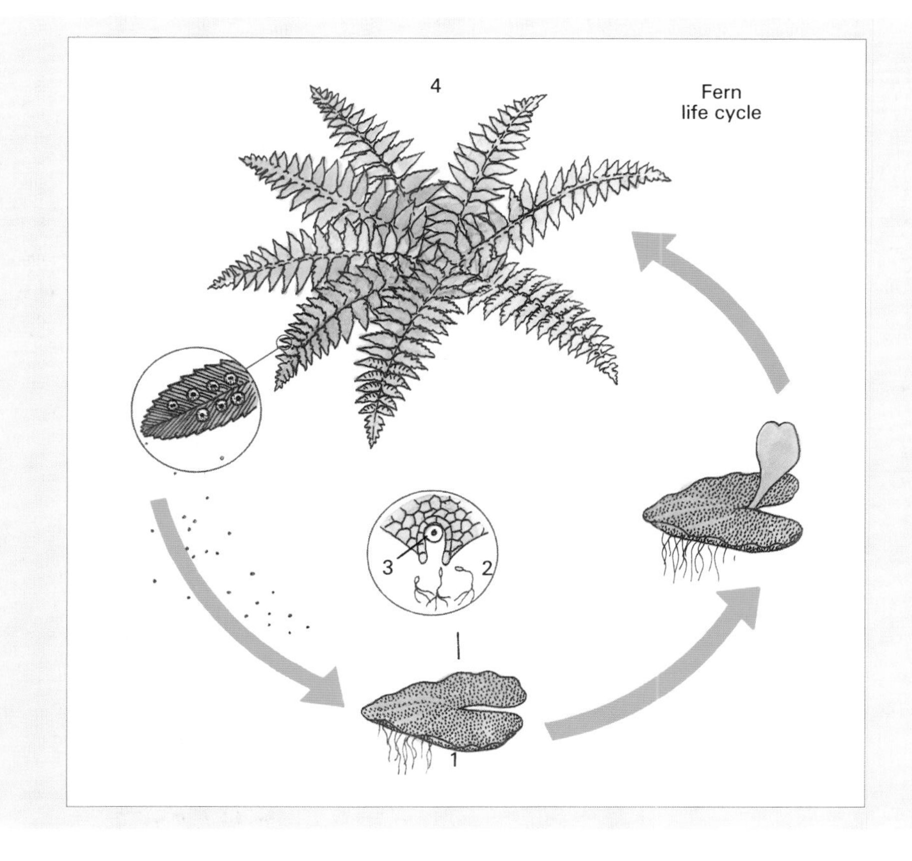

Beech forest

Few native trees are more familiar than the beeches (*Nothofagus*). In the moist west of the country, beeches may be found growing singly, as members of the conifer-broadleaved forest. But travel away from regions where the climate is kind, and beech slowly takes over. The trees seem to thrive in adversity, gaining a competitive advantage over others as the environment trends from moist and warm conditions to dry and cool conditions. By the time the high country is reached, or the drier east and cooler south of the country, beeches will often occupy the land to the virtual exclusion of all other trees.

The purity of these beech forests is in stark contrast to the fecund complexity of the conifer-broadleaved forest. Rank upon rank of furrowed trunks hold out plate-like tiers of foliage. The interior is spacious and airy, suffused with an even, green light that filters through the accordance of tiny leaves. Often the most common plants of the understorey are beech seedlings themselves. Scattered among them are small-leaved shrubs such as mingimingi, weeping matipo (*Myrsine divaricata*) and numerous coprosmas. At knee height are harsh-leaved ferns, particularly crown fern and prickly shield fern, while on the forest floor lies a mat of fallen twigs and leaves, scattered with soft turfs of moss and tiny colourful fungi. There are few, if any, large epiphytes, though mosses, ferns and lichens drape trees in wet parts of the country.

The life cycle of beech is, in many ways, perfectly adapted to its environment. The trees achieve pollination by the wind, although this has evolved from insect pollination. With a hand lens you can find traces of petals which have been made all but redundant by the changeover. It is often surprising to learn that some flowering plants, whose elaborate floral structures evolved to use animals as pollinators, have reverted to using the wind. After all, wind pollination is usually associated with the less sophisticated conifers. In the beech's case, the reason may simply be that wind is rarely in short supply in the temperate regions which beech usually inhabits. The gales that frequently sweep across New Zealand can carry pollen from one end of the country to the other, cross-pollinating trees that are hundreds of kilometres apart. Notwithstanding this, beech usually grows in forests where there are few, if any, other types of tree, so no matter which way the fickle wind blows, there is always likely to be another beech tree standing in its path, ready to catch pollen grains as they blow past.

After they have been fertilised, beech flowers produce

Nature of beech forests
Beeches (*Nothofagus*) are found in many parts of the country. Sometimes they grow as members of the podocarp-broadleaved community, but in cool and dry regions they often appear in pure stands of beech forest. There are several exceptions to the expected distribution of beech within New Zealand, because their seeds are dispersed only very short distances by wind or rivers. Beech is still slowly spreading into some parts of the country from where it was evicted during the Ice Age. Beech has also failed to colonise offshore islands such as Stewart Island, being unable to cross the small water gap.

their seeds in the form of nuts. Some species equip these with tiny wings, although this is no more than a token attempt at achieving wind dispersal. Few are blown more than a few metres before their weight brings them to earth. The characteristic of beech nuts is that they are produced in huge numbers, rather erratically, during what are called mast years. These are three to five years apart and seem to be triggered by a preceding warm, dry summer. When this happens the forest can blush copper with millions of tiny flowers, and later, fallen nuts litter the ground, several thousand to a square metre. This infrequent mass seeding is thought to help prevent most of the nuts being eaten by animals. A forest such as that of beech, which consists of large numbers of one type of tree, is an open invitation for an equally large number of herbivores to target that tree as a source of food. For any tree to shower the forest floor with nutritious nuts each year would be asking for trouble. So by shedding their seed at very irregular intervals, beeches make them an unreliable source of food. This makes it impossible for a large population of seed-eating animals to exist from one year to the next. Then when the beeches do seed, they produce such a glut that most escape consumption.

Fallen beech seeds germinate and grow very slowly beneath their parents. Some seedlings may persist for decades, their growth held almost static by the half-light of the forest floor. A visitor to any natural beech forest will encounter thousands of these spindly juveniles, waiting for a parent to fall so they can claim a spot in the canopy. Their wait may be extensive, since beeches can live for over 300 years. However, things often happen faster than this. Heavy storms will topple stands of beech like so many skittles, unleashing a rush of growth among the waiting seedlings. Such catastrophes are not uncommon in the temperamental landscapes that beech inhabits, and the 'waiting game' strategy of the seedlings is superbly suited to dealing with them. The standing population of saplings is ready to reform the beech forest canopy before any other trees get the chance to invade and take over.

Starting life Barely more than 5 centimetres high, a silver beech seedling (*Nothofagus menziesii*) sprouts on the forest floor. It will grow slowly throughout its early life, hardly gaining size in the weak light that filters through the canopy above. During this time the young plant will probably succumb to competition, disease or be eaten. But if it is very lucky, a fallen parent will release it from the shade and it will be able to make a bid for the canopy. If so, it may grow 30 metres tall and live for 300 years.

The beeches There are four species of beech. Which one is most commonly encountered varies across the land. Each has its own preference for soil and climate. Hard beech (*Nothofagus truncata*) and black beech (*N. solandri*) are both trees of the lowlands, with black preferring the cooler and poorer-drained sites. Forests of red beech (*N. fusca*) cover the foothills and inland river valley floors, particularly where soils are fertile and well drained. Silver beech (*N. menziesii*) and mountain beech, a variety of black beech, mantle the high country, often extending an unbroken green canopy to the treeline. Silver beech dominates the moister mountains to the west, while mountain beech thrives on the drier inland ranges.

The cosmopolitan beeches

The southern beeches of New Zealand are members of the Fagaceae, a family that has achieved outstanding success in temperate regions of the world. In the Southern Hemisphere they include the southern beeches (*Nothofagus*), of which there are four species in New Zealand, and about 30 others in south-east Australia, Tasmania, New Guinea, New Caledonia and southern South America. In the Northern Hemisphere, the Fagaceae include the 'true' beeches (*Fagus*), the oaks (*Quercus*) and the chestnuts (*Castanea*), which grow in a great forest belt girdling the temperate regions of North America, Europe and Asia.

The Fagaceae are thought to have evolved early in the history of flowering plants. The wide southern distribution of *Nothofagus* had its roots in the primeval supercontinent of Gondwana, over 100 million years ago. Beech forests once grew along the southern fringe of this continent, on lands which have since split into South America, Australia and New Zealand. According to fossil records, Antarctica too was one of these southern beech-forested continents, until it was overwhelmed by the spread of ice sheets several million years ago.

During the passage of time New Zealand has lost some of the beeches once living here. There were some warmth-loving species that failed to survive the harrowing effects of the Ice Age. Nevertheless, the character of the forests that remain is probably similar to how it has always been. The beech forests of New Zealand and South America retain an uncanny likeness to one another, made all the more remarkable when one considers that they are separated by about 80 million years of time and 9000 kilometres of ocean. Not only do the trees still bear a resemblance to one another, but the forests also share some closely related fungi, mosses, lichens and insects.

DIVARICATING PLANTS — LEGACY OF THE ICE AGE, OR BROWSING MOAS?

Few things have been the subject of more botanical debate than New Zealand's curious divaricating shrubs. These branch in a seemingly unrestrained manner to produce a zig-zag mass of interlaced stems and twigs. As a consequence, their leaves are held within the protection of an impenetrable tangle of branches, where they are forced to grow within the shrub's own shade. Even some native trees adopt a divaricate form during their youth, then grow normal branches once they get larger. Just why these plants should adopt such a bizarre growth form is a mystery. The divaricate habit is relatively uncommon overseas, yet in New Zealand it has evolved in about 60 different species. Many of these come from different plant families.

When so many unrelated species evolve a similar form it implies that an overall natural selection process is at work. Some clues as to what this might be can be gleaned by studying the ecology of divaricating shrubs. They are most common in dry beech forest and open areas to the east of the main divide, which experience strong winds, droughts and extreme temperatures. This has prompted the suggestion that the growth form is an adaptation to adverse weather conditions, the twiggy mass being intended to shelter the leaves from wind and frost by holding them within a protected microclimate.

Coprosma crassifolia

This argument might seem flawed by the fact that divaricating plants are less common overseas, in regions of similar climate. However, New Zealand's unusual island isolation may explain this. During the last few million years New Zealand has experienced an abrupt change of climate, from a long and benevolent period of warm-temperate conditions to bitter cold and high winds during the Ice Age and uplifting of the alps. New habitats were created, but because New Zealand was surrounded by thousands of kilometres of sea, these could not easily be colonised by ready-adapted plants from cooler parts of the world. Instead, its own isolated collection of plants was left to evolve solutions to the deteriorating climate. This was something they were sorely pressed to do, being essentially subtropical plants, adapted to millions of years of warm climates. So, lacking evolutionary experience of cold and windy conditions, many of the plants came up with a solution which was relatively simple to evolve — the divaricating habit.

A rather more intriguing explanation for the divaricate shrubs is that they evolved to cope with browsing by moas. According to this theory, the impenetrable network of branches is intended not so much to offer shelter from the wind as to frustrate the beaks of these birds. Certainly moas had prodigious appetites, and examination of their fossilised gizzards shows they were partial to divaricating plants. Adding fuel to this theory is the observation that divaricate plants are common in habitats that the moas are thought to have favoured, while they are rare among plants of cliffs and offshore islands, where moas were absent.

The debate continues. Protagonists of the climate theory point out that if divaricating shrubs evolved because of moas browsing, why do they remain so common now that moas are extinct? On the other hand, a fossil specimen of a divaricating plant has been discovered that pre-dates the climatic turmoil of the Ice Age.

A walk to the treeline

A forest changes perceptibly as you climb a mountain slope. Lowland trees such as rimu, kahikatea, puriri and tawa are left behind. So are large tree ferns and the tangle of lianes. In their place newcomers appear. There are mountain toatoa, southern rata and beeches. In wetter areas, mountain cedars may be encountered, rising in stately symmetry like church spires.

The changeover of trees is caused mostly by cooling temperatures, which fall about 1 degree Celsius for each 200 metres climbed. Similar changes could be observed by staying at sea-level and walking from the warm north of the country to the cool south. For example, the kamahi forest in the photograph grows at about 800 metres above sea-level in the North Island, yet it can be found near the coast in the south of the South Island.

Other factors, too, will influence how the forest changes with altitude. Both humidity and rainfall vary up a mountain slope. Rising air cools, causing the moisture in it to condense as rain. Ranges facing the prevailing winds are therefore very wet. Where clouds gather at their mid slope the vegetation is almost perpetually drenched with mists. Here will grow fog-shrouded elfin forests of gnarled kamahi or silver beech trees. Mosses and lichens festoon twisted branches and water oozes everywhere. Conversely, the other side of the range is drier, the descending air having lost much of its moisture. There are fewer mosses and the trees are of a different type. Often they are mountain beech, which can survive drier conditions.

If you continue to climb, the forest becomes visibly more stunted by wind and cold. There are fewer and fewer types of trees. Subalpine shrubs begin to make an appearance. Then, quite suddenly, at about 1400 metres in the North Island and 1100 metres in the South Island, you emerge into the windy realms of the alpine zone. Here at last is the treeline, where trees yield to tussocks and shrubs.

The treeline is one of nature's most pronounced boundaries. Where it is dominated by silver or mountain beech the treeline forms an almost ruler-sharp division between forest and alpine regions. Just how high up a mountain trees can grow does not depend, as you might think, on how cold and bleak the winter is. It is more governed by how warm and favourable the summer is. Research on beech has shown that the summer growing season must be long enough for new branches to complete their growth cycle and harden off their foliage before the onset of winter. As autumn advances, the young leaves become more leathery and acquire a thick waterproof cuticle of waxes. If this is not completed in time, frosts will freeze the tender tissues, rupturing their cells, while dry winds will strip the unprotected leaves of moisture until they shrivel. The treeline is at the altitude where the summer is just long enough for trees to secure their new growth against such hazards. Any tree that tried to grow higher on the mountain would make no gains. All of its summer growth would be destroyed each winter.

Forest in the clouds
Elfin forests of kamahi (*Weinmannia racemosa*) grow on mist-covered slopes near the treeline. Mosses and lichens flourish in the cool humidity.

Associations and interactions in the beech forest

The beech forest lacks the diverse mixtures of plants and animals found in conifer-broadleaved forest. At times it appears to be filled by beech trees and little else. But, as in any forest, the intricate web of relationships that is a community will be found if you look carefully enough. In beech forest there are numerous examples of associations and interactions between different organisms. Some of these give mutual benefit, others are benign. A few even lead to death. But all these relationships are ways that organisms seek their share of resources within the forest community.

Fungal partners and parasites

Many of the fungi found in the forest are saprophytes, which live by breaking down dead and decaying matter (page 59). There are also fungi that obtain their nourishment directly from other living organisms. Some do so as parasites, feeding at the expense of their host. Others live in partnerships, providing some return for what they take.

The most important and common fungal partners of forest trees are called mycorrhizae. In this alliance fungi sheathe live roots with their thread-like hyphal strands and take sugars from their host for food. In return the tree takes minerals which the fungus absorbs and transports from the surrounding soil. Obtaining some of these minerals can otherwise be difficult for plants. Phosphorus, which is essential for plant growth, is scarcely mobile in soils. Roots soon exhaust the supply in their immediate vicinity and can only get more by continually growing into fresh soil. This uses resources and is a substantial expense to the tree. By comparison, fungi, with their extensive cobweb of fine strands, are very economical at exploring the soil. So by 'paying' its mycorrhizal fungus with sugars to search for minerals, the tree saves considerably on the cost of growing roots for the same purpose.

The partnership has been an enduring one. Fossils show that mycorrhizae appeared very early in the colonisation of land by plants. They are now also very widespread, particularly in beech forests where over 170 species of mycorrhizal fungi exist. Many of the colourful mushrooms and toadstools that sprout from the forest floor in autumn belong to these fungal help-mates. Among them are species of *Russula*, *Lactarius*, *Cortinarius* and *Amanita*. With their help, beech can exploit soils which would otherwise be too infertile.

By contrast, parasitic fungi gain nourishment from their host without providing anything in return. Among the most common and aggressive in beech forest are the honey fungi (*Armillaria*). Honey fungi owe their success to their ability to spread between host trees via long runners called rhizomorphs. Pull back the bark of an

Fungal partner
Mycorrhizal fungi such as this *Thaxterogaster porphyreum* (top right) work in partnership with beech trees, taking sugars and supplying minerals in exchange.

Fungal parasite
The beech strawberry fungus (*Cytarria gunnii*) (bottom right) is a specialised fungal parasite living only on silver beech.

Virulent parasite
Though parasitic in the early stages, the honey fungi (*Armillaria*) (far right) may eventually kill their host and live in the dead wood.

infected tree and you will often see these strands, looking like black bootlaces. They conduct food and water, enabling the fungus to mount a sustained attack on one tree while still drawing nourishment from its last victim. Eventually the new tree is killed and the fungus continues to live on the dead wood, reproducing itself by producing more rhizomorphs, as well as clusters of honey-coloured mushrooms.

More specialised parasites do not kill their host. A live host, after all, provides a source of nourishment for much longer than a dead one. For a parasite to cause minimal damage it must evolve a lifestyle that is very compatible with its victim. Often this means becoming so specialised that it can invade only the one organism. The beech strawberry fungus (*Cyttaria gunnii*), for instance, attacks only silver beech trees. It causes woody galls, or growths, on the tree's branches from which fungal fruiting bodies appear in spring, like clusters of yellow golf balls. Galls are caused by many specialised parasites of plants, including parasitic mites and insects. By compelling the plant to produce a large growth which is well supplied with sap, the parasite can obtain the shelter and food it needs to complete its life cycle without mounting a widespread invasion which could kill its benefactor. A tree may carry hundreds of galls and still function normally.

Orchids Orchids such as these tiny spider orchids (*Corybas oblongus*), which inhabit the mossy forest floor, could not survive without fungi. When an orchid seed pod opens it releases clouds of spore-like seed to be blown away on the wind. Each seed is so minute that it contains almost no food supply. It is barely more than an embryo, which has to be 'infected' by a specific fungal partner in order to germinate. The fungus provides the growing plant with all its minerals and food until it can unfold its first green leaf. There is a huge element of chance in a seed landing by a suitable fungus. But since orchids do not provide their seed with a food resource they can afford to counter these odds by liberating them in vast numbers. A single plant may shed over a million.

LICHENS

A lichen cannot be considered a single organism. Rather it is a composite of two entirely different organisms, a fungus and an alga. The fungus provides the alga with physical support and shelter within its weft of hyphal threads, while the green alga provides the fungus with a photosynthetic source of food.

So intimate a partnership causes problems when it comes to reproduction. A lichen can only reproduce itself as an entity by vegetative means, budding off a few fungal and algal cells together that blow away to find a new home. When a lichen reproduces sexually, only fungal spores are liberated. If these are to form new lichens they need to find and capture suitable algal partners. Details of this, however, are largely unknown, since the event has rarely been witnessed.

Some people contend that the fungus-alga partnership is mainly a one-sided arrangement, in which the fungus gains. However, by growing as a team, both partners can live in a far wider range of environments than each could as an individual. It is such a hardy combination that lichens flourish on tree trunks, sun-baked rocks and windswept alpine summits, where they survive extremes of drought and temperature that would kill other green life.

The remarkable resilience of lichens is not due to their evolving special methods to prevent desiccation. Entirely the opposite is true. When the surroundings dry out, lichens simply dry out too, becoming brittle and seemingly dead. They enter a state of 'suspended animation' in which searing

sun or arctic cold can be endured. Then, when water is available, lichens soak it up like blotting paper through all their surfaces and resume photosynthesis. At the same time they possess a remarkable ability to mop up mineral nutrients in the water and concentrate them within their tissues.

A lichen's growth is therefore geared to take advantage of sporadic wetting. This might be a downpour of rain or just the dampness of a dewy morning. Each time it grows by a minute increment, gaining a few millimetres each year. Nevertheless, in terms of their extraordinary tolerances, the lichens could well be considered the best adapted of all terrestrial plants. No others can endure the capricious nature of life on land so well.

The parasitic plants

Some plants have discarded the conventions of their leafy kind by not photosynthesising a personal supply of organic materials for growth. Instead they have become parasites, stealing all the food, water and minerals they need from other plants. Parasitic plants can therefore do away with green leaves, as well as roots, and live happily on the dark forest floor. Many, in fact, spend a great deal of their life underground, attached to their host's roots. They only put in an appearance above ground to poke a non-green shoot through the leaf litter when flowering. One example is *Dactylanthus taylori*, which the Maori named pua reinga, meaning flower of the underworld, on account of the unexpected emergence of its flowering stem from the forest floor. When a seed of *Dactylanthus taylori* germinates it sends out a root-like probe which searches for a suitable host. This may be any of a number of forest trees, including *Pseudopanax* and *Pittosporum*. Once it encounters a root it penetrates the tissue and plugs into the host's vascular system, which conducts food and water. From then on it can take what it wishes.

The most common parasitic plants found in the beech forest operate in a slightly different way. These are the potato orchids (*Gastrodia*). Their seeds start life like other orchids, by associating with a fungus. But instead of producing green leaves, the growing orchids remain dependent on their fungal hosts throughout their lives. They have therefore achieved one of the most bizarre associations in the plant kingdom by becoming parasitic on fungi. The fungal host in turn feeds on decaying litter. Sometimes it may itself, too, be a parasite on other living plants.

More benign in their habits are the hemiparasites. These unfold their own green leaves and so can provide their own food requirements, but tap their host for water and minerals. The best-known hemiparasites belong to the worldwide family of mistletoes, Loranthaceae, which usually attach themselves to branches in the canopy. When a mistletoe seed germinates on a branch it produces a special root which penetrates the bark and latches on to its host's xylem vessels, which carry water and minerals from the soil. Thus provisioned the mistletoe can enjoy a privileged perch in the sunlit canopy to photosynthesise its own food supply. To spread between trees, mistletoes produce berries with sticky seeds. Some of these get caught on the beaks of feeding birds, which then wipe the seeds into the bark of other trees in an attempt to clean themselves.

Stealing water
The mistletoe (*Peraxilla tetrapetala*) (right) perches high in the sunlit branches of the beech forest like an epiphyte. But instead of obtaining water from rainfall, it produces special roots to steal a supply from its host. This allows mistletoes to inhabit forests which would be too dry for normal epiphytes. Mistletoes are important members of the beech forest community. In summer their blooms offer a heavy crop of nectar and berries for forest birds, compensating for the absence of nectar produced by the beech itself.

A parasitic orchid
The ghostly flower stalk of the potato orchid (*Gastrodia cunninghami*) is often found rising from the beech-forest floor in early summer. Instead of producing green leaves to photosynthesise its own food, the potato orchid has become parasitic on a fungus for all its requirements. The fungus in turn obtains nutrition from decaying plant matter.

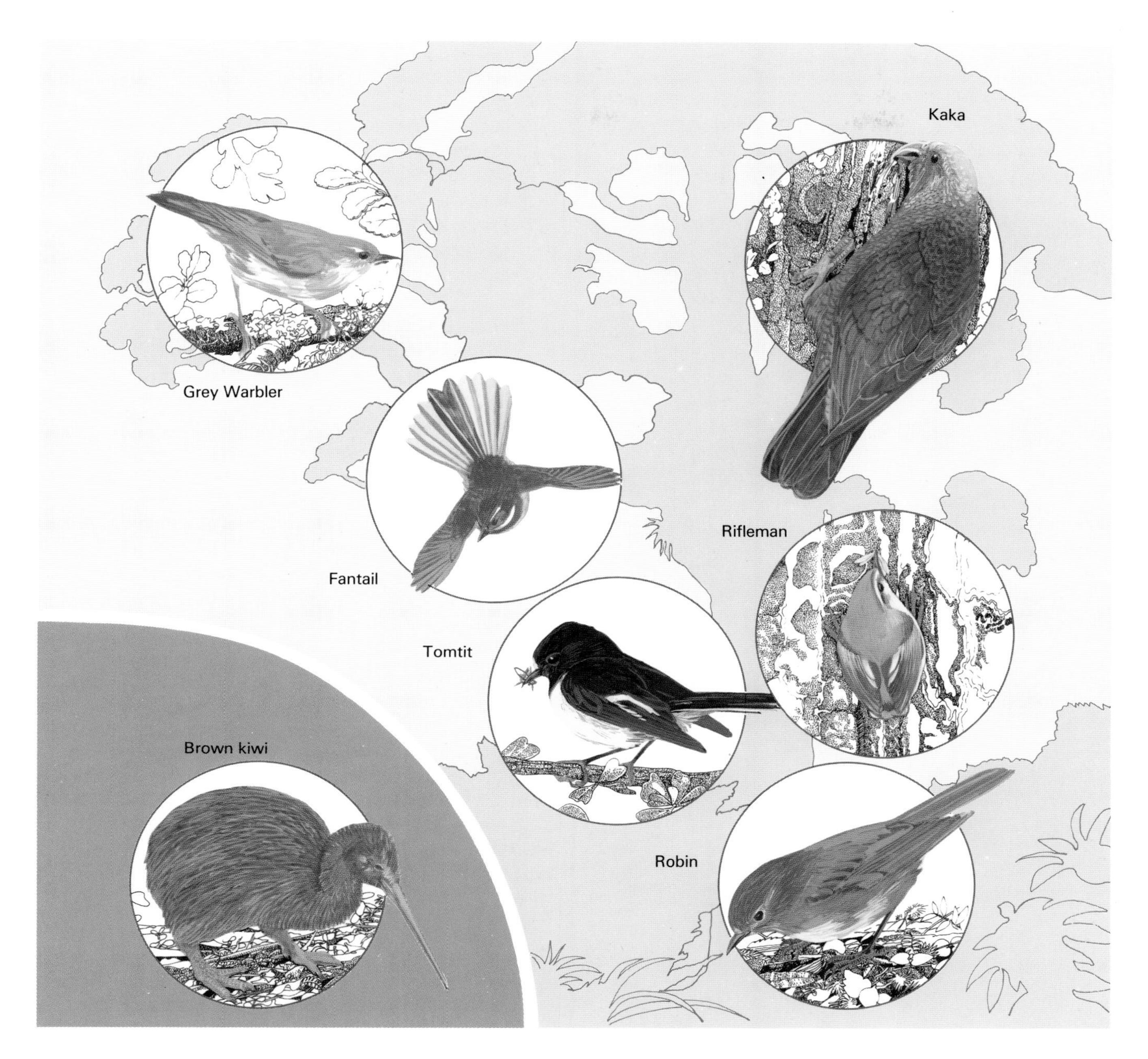

Birds of the canopy — the insect eaters

The scarcity of nectar and fruit in the beech forest means that there is little food for birds such as tuis, bellbirds and pigeons. However, the ample supply of insects supports many different insect-eating birds. In fact, the number of bird species snapping up beetles, spiders, caterpillars and other small invertebrates might seem to contradict one of the golden principles of ecology. This is that when different species compete for the same food source one eventually prevails and displaces the other. How can so many different birds coexist on a similar diet?

The answer is that each species of bird avoids competing by concentrating its search for insects in a different part of the forest. The robin (*Petroica australis*) fossicks for insects in the leaf litter, while the tomtit (*P. macrocephala*) searches leaf and branch surfaces in the understorey. The rifleman (*Acanthisitta chloris*) feeds by methodically exploring tree trunks, picking insects from the surface or tweezering them from cracks. The kaka (*Nestor meridionalis*) uses its strong beak to rip back bark for grubs underneath, while the agile fantail (*Rhipidura fuliginosa*) snaps up prey in mid air. Other birds, the grey warbler (*Gerygone igata*) and brown creeper (*Mohoua novaeseelandiae*), search for insects in the high canopy. The brown kiwi (*Apteryx australis*) separates its feeding niche from other birds in both time and space. It comes out at night when the other birds are asleep and probes deep below the litter with its unusually long beak.

Forest insects

Frequently overlooked and usually maligned, the insects perform a vital service to plant communities. Without them organic matter and minerals would not be recycled effectively (page 58) and insect-pollinated flowers would not set seed (page 50). It is true that some attack and damage live trees, but even this can be seen as having benefit to the forest as a whole. It is usually the old and weak trees that are overwhelmed, so their death paves the way for the more vigorous and productive individuals to grow.

Insects that feed on live plants can be divided into those which eat sap and those which chew whole tissue. Sapsuckers include plant hoppers, scale insects and cicadas, which have mouthparts specialised for piercing plant tissue. Chewing insects include stick insects, wetas, grasshoppers, caterpillars, beetles and their grubs. Some of these insects are polyphagous, feeding on a number of host plants; others are monophagous, specialising in just one. Beech forest is unusually rich in monophagous insects. There are over 20 insect species that specialise in beech trees alone. This situation has probably developed over the extraordinarily long time that beech forests have existed. Their resident insects have had millions of years without disruption in which to evolve specialised feeding relationships.

There are advantages to eating only one food source. It becomes worthwhile for an insect to evolve elaborate camouflage to match the host, and ways to deal with the host's particular defensive mechanisms. It also allows the insect to evolve a specialised lifestyle to utilise its host effectively for food or shelter. One of the best examples of this is not an insect but a mite called *Aceria waltheri*. When this minute creature invades a beech branch it causes the tree to produce a gall, called a witch's broom. The mite then lives inside this, the tree

Camouflage
You may have noticed the small male stick insect in this photograph straight away. But did you notice the much larger female he is mating with? Stick insects (Family Phasmatidae) spend their entire lives in the canopy browsing the leaves of a number of trees and shrubs. They are therefore always exposed to predators. Many insects that spend their lives in the open have escape mechanisms such as flight or leaping to avoid predators. Others may rely on being distasteful or toxic. The stick insect, however, stays perfectly still and blends with its twiggy surroundings. At most it sways gently from side to side, perhaps mimicking the trembling of a small branch in the breeze.

TREE DEFENCES

A tree is under attack throughout its life. From the moment it germinates on the forest floor it may fall victim to insects that chew through its wood and foliage. Since plants cannot run from their many predators and parasites, they have evolved ways to repel them instead. The tree nettle deters animal browsers with needle-like hairs which inject a painful cocktail of irritants. In a similar way, many forest grasses cover their leaves with sharp silica crystals to provide an unpleasantly abrasive mouthful.

More subtle and ubiquitous are the chemical tactics plants employ to repel their assailants. Some of these chemicals, such as the tannins that add taste to our cup of tea, are intended to make the leaf proteins indigestible. Other chemicals act as outright poisons. The leaves of pigeonwood are laced with alkaloids, while ngaio uses terpenoids. Sometimes these chemicals are remarkably selective in how they work. The bark of podocarp trees contains substances called ecdysones, which mimic the moulting hormones normally produced by insects. Any insect that chews its way into the tree, ingesting the 'hormone', has its normal growth and development sabotaged.

Synthesising a chemical weaponry represents an expense to the plant. It consumes resources that could otherwise be put into new growth. So for greatest economy, plants often place their poisons where they will be of best use. Rangiora invests most of its toxins in vulnerable young shoots. The edible fruit of the karaka tree are intended to be swallowed by pigeons and later voided to germinate on the forest floor. But lest a creature decides to dine on the seed itself, this is protected by a deadly dose of a glucoside called karacin.

These are just a few examples of the ploys plants use to protect themselves. Their chemical arsenal is extraordinarily varied and as yet remains little studied. Countless useful substances await discovery, some of which could offer enormous benefit to humankind. All species, no matter how obscure they seem, have their value. Who knows what secrets they may contain.

providing it with both food and shelter. The disadvantage of such a specific feeding role is that if the host is threatened with extinction, so is the insect. Only polyphagous insects have been able to switch from the declining native vegetation and turn their attention to the increasing introduced vegetation.

The wood eaters (left)
Wood lies in abundance on the forest floor, and many insects use it as food. One is the huhu beetle (*Prionoplus reticularis*). The huhu spends several years as a grub, feeding within the dead trunks of trees. As an adult it takes wing on its heavy, droning flight, in search of a mate or a place to lay its eggs. The adult is short lived and probably does not feed. Its formidable mandibles may be used only once, to chew its way to freedom from the log in which it lived as a larva.

Insects like the huhu face the problem that wood is difficult to digest. The enzymes necessary to break down the cellulose of plant cell walls are notably absent amongst animals. This is overcome by relying on a symbiotic association with micro-organisms, usually bacteria or protozoa, which live within the animal's gut. These break down the wood, making it available as food to the insect. A slightly different tactic has been evolved by the ambrosia beetles, some of which bore into beech. These beetles cultivate fungi on the walls of the tunnels they excavate. The fungi grow on the wood, while the beetles and their larvae feed on the fungi.

THE HONEYDEW STORY

In the complex web of the forest, the most seemingly insignificant organism can play a crucial role. The sooty scale insect (*Ultracoelostoma assimile*) is one example. This tiny insect burrows into the bark of beech and feeds on its sugary saps, excreting excess sap as honeydew from the end of a wax tube.

In summer, the amounts of honeydew produced are so prolific that many birds, insects and lizards come to feed on it. Droplets that fall on the bark and soil nourish a fungal carpet of black sooty mould as well as soil organisms. Even the tree gains a small benefit. Among the soil organisms that utilise the honeydew are bacteria able to fix atmospheric nitrogen into forms which are available to the tree. Thus the beech reaps a return from its lost energy resource as nitrogen fertiliser.

Unfortunately, introduced wasps have now become interlopers in the honeydew story. Not only do they compete aggressively with all other creatures for the sugary liquid, they are also carnivores, using their sting to kill other insects. Soaring wasp populations have become one of the greatest ecological threats to beech forest in many parts of the country.

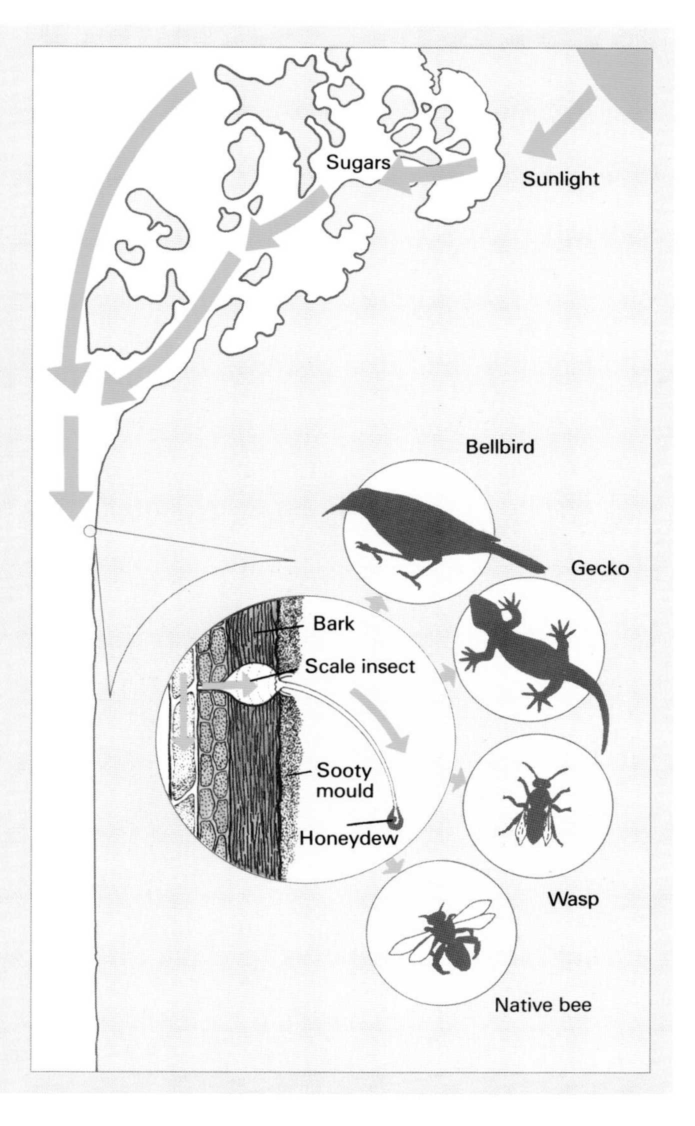

Scrub

Scrub is usually a transient habitat. It springs up in the wake of forest clearances as part of the process of regeneration, in which plants reclaim the bare ground and return it to forest. Thus it rarely persists for more than 100 years before it is shaded out by the trees which germinate beneath its shelter. There are exceptions though; for example, where conditions do not permit the return of normal forest, because of boggy or infertile soils. This is the case for large areas called pakihi on the South Island West Coast. Here a scrubby vegetation of silver pine and stunted manuka grows with sedge, tangle fern and tiny sundews on dark, waterlogged peat soils.

Since the huge forest clearances that have accompanied human settlement, scrubland has become prevalent. It is usually viewed contemptuously as something which frustrates human attempts to turn the land to a more 'useful' purpose, such as farming or forestry. Scrub, though, is a diverse and valuable habitat in its own right. It consists of a variety of shrubs and small trees, with an understorey of herbs and ferns. The shrubs and trees often include coprosmas, tutu, dracophyllums, wineberry, cyathodes, and hebes, though by far the most common members are manuka (*Leptospermum scoparium*) and its relative, kanuka (*Kunzea ericoides*).

Like many successful plants, manuka and kanuka have accumulated a multitude of plants and animals that associate with them. Because of their peeling bark, epiphytes are not present, but the branches are often laced with small vines, including species of *Muehlenbeckia*, *Parsonsia*, and the showy *Clematis*. They are also host to some mistletoes, and have an exclusive association with the leafless dwarf mistletoe (*Korthalsella salicornioides*). In Northland, manuka and kanuka are major hosts for two twining parasites (*Cassytha*). These plants embrace stands with a stringlike mass of twining pale green stems that penetrate the branches of their host at intervals to obtain nutrition.

Both manuka and kanuka flower prolifically and their nectar is sought by many insects, including the introduced honey bee. Other insects eat the wood and leaves, among them the manuka moth (*Declana floccosa*), manuka beetle (*Pyronata festiva*), longhorn beetle (*Ochrocydus huttoni*) and various stick insects.

There are few birds that specifically inhabit scrub. Fantails, pipits and harriers are commonly encountered here, as well as in other habitats. However, one bird in particular frequents boggy pakihi scrub. This is the fernbird (*Bowdleria punctata*), a rather retiring member of the warbler family. Its cryptic plumage and shyness of flight hide it well in its habitat, where it feeds on insects. It would rarely be noticed if it wasn't for the sharp, metallic calls that individuals make to one another.

Associating with manuka and kanuka are numerous mycorrhizal fungi. Many are species of *Russula* and *Lactarius*, which crumble in the hand with a tell-tale brittle texture. Flowering orchids are also common, perhaps because of the presence of mycorrhizal partners which they need in order to establish their seeds. In early summer the understorey beams with royal-blue sun orchids, red and green bearded orchids and curious horned orchids. All in all, scrub has much to offer as a habitat. Moreover, a search in the undergrowth will usually reveal seedlings of totara, rimu, beech and other trees — scrub is the nursery for tomorrow's forest.

Clematis vine
The showy white flowers of the climbing vine *Clematis paniculata* (right) celebrate springtime in the scrub. There are many species of clematis worldwide, but those in New Zealand are unusual as they bear male or female flowers on separate plants. Since clematis flowers do not offer any nectar, insects visit them to collect pollen for food. This poses the question of why female flowers should be visited by pollinating insects. Possibly they rely on an error of judgement by the insect, mistaking them for male flowers.

Scrubland orchids
The sun orchid (*Thelymitra venosa*) (far right) is common in scrub, growing on boggy ground.

Geckos With generous offerings of insects and nectar for food, and a well-lit canopy for sunbathing, scrub is an ideal habitat for geckos. This one, *Naultinus grayi*, is common in scrub in the northern North Island. There are 16 species of gecko in New Zealand, though more may yet be discovered. They belong to a family of lizards known as the Geckkonidae, which is found almost worldwide in warmer regions. Many like *N. grayi* are arboreal, scrambling amongst branches, using their tail as a fifth limb. However, much of their climbing ability can be attributed to a remarkable talent for gripping with their feet. Geckos possess toe pads that have an extremely fine structure of tiny projections that interlock with the smallest irregularities of any surface, even ones that appear utterly smooth. Geckos are also renowned for being among the most vocal of lizards, with a repertoire of clicks, chirps and barks.

MANUKA AND KANUKA — PLANT PIONEERS

Manuka (*Leptospermum scoparium*) and kanuka (*Kunzea ericoides*) are superbly adapted to colonise ground which has been bared by forest destruction. Both flower from an early age and produce copious quantities of tiny windborne seeds, so they can spread quickly across the cleared area. Like successful pioneer plants, manuka and kanuka are also opportunists, able to grow under a huge range of conditions so long as there is enough light. Manuka in particular springs up almost anywhere. It grows in the warmth of Northland and along the chilly Stewart Island timberline. It manages in the bogs of Westland and on the dry plains of Canterbury, regardless of whether the soil is fertile or infertile. Manuka even has a way to cope with fire, an all too frequent scrubland hazard. Although the parent plants may themselves be destroyed, the intense heat triggers protective woody seed capsules on their branches to open, quickly resowing the ashes to produce a dense new stand.

Like many plants occupying a large range of natural environments, manuka and kanuka have evolved local races, adapted to the peculiarities of the local conditions. Manuka has grown in some South Island pakihi bogs for so long that it has evolved dwarf forms adapted to the waterlogged conditions. This characteristic has become genetically fixed. That is, if seeds from one of these plants were grown outside the bog, they would still grow as dwarfed forms. In other parts of the country there are numerous variations in leaf shape, flower colour and form. From this wealth of genetic diversity, plant breeders have been able to provide the huge range of cultivated manuka now popular as garden plants.

Manuka (*Leptospermum scoparium*) growing on geothermal sinter stone.

Exotic forest

Today, large areas of New Zealand are clothed in a tree cover very different from beech or conifer-broadleaved forest. This is exotic coniferous forest, such as that grown at Kaingaroa in the North Island and Golden Downs in the South Island. Exotic forests have had a considerably shorter history in New Zealand than native forests. They have virtually all been planted during the last hundred years, predominantly as a timber resource and for erosion control.

At its inception, earlier this century, the planting of extensive exotic forests was a bold experiment. Not only was New Zealand one of the first countries to begin large-scale reafforestation, it also undertook this entirely with introduced trees. Native species were considered too slow growing, so suitable trees were tried from all over the world. Early choices were made somewhat on a trial and error basis. Some, the spruces and redwoods, were disappointing, while others, particularly *Pinus radiata*, exceeded all expectations.

Most trees now grown commercially are conifers that have been introduced from the west of North America. These include *Pinus radiata*, Douglas fir (*Pseudotsuga menziessi*) (below), Ponderosa pine (*Pinus ponderosa*) and lodgepole pine (*Pinus contorta*). Europe has also contributed one or two tree species. The Corsican pine is a variety of *Pinus nigra* which is native to the Mediterranean island of Corsica. The larch (*Larix decidua*) has been grown as a timber tree in England for hundreds of years.

In the early days, when these various trees were being tested in New Zealand conditions, it was not appreciated that success meant not only choosing the right species, but also collecting its seeds from the right place. In their natural habitats, Douglas fir, lodgepole pine and Ponderosa pine grow for thousands of kilometres along the mountains and foothills of the North American Rockies. Where in this huge area the seeds were collected from had a crucial effect on their suitability for New Zealand. For instance, plantings of Ponderosa pine taken from Canada grew at different rates in New Zealand from those taken out of California, even though they were both the same species. This is because plants which occupy large natural ranges tend to evolve local varieties or strains in response to the peculiarities of local environments. So the Canadian trees were adapted to Canadian conditions while Californian trees were adapted to the very different conditions found in California.

Douglas fir stands (*Pseudotsuga menziessi*)

BIRDS OF FARMLAND

White-faced heron (*Ardea novaehollandiae*) This bird crossed the Tasman Sea from Australia earlier this century, and is now the commonest heron. It feeds on fish, frogs and aquatic insects, as well as on terrestrial insects and small mammals. It prefers exotic conifers for nesting, particularly *Pinus radiata*.

Australasian harrier (*Circus approximans*) Open country is ideal hunting ground for the harrier. For this reason, it has benefited from the creation of farmland, where it finds an ample diet of small mammals and birds, lizards, insects, and various kinds of carrion, including possums killed on the road by passing cars.

Skylark (*Alauda arvensis*) The twittering song and the way it flutters high above its nest site are easily recognised habits of the skylark. It is at home in pasture and other open ground, nesting in a hollow, such as a hoof-print, among taller grasses. Although skylarks may occasionally damage crops by uprooting seedlings, they are thought to be beneficial on the whole by feeding on insect pests.

White-backed magpie (*Gymnorhina hypoleuca*) A common bird of pastures and ploughed land, where it feeds on many kinds of insect, including grass grubs. It nests in tall trees, and occasionally in hedgerows. If humans or animals approach too close to its nest it dives on them.

Kingfisher (*Halcyon sancta*) Contrary to its name, the New Zealand kingfisher only rarely includes fish in its diet. It is more likely to be seen by the roadside, perched on a telephone wire or power cable, scanning the adjacent pasture or ploughed land for insects, worms, lizards, small mammals and birds. The kingfisher is particularly at home in open settled areas, often nesting in road cuttings or other excavated sites.

Weeds

A simple definition of a weed is 'a plant growing where it isn't wanted'. From the point of view of the farmer, there is more to a weed than that. Some weeds are poisonous and grazing animals may avoid these because of their taste. However, poisonous weeds can get into hay and may then be more readily eaten by stock. Ragwort and the highly poisonous Cape tulip are examples. There are weeds, too, that reduce crop yield, such as Nasella tussock grass, which invades pasture and is also unpalatable to stock. Weeds may also taint meat and dairy products. Twincress, for instance, causes unpleasant flavours in milk from animals that have grazed on it, and this is passed on to cream and butter. Other problem weeds include those with stringy stems, such as hedge mustard and wireweed, which become tangled in harvesters and other farm machinery, and species such as ripgut brome, which have seeds with reversed bristles that help the seed work its way into the skin of sheep, damaging the hide.

One pest helps another
The giant buttercup (*Ranunculus acris*) is a common and persistent weed of pastures. It is poisonous to stock but is usually avoided because of its acrid taste. Stock leave the buttercup well alone — and also the grasses growing in the vicinity of the buttercups. The ungrazed grasses are eaten by caterpillars of the porina moth. Porina moths flourish in these 'protected areas', which became a focus for further damaging attack by the caterpillars on nearby fodder plants — grasses, clover and lucerne.

Insect and weed benefit each other, since the bare patches in the pasture, caused by the attacks of the caterpillars, give space for more buttercup seedlings to grow.

There are thousands or even tens of thousands of weed seeds per cubic metre of arable soil. Each year, those in the upper layers germinate and renew the infestation. Cultivating the soil brings a new supply of seeds to the surface. Add to these the myriad seeds that blow in from nearby areas and it is easy to understand the origin of the gardener's maxim 'One year's seeding is seven years' weeding'.

Weeds are the opportunists of the plant world. They rush in to establish themselves quickly in newly cleared areas. Land clearance has occurred only recently in the history of New Zealand and consequently there are few native plants that have adopted the weed habit. The native weeds of farmland include bracken, manuka, kanuka, willowherbs, and several rushes and sedges, but the majority of weeds in New Zealand have been introduced from overseas.

The secrets of their success

Some plants possess features that distinguish them as being highly adapted to the weed lifestyle.

The ability of some plants to compete with other species is one major feature. Fennel and old man's beard, for example, quickly establish a dense or mat-like growth that smothers other plants. Daisy, plantain and several other weeds produce leaf rosettes, which spread widely and grow close to the ground, preventing other plants growing nearby. Leaf rosettes are also resistant to grazing.

Seeding strategy is also a key to the success of weeds, and this may manifest itself in a number of features. Rapid seed production is one. Most weeds are annual and go through their life cycle in a few weeks or months. This allows them to grow, flower and seed within the crop stand before harvest time comes around. For example, groundsel seeds germinate immediately they find the right conditions and can seed five to six weeks later. Large-scale seed production is another weed feature. Scarlet pimpernel produces up to 12,000 seeds per plant and has two or more germinations in a year. Nasella tussock grass produces up to 120,000 seeds per plant. Year-round activity is also common among weeds. Shepherd's purse, for instance, germinates and grows in any season, producing several generations each year.

The distribution of the seeds of weeds is usually wide

NOT A SPIDER

This is a harvestman — so-called because in Europe, from where this species was introduced, it was often very common in the fields at harvest-time. The eight long legs make it look like a spider, but the body is in one piece, whereas in spiders there is a 'neck' between the head-thorax and the abdomen. Also it has only two eyes, compared with the eight eyes of most spiders. There are similar long-legged native harvestmen living in forested areas.

Harvestmen are mainly scavengers, feeding on the bodies of dead insects, but some are able to catch living prey.

Native pests While most native animals have suffered with the expansion of agriculture, two have profited, almost beyond measure. These are the porina moth (*Wiseana*) (left) and the grass-grub beetle (*Odontria striata*) (below), both of which are so numerous as to be major agricultural pests. The female porina moth lays eggs in pasture soil. The caterpillars live near the soil surface under debris or in silk-covered depressions in the soil. Later they burrow deeper into the soil, forming vertical tunnels which they line with silk. They camouflage the mouth of the tunnel by dragging leaves into it, emerging at night to feed on the leaves of plants. The adult grass grub beetle feeds on the leaves of trees, shrubs and pasture plants. After mating, the female deposits eggs in the soil. The grubs feed on the roots of the grasses and pasture plants, completely severing the roots so that the plants die. Weeds may take over the bare patches of soil. After three stages of growth, the grub becomes a pupa in the soil. A few weeks later, the adult beetles emerge and the cycle begins again.

permanent residents of the country. Some of these have been carried around the world from place to place, wherever agriculture has been practised. Often they have been associated with farming for so long that their place of origin is unknown. Some of these, such as lucerne, have been introduced as crops and have subsequently escaped to become established in the wild. Others have been introduced accidentally, perhaps in soil surrounding imported crop plants or as contaminants in imported seed. Animals have also been brought into the country. Some, such as the thrush, blackbird and skylark, bring their pleasant songs to the countryside. Others, such as the rabbit, stoat and pig, have become pests.

Finally, there is the farmstead itself. No matter how successful the farmer is in maintaining a monoculture of exotic crop plants and no matter how successfully the animal pests are eliminated, the farmstead remains an oasis of wildlife. The yards, the dams and the gardens provide living-space and shelter for wildlife of all kinds. Semi-natural communities may become established in neglected areas. The house and outbuildings are a sanctuary for birds, insects, spiders and many other creatures. If the buildings are old, their timbers are likely to be the home of wood-boring beetles such as the common house borer and others. Some species seem to be spread mainly as a result of farming activities. An example is rayless chamomile (*Matricaria dioscoidea*), sometimes known as pineapple weed. The seeds of this plant are carried on the tyres of tractors and other farm vehicles from one muddy place to another. This accounts for the frequent occurrence of this weed on farm tracks and particularly at gateways, where congregating livestock make the mud even stickier than usual. Farmyards on damp soils are a haven for several other mud-living plants, such as the native *Limosella lineata*, a close relative of the European mudwort. Other lovers of well-trodden mud are orange foxtail grass (*Alopecurus aequalis*), kneed foxtail grass (*A. geniculatus*), water pepper (*Polygonum hydropiper*) and many sedges, such as the native cyperus sedge, *Cyperus ustulatus*. Where these are established, a host of associated animals join them. On balance, farmland sometimes seems to have as many species as the native habitats it replaces.

The katydid The staccato zit-zit-zit of the katydid (*Caedicia simplex*) is often heard late on a summer's afternoon, but the insect itself is not as easily seen. Large green wings virtually enclose its body, giving it the appearance of a leaf. Wing markings that look very much like leaf veins complete the disguise.

The katydid belongs to the long-horned grasshoppers, a group that differ from the true grasshoppers commonly found in alpine and subalpine regions in having very long antennae. It also produces its 'song' in a different way, by rubbing its forewings together rather than using friction between its hindleg and forewing.

GORSE — PEST OR PIONEER?

Gorse (*Ulex europaeus*) is a survivor. It has numerous adaptations that help it establish and thrive in open areas. Its leaves are reduced to spines, with the double bonus of reducing evaporation, allowing the plant to survive in dry soils, as well as providing a prickly mouthful for prospective browsers. Being a member of the legume family, its roots bear nodules containing nitrogen-fixing bacteria. This enables it to survive in poor nitrogen-deficient soils. Once established, the plant casts an evergreen shade that helps prevent other plants from growing beneath it. In addition to this it produces huge numbers of seed which can germinate rapidly, and remain viable in the soil for over 50 years — all features of a successful weed. Since being introduced from Europe, gorse has occupied over 20,000 hectares of pastureland.

Burning and clearing are little use in combating gorse. These techniques simply re-create bare areas which gorse can quickly reoccupy. Studies indicate that one way to get rid of gorse is to do exactly the opposite and leave it alone. Gorse has the advantage that it can establish in areas difficult for many natives. If allowed to grow, it creates a sheltered environment beneath its canopy, protecting the soil below from the drying effects of wind and from extremes of temperature. The litter from the gorse and smaller early colonisers provides nutriment for the soil and increases its water-holding capacity. If the gorse canopy is not too dense and the soil conditions below are just right, native trees such as manuka can grow there. In 10–15 years the natives begin to take over from the gorse. Other woody trees follow and the area begins to revert to forest. Without the gorse being there to begin with, these plants might never have succeeded in obtaining a foothold so soon.

In areas where the gorse is too dense to allow other plants to take over in this way, a longer waiting period may be involved. After 20–25 years, stands of gorse mature and begin to become thinner as the plants die. It is believed that native shrubs and trees will take over from the ageing gorse after 25–30 years, and the area will eventually turn to forest. So one practicable technique with gorse seems to be to have patience and let natural forces operate in their own way.

RAGWORT — PORTRAIT OF A WEED

Ragwort (*Senecio jacobaea*) arrived in New Zealand over 100 years ago and is now widespread in pastures, waste areas, open forests and swamps. It has a serious impact on pasture because it competes successfully with the pasture plants, and is toxic to cattle and horses, though sheep are less affected by it. It also taints milk and honey.

Part of the success of ragwort is due to its complex seeding strategy, in which two types of seed are produced. What appears to be a single ragwort flower actually consists of dozens of flowers, or florets, packed together. The central disc is made of florets with visually insignificant petals. Surrounding these are a dozen or so longer-petalled florets, the rays. Those seeds produced by the disc florets are very light and are equipped with a tuft of hairs that aids dispersal by wind. Although many of these seeds do not in fact spread more than a few metres from the parent plant, a few that get carried high by upward air currents can travel for several kilometres. Plants have been found growing in Arthur's Pass that are thought to have been wind-dispersed from Westland, crossing the Main Divide. The disc floret seeds also have stiff hairs that may stick in fur and thus aid dispersal by animals.

The other type of seed, produced by the ray florets, has neither the tuft of hairs nor the stiff hairs. These seeds are heavier than the others and simply fall close to the parent plant. The spreading rosette leaves of the parent prevent adjacent plants from crowding in, giving these seeds ideal conditions for germination. They eventually replace the ageing parent plant.

Some ragwort seeds may germinate quickly, within one to two weeks. Others, which become covered by 25 millimetres or more of soil, enter a dormant state and remain viable in the soil for a long time, some for up to 20 years. Thus there is always a reserve of seed in the soil, waiting for the opportunity to germinate. Disturbance of the soil, by cultivation, by grazing or by trampling, for example, brings dormant seeds to the surface. They soon germinate and grow quickly into plants, each capable of producing up to 200,000 more seeds!

A healthy continuous pasture prevents the establishment of ragwort plants. But, once a gap occurs and ragwort succeeds in growing beyond the rosette stage, it becomes very difficult to eradicate. Even attempts to eliminate the plant by uprooting it usually fail, as even small pieces of root left in the soil are able to produce buds.

to help the species spread from one area to another. The feathery seeds of coltsfoot and other members of the daisy family are carried for kilometres by the wind. Some other weeds, such as pearlwort, produce large quantities of dust-like seeds that are blown away by the wind. Once fallen to the ground, many weed seeds are able to remain dormant for long periods, a few germinating each year to maintain the plant's presence. Dock seeds are viable for over 60 years.

Perennial weeds can have the added ability to spread successfully by vegetative means. Bracken, couch grass and others spread rapidly by underground food-storing stems (rhizomes) or rooting stems (stolons) that grow rapidly over the soil surface. The rhizomes of couch can spread more than 3 metres in a year. Couch grass and other perennial weeds, for example field bindweed, also reproduce readily from very small pieces of stem or rootstock, which may be cut and moved from place to place by ploughing or digging.

Weed climber In Europe, from where it was brought, the vine old man's beard (*Clematis vitalba*) is often called traveller's joy. In New Zealand, it is looked upon less favourably, for it has the habit of smothering native vegetation. It often establishes in scrub or along the margins of forest remnants, where it grows profusely, spreading over tree tops and depriving them of light.

Keeping the balance

Farming has sometimes been considered to be a battle against nature. At times the impact of agriculture has certainly been devastating. Modern trends, however, more and more favour farming methods that work according to nature's principles rather than against them.

Problems with pesticides and fertilisers

Pesticides have become a useful tool in modern agricultural practice. They offer one easy way that farmers can maintain crop monocultures without them being ravaged by epidemics of pests and diseases. Unfortunately many of these chemicals can affect more than the troublesome organisms they are intended for. The widespread use of pesticides is also a threat to the local living communities, particularly as it is often impossible to restrict their action to the farm itself.

Indiscriminate use of insecticides can kill beneficial insects such as bees, without which many flowers go unpollinated and fail to set seed. The problem is particularly bad when pesticide sprays drift onto surrounding areas, an all-too-easy occurrence in New Zealand's windy climate. Pesticides may also be washed off the land into waterways, where they kill fish and other aquatic life. Often the consequences are hard to monitor, especially when the pesticide enters a food chain. For example, a bird may eat seed dressed with insecticide and then fly to an area of bush where it is eaten by a bird of prey. The bird of prey is poisoned and dies. Animals which are the food of the bird of prey thus escape being eaten. These animals themselves may be pests. There is no telling where the chain of events will end.

Fertilisers, like pesticides, can cause problems for natural communities. Farmers require fertilisers to obtain high yields of agricultural crops. But inevitably some of the fertiliser is carried away, dissolved in water draining from the site. If this mineral-rich solution enters a stream or river, it can cause an effect known as eutrophication. It allows algae and other water plants to grow rampant. This in turn upsets the natural ecology and, among other things, can deprive water creatures of the oxygen they require.

Controlling the cabbage white The cabbage white butterfly (*Pieris rapae*) was one of the early introduced insect pests to yield to biological control. It reached New Zealand in the 1920s, possibly on vegetables imported from England. It soon appeared in large numbers, its caterpillars devouring vegetable crops such as cabbage and cauliflower. Two parasitoid ichneumon wasps were then brought in from Europe and, since then, the cabbage white has been much reduced in numbers. This instance of biological control cannot be considered a complete success since one of the parasitoids also attacks the native red admiral butterfly. Nowadays more stringent tests are carried out to ensure that newly introduced control species attack only the target species.

Erosion

As forests have been cleared for farmland, so some parts of New Zealand have suffered from erosion. Trees protect soils. They shelter them from the drying action of wind and the heat of the sun. Their crowns deflect rainfall, protecting the ground beneath. Trees take up a large proportion of the water that reaches the ground, so reducing the amount of leaching of mineral nutrients from the soil. Their fallen leaves decay, enriching the soil with nutrients and contributing humus, which improves its water-holding and other properties. The roots hold the soil together, preventing it from slipping. Clearing forest removes this protection. We lose the trees, we lose the plants and animals that once gained food and shelter from the trees — and we may lose the soil.

The Gisborne Plains have suffered in this way. Over-exploitation of the hill forests has allowed floods to deluge the plains with silt. Reafforestation projects began decades ago to help alleviate the problem, but more still needs to be done. In 1988, Cyclone Bola emphasised this problem in an all too dramatic fashion. Silt deposits effectively entombed the worst-hit farmland areas. They lay so thick on the ground that air was cut off from the roots of orchard trees and crop plants.

Biological control

Biological control is one way of keeping a check on pests without using pesticides. It relies on the principle that all living things, even pests, have organisms that attack them. The reason so many introduced weeds and other pests do so well in New Zealand is that the natural enemies they have in their native lands are not present here. Free from insects to eat them or diseases to weaken them, they flourish and spread.

To biologically control a target species (the pest), we have to find and introduce a control species, an animal or disease that attacks only that particular pest. It is no good introducing a control species that will destroy other, perhaps useful, species when it has eliminated the target. We would only be replacing one pest with another. Fortunately, many animals are very selective in their food. Knowing the country or region the target species comes from, we search that region for its natural enemies. Any potential control species that are discovered have to be very carefully tested, at first overseas and later in

New Zealand in quarantine, to check that they do not attack other species of value.

Once a species has been shown to be safe, it is bred in sufficient numbers to be released in the field. At this stage we have to find out if it will survive in its new environment. Having passed this hurdle, there is still the possibility that the control species may fail to attack the target with sufficient vigour. Only after several seasons will it be known if the project is successful.

Biological control does not eliminate the target species completely. As the control species increases in numbers, the target species decreases. As this occurs it becomes more difficult for the control species to find food. Its own numbers may fall too. Eventually, we hope to reach a delicately balanced situation in which both species exist permanently, but in very small numbers. If, at any later stage, something happens that temporarily favours the target species and causes its numbers to increase, the control species is then able to obtain food more easily and its own population increases for a while, attacking the target species more effectively. Gradually the balance is restored and the two populations return to their original low levels.

One of the first successes using this method was in the control of St John's wort. This was a serious weed in some areas before 1945, and has since considerably diminished, partly because of the introduction of the St John's wort beetle, which eats this plant. Another success has been against alligator weed, which blocks waterways in Northland and spreads onto the surrounding land. This has been controlled by introducing an aquatic flea beetle into the streams. Control schemes have also begun against gorse, broom, ragwort, nodding thistle and Californian thistle.

Insect pests, too, have been subject to biological control attempts. In an attempt to control the German wasp and the common wasp, the parasitic wasp *Sphecophaga vesparum vesparum* has been introduced. This parasite lives only in the wasp nest, feeding on the larvae. Investigations have shown that it is becoming established in certain areas, and there are strong hopes that it may eventually reduce the numbers of German and common wasps in the country.

Trees on the farm

Trees, both native and exotic, that have been planted around the farmstead and beside the roads are an attractive feature of many farms in New Zealand. But their value is more than aesthetic. They provide valuable shelter in this windy land. The reduction in wind force allows crops to grow more profusely and to fruit earlier. In the long term, trees are also a cash crop, as timber.

Agroforestry — the inclusion of tree crops with the usual range of farm crops — is a modern approach to land use that is becoming increasingly favoured. The conventional farm crops provide an income for the farmer while awaiting the longer-term profits from the trees. During the early stages of tree growth, the land can also support the grazing of cattle or sheep. In severe climates, the shelter provided by the trees brings the benefit of more successful lambing and protects newly shorn sheep. The combination of trees with other crops brings diversity to the local environment, assists with soil conservation, and gives greater ecological stability.

For the same reasons, hill farmers are beginning to plant trees and shrubs as fodder crops. One of the favourites is tagasaste (*Chamaecytisus palmensis*), a drought-resistant leguminous plant which grows well on poor soils. Other trees used for fodder include honey locust, carob, oak, and willow. With thoughtful planting, the farmer can provide a variety of fodder trees suited to the microclimatic conditions in different parts of the farm, and supplying a succession of fodder throughout the year. This type of approach, as well as such techniques as biological control, is part of an increasing trend towards agricultural systems modelled more on natural systems. The future health of farming, and the natural world in general, depends on growing food in ways that mirror nature as closely as possible.

A native control species? Sometimes we find that biological control has already been achieved naturally. An example is groundsel, a weed that causes much trouble in Europe, but has not done well in New Zealand. Possibly this is because it has become one of the main food plants of the caterpillars of the native magpie moth (*Nyctemera annulata*) (left), which does not occur in Europe. The moth has a striking yellow and black coloration, which is a warning to birds that it is dangerous to eat. The magpie-moth caterpillar eats mainly members of the plant genus *Senecio* (to which groundsel belongs), many of which contain toxins. The caterpillar probably accumulates these toxins in its body as it feeds, so becoming distasteful to potential predators. Interestingly, unlike most moths, the magpie moth brazenly flies by day, presumably because of its immunity to attack by birds.

CHAPTER 5

THE INLAND WATERS

With mountains that rise into the moist westerlies blowing across the Tasman Sea, New Zealand is generously doused with rain. This water is the erosive agent which carves out valleys and deposits plains. It is the life-giving substance that sustains the green fields and tall forests. For the organisms of this chapter, water is also a home.

As it flows from source to sea, water can provide several habitats. In the uplands, small torrents move so fast that organisms must clutch at rocks, or find shelter in calm backwaters. Yet later, the water may pause in large lakes, calm enough for pond skaters to ripple the surface and minute water fleas to swim freely below.

On the plains, large rivers flow sedately between banks of waterweeds. Fish idle in the current and shags sit watchfully nearby. Sometimes the current slows to the merest trickle, seeping through the habitat of half water and half land that is called wetland. Behind serried ranks of vegetation and within peat-stained depths, scores of animals unfold their obscure lives.

By the time it returns to the lapping ocean, the rain that fell upon the mountains will have been home to tiny plankton and shoals of migrating whitebait. It will have been stirred by the movement of trout and sprayed into glistening beads by the thrashing wings of waterfowl. All these things are part of the inland waters. It is easy to understand the naturalist's wonder.

Forest stream, South Westland

Lakes

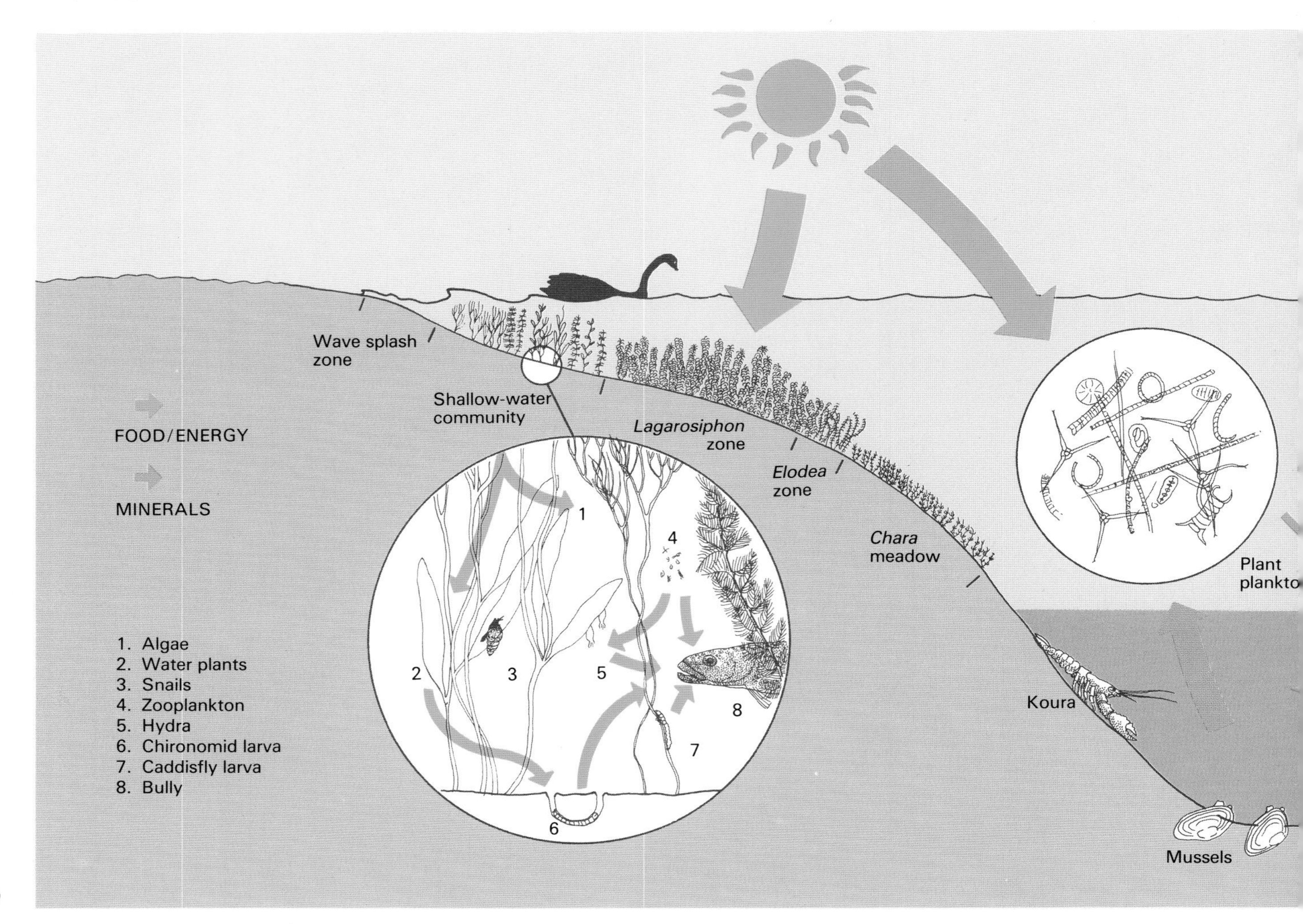

The lake food web

The lake food web

The clear blue waters of a lake may appear sterile to our eyes, but nothing could be further from the truth. Billions of microscopic algae, diatoms and cyanobacteria, far too small to see, photosynthesise and grow in the sunlit surface layers. Collectively called phytoplankton, they are the primary producers of food upon which most lake animals ultimately depend.

In the warming months of spring, phytoplankton numbers burgeon, sometimes on so grand a scale that the surface of the water takes on a greenish tinge. This spurt of growth is called a bloom. It is only prevented from developing into a 'soup' by the phytoplankton eventually exhausting the available supply of dissolved minerals that they require for growth. Diatoms, for instance, take silica from the water for their shells, and this ends up in short supply. Even though silica is constantly released as fallen diatoms decompose on the lake floor, this is not immediately available for use at the surface. It remains trapped within the cool, deep waters of the hypolimnion until the following winter, when the turnover of water stirs and replenishes the layers of the lake.

The growth of phytoplankton may therefore slow during summer for want of minerals. But blooms do reappear after heavy rains wash fresh minerals in from the surrounding lands. If these lands have been heavily fertilised for agriculture, then the supply of minerals can be so lavish as to cause a problem called eutrophication. Rampant algal blooms form such a scum on the water that aquatic creatures are deprived of oxygen. In some cases the blooms are also toxic.

Browsing upon the floating meadows of phytoplankton are hordes of different animals, collectively called zooplankton. Among them are minute rotifers, water fleas and copepods. They ply through the water, propelled by beating cilia, twitching antennae or paddling legs. Some sweep at the water as they go, using brush-like devices to sift out algae and specks of other plant matter.

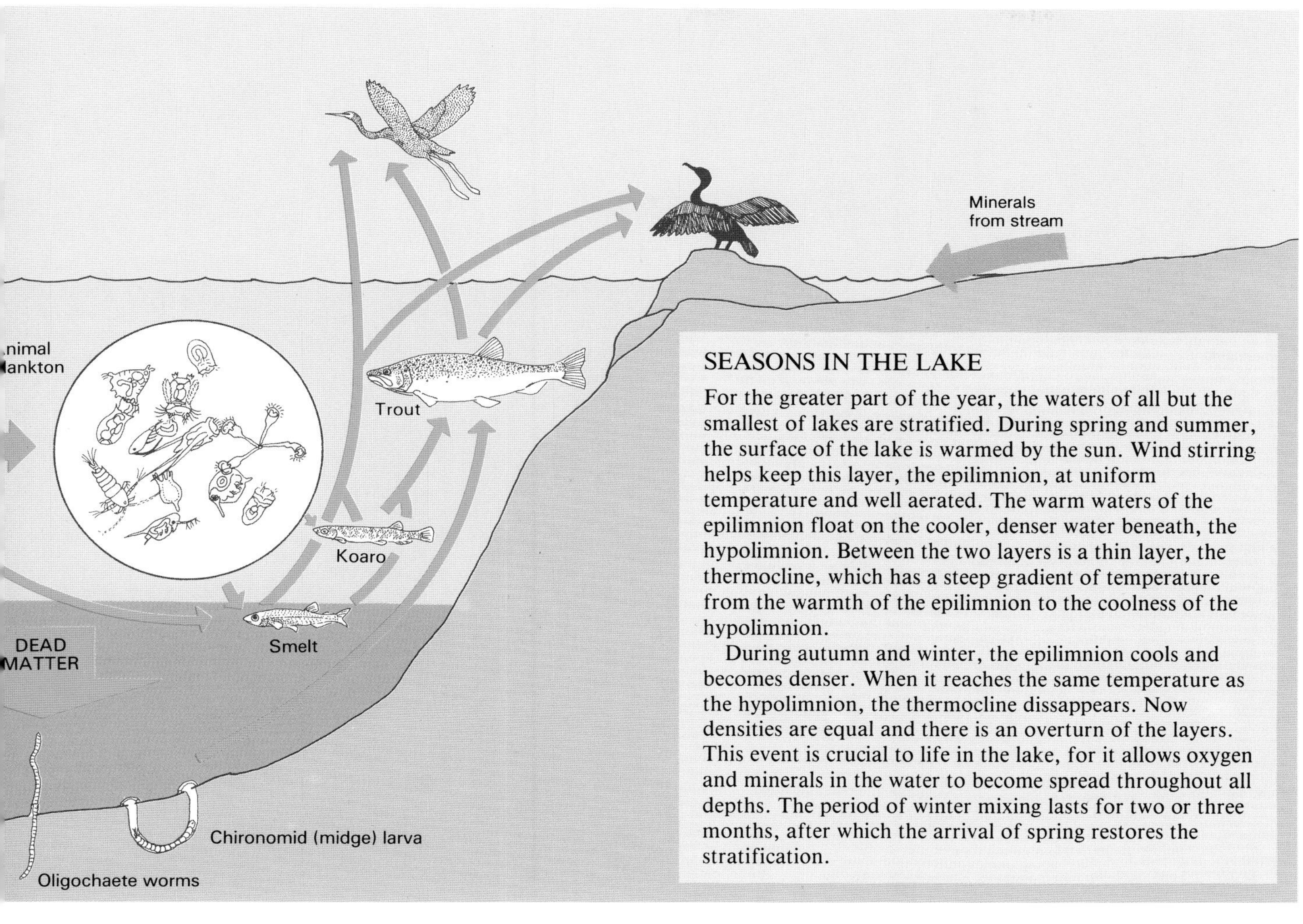

SEASONS IN THE LAKE

For the greater part of the year, the waters of all but the smallest of lakes are stratified. During spring and summer, the surface of the lake is warmed by the sun. Wind stirring helps keep this layer, the epilimnion, at uniform temperature and well aerated. The warm waters of the epilimnion float on the cooler, denser water beneath, the hypolimnion. Between the two layers is a thin layer, the thermocline, which has a steep gradient of temperature from the warmth of the epilimnion to the coolness of the hypolimnion.

During autumn and winter, the epilimnion cools and becomes denser. When it reaches the same temperature as the hypolimnion, the thermocline dissappears. Now densities are equal and there is an overturn of the layers. This event is crucial to life in the lake, for it allows oxygen and minerals in the water to become spread throughout all depths. The period of winter mixing lasts for two or three months, after which the arrival of spring restores the stratification.

Each day, as the afternoon draws to a close, swarms of zooplankton embark on a curious migration. Attracted by the fading light they propel themselves en masse towards the surface. There they remain during the evening and night, except perhaps on black moonless nights. Then early the next day, as the light gathers strength, they migrate back towards the depths.

There has been no satisfactory explanation of this widespread phenomenon. It may ensure that the zooplankton optimise their time spent where plankton are most plentiful, yet avoid the harmful effects of ultraviolet light at midday. The phytoplankton too may engage in a daily migration, diving and surfacing with the help of pulsating flagella or gas-filled bladders. This is thought to help them renew their supply of minerals by visiting deeper waters.

The zooplankton provide food for the carnivores of the lake, the fish. The fish in turn provide food for birds, such as shags and herons, that frequent the lake. Since the birds are free to roam as they please, some of the energy originally trapped by the phytoplankton may be lost from the lake ecosystem. However, most of the plants and animals end up sinking to the lake bottom as dead or excreted matter.

This steady rain of falling material supports a host of scavengers that wait in the dark cool depths of the hypolimnion. Among them is the koura, or crayfish, which can descend to 60 metres to feed on debris. Most of the bottom dwellers, or benthos, are burrowing animals such as mussels, earthworm-like oligochaetes and the larvae of chironomid midges. Each harvests its food in a different way. The mussels, like their marine counterparts, filter it from the overlying water. The oligochaetes ingest the silty sediment and extract the organic nutriment from it. The chironomid larvae secrete a mat of sticky mucus at the entrance of their burrows to trap particles. These bottom-dwelling animals, as well as the ubiquitous bacteria and fungi, break down the organic rain, rendering it to its chemical constituents and so unlocking the minerals to be used again in the food web.

Lake-shore aquatic plants

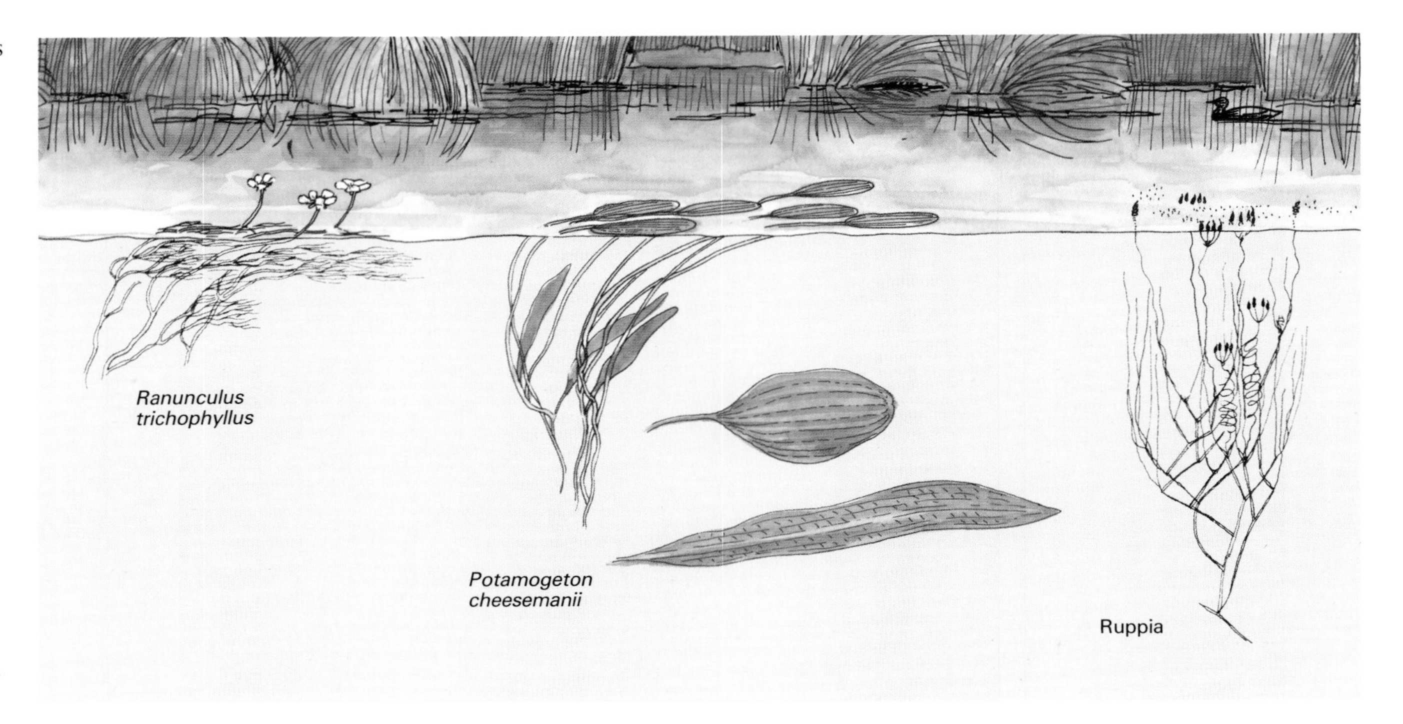

Plants that grow underwater

Apart from the teeming millions of microscopic algae that inhabit the surface waters of a lake, there are also many larger plants to be found rooted in the shallows by the lake shore. Wherever the shelter is sufficient, they grow like verdant underwater gardens, every bit as prolific as their counterparts on land.

Among the assembled 'waterweeds' are many flowering plants. This is of interest, since flowering plants evolved on land from ancestors that were originally aquatic. By returning to water, they have been able to relinquish some of the adaptations they developed for terrestrial life. For instance, submerged plants can obtain the water and minerals they need directly through their leaves, so the roots of aquatic flowering plants have become simplified to serve a purpose more limited than that of their land relatives, and act mainly to anchor them to the bottom. At the same time their submerged leaves have largely been able to discard the watertight covering, called the cuticle, that their land-dwelling ancestors needed to conserve moisture. Likewise, aquatic flowering plants do not need the stomatal pores which land plants use to obtain carbon dioxide from the air for photosynthesis. Instead they can absorb carbon dioxide directly through their leaf surfaces, from the rather small amounts that are dissolved in water.

Herein, however, lies a problem for aquatic plants. Carbon dioxide diffuses 100,000 times more slowly in water than in air, so their leaves have trouble absorbing it quickly enough. In answer to this most aquatic plants have leaves which are feathery or thin and ribbon-like, to increase the surface area available to absorb carbon dioxide from the water. The most interesting plants in this respect are those which have some leaves below water and some above. These produce two entirely different types of leaf, one to suit each of the two environments. This phenomenon, called heterophylly, is displayed by *Potamogeton cheesemanii*, which produces very thin ribboned leaves underwater, while on the surface it produces conventional oval leaves.
The surface leaves are also conventionally equipped with masses of stomata and a thick cuticle.

Water also provides an unusual environment for aquatic plants to flower and achieve pollination. Some, like the water buttercup (*Ranunculus trichophyllus*), raise their flowers above the surface and rely on insects to ferry their pollen from bloom to bloom, in the same way as their land-living relatives do. Many others, however, have taken special advantage of the wind. Normally wind is an extremely haphazard way of distributing pollen. Grains shed by one flower have very little chance of reaching another flower because they can be blown in any of three dimensions through the air. Most simply end up on the ground. Aquatic plants improve these odds by spreading their pollen in two dimensions across the water's surface. One plant that does this is *Ruppia*. It grows submerged in relatively deep water, so when it is ready to flower it extends its blooms to the lake surface on the end of long stalks. Male flowers then drop floating pollen grains onto the water, to be blown across the surface. Female flowers, because they are also held at the surface, have a far greater chance of picking up the pollen than if it were dispersed three dimensionally in the air. After it has been fertilised the female flower stem coils up, withdrawing the developing seed back underwater.

Life at the extremes of heat

In parts of the North Island where molten magma lies close underground, springs of hot, mineral-laden water gush onto the surface. Sometimes they erupt from the ground in awesome spires of steam. Elsewhere they well up in brimming turquoise pools, or trickle across rocks the colour of burnt ochre. It is a contrary landscape: beautiful, yet hostile.

In pools too hot to touch, there are no green plants. Neither are there any fish or insects to ripple the surface. But life is not precluded altogether. If a glass microscope slide is dropped in the scalding water and later examined, it will be found to be coated with colonies of simple bacteria. These are not organisms which struggle to survive in the heat. Their normal growth demands it. Even in the very hottest of the pools, where water is simmering, there are thriving populations of such bacteria.

One hundred degrees Celsius, the boiling point of water, is the hottest temperature that life can live at on land. It would be fruitless to search for bacteria on hotter surfaces. Nevertheless this limit is not due to temperature itself, but to the availability of water. All life depends on liquid water, and when temperatures exceed 100 degrees Celsius, water can only exist as steam. To find bacteria that live at higher temperatures one must look to the sea. At the bottom of the ocean, the overlying sea exerts such pressures that water will not boil till well over 100 degrees Celsius. Here, near thermal vents, bacteria have been discovered that can grow at 110 degrees Celsius.

Just how high a temperature life can exist at we do not know. Other bacteria may yet be found living in even hotter conditions. Water issuing from the deepest thermal vents has been recorded at over 350 degrees Celsius, but it would be remarkable if any organism could survive even half this temperature. The difficulty is that as the environment gets hotter, so the organic molecules upon which life depends become increasingly unstable. Hot-pool bacteria living at temperatures near 100 degrees Celsius have found ways to prevent their genetic material — encoded in DNA molecules — from melting down. They are also able to construct proteins that are remarkably heat-stable, much to the interest of biotechnologists studying these proteins for their possible industrial uses in high-temperature chemical processing. Nevertheless, despite the ability of bacteria to heat-stabilise many complex organic compounds, there are limits. There comes a point, probably before 150 degrees Celsius, when many simpler organic compounds disintegrate so quickly that the bacteria can no longer keep pace with the job of repairing their metabolic systems.

As well as their extraordinary ability to tolerate heat, hot-pool bacteria display other talents. Living in water laden with mineral salts, they have some unusual metabolic pathways. Some bacteria feed on organic compounds in the pool, which they break down as a source of energy using sulphur, in a similar way to that in which air-breathing organisms such as ourselves obtain energy from organic compounds using oxygen. They can therefore live in the absence of oxygen. Indeed for most, the presence of oxygen is lethal. There are other bacteria which can derive the energy they need from the mineral salts themselves. In effect, they feed on the chemical compounds in the hot spring, such as those of sulphur and iron, using the energy derived to build the organic compounds of which their tissues are made. Thus they achieve something very unusual. They bypass the conventional source of energy that powers virtually all other life, which is the sunlight absorbed by green plants, and tap a source that emanates from the earth instead.

Heat-loving organisms have not evolved recently in order to exploit the extreme habitat offered by thermal waters. Far from it. When life first appeared about 3500 million years ago, conditions were not unlike those found in hot pools. Then, there was no free oxygen in the atmosphere. The young Earth was still rapidly cooling after its creation and its surface may have been close to the temperature of boiling water. Sulphurous hot pools were probably commonplace. So life may have evolved in these conditions. Indeed, studies of some modern-day groups of thermal bacteria would support this. Those living at the very hottest temperatures belong to a distinct and slowly evolving group called Archaebacteria. Organisms very like them were probably among the earliest life forms on Earth.

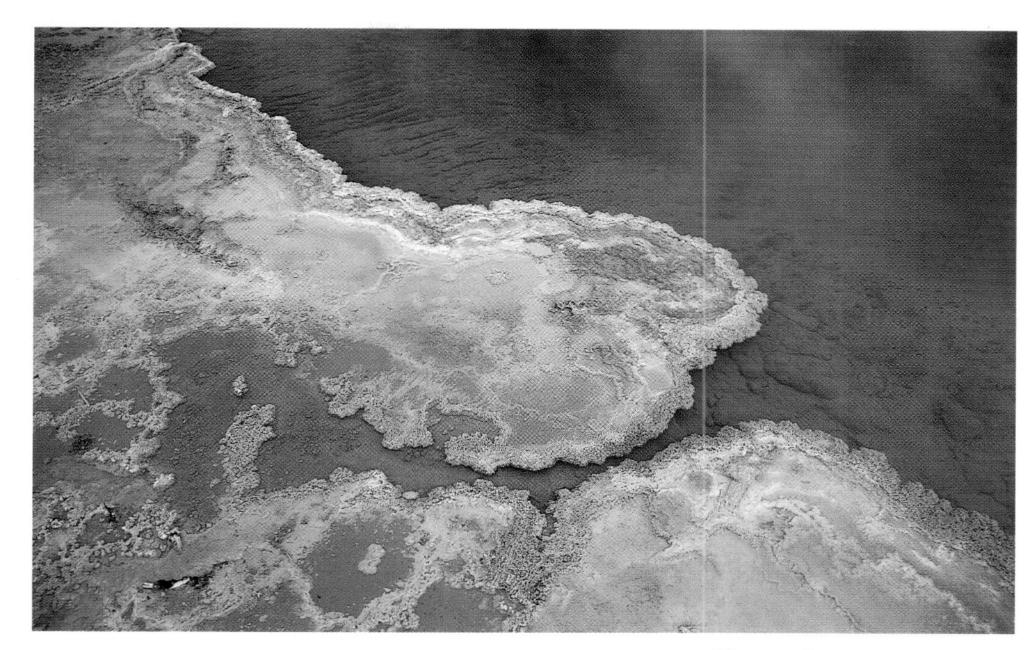

Thermal waters
With mineral-rich waters at a scalding 70 degrees Celsius, the champagne pool at Waiotapu provides a habitat for thermal bacteria.

Freshwater fish

It is sometimes a surprise to learn that New Zealand has native freshwater fish, so inconspicuous are they compared to their introduced relatives. With only about 30 species, it is a modest collection. About half of these are members of the Galaxiidae, a family found in other temperate lands of the Southern Hemisphere. Others include two eels, the common smelt, the torrent fish and several bullies.

Since the arrival of Europeans a further 20 species of fish have been introduced from overseas. Best known are members of the family Salmonidae: the salmon, trout and char, brought here from the Northern Hemisphere for fishing. Among other sport fish are the perch and tench. Then there have been a few unofficial liberations such as the rudd and the aquarium goldfish. The most enterprising of aquarium escapees, however, must surely be the sailfin molly, the guppy and the swordtail. All are strictly warm-water fish, but survive in the wild by inhabiting geothermally heated streams in the North Island.

Fish are often considered lesser animals. They are easily dismissed as cold-blooded, unthinking creatures, still tied to the watery world our forbears left countless millions of years ago. However, a great deal of mystery still prevails over their lives. Between birth and death many undertake extraordinary migrations and achieve feats of navigation that leave even the scientist incredulous.

The whitebait story

Next time you yearn for that delicacy whitebait pause a moment to consider the natural history of these tiny creatures. Whitebait are the young of several different species of native galaxiid fish, caught in estuaries as they migrate upriver from the sea. By far the commonest species is the inanga (*Galaxias maculatus*), and the reason it happens to be swimming in the estuary is a story as mysterious as it is marvellous.

Inanga whitebait (*Galaxias maculatus*)

The adult fish live inland, in streams, lakes and swamps. In autumn, ready to spawn, they travel down to the river's tidal mouth, timing their journey to coincide with the night of the full or new moon. How they know when to head downstream is a mystery, but the timing is utterly critical, since this is when very high spring tides occur. In the estuary, water levels rise well up the grassy banks and spill into surrounding salt marshes. The fish, their silver bodies perhaps gleaming in the moonlight, thrash around in these flooded meadows, shedding eggs and sperm.

At first the eggs stick to surrounding vegetation so they do not drift away. But once the tide has fallen they drop to the ground and remain moist among the vegetation. Here the eggs lie, marooned for a fortnight while the smaller neap tides come and go. By the time the next spring tide floods back over the vegetation, the eggs are ready to hatch. Once again timing is critical, for there is only an hour before the water recedes and they would be left stranded. The young fish larvae, about 5 millimetres long, break out of their eggs en masse and drift out to sea with the falling tide.

For about six months the larvae live as part of the ocean's plankton, perhaps drifting for hundreds of kilometres at the mercy of the currents. During this time they probably feed on other animals in the plankton, steadily growing to about 50 millimetres, when they are ready to return to fresh water. In spring, they congregate offshore and cease feeding, preparing themselves for the change to fresh water. Then, shoals of the young fish, now the familiar whitebait, swarm up the estuary with the rising tide. Those that evade the whitebaiters and other predators make their way upstream.

In streams, lakes and swamps, the inanga grow to adulthood, feeding on small aquatic animals. Then, one full or new moon in autumn, the 'call' urges them downstream and the timeless saga is re-enacted.

Eels

Like the whitebait galaxiids, freshwater eels (*Anguilla*) spend part of their life cycle at sea. But instead of shedding their eggs at the river mouth, the adults migrate vast distances across the Pacific to spawn. No one is sure where they go, except that it is to warmer seas far to the north, possibly as far away as New Caledonia. Since eels are so rarely caught at sea they probably travel at depth, navigating through the watery twilight by means which are hard to imagine. After spawning, the parents die but the leaf-like eel larvae drift back with the ocean currents. Once they reach the continental shelf they change into slender, transparent 'glass eels'. These migrate into estuaries on the flood

Long-finned eel (*Anguilla dieffenbachii*) (left)

tide and later head upstream, feeding and developing into greyish-brown elvers. They slither adeptly across wet surfaces to get around waterfalls and reach the headwaters. As the eels grow so do their appetites. From a diet of insect larvae and snails they progress to crayfish, trout and even duckling.

The eels spend many years in the headwaters before they return to the sea. The long-finned eel (*A. dieffenbachii*) will usually migrate after 20 years and the short-finned (*A. australis*) after 10 years. Before departing, their eyes enlarge, perhaps in preparation for the darkness of the deep sea. They also cease feeding, relying entirely on stored body fats to last them through the long journey to their breeding grounds.

The salmon migration

Salmon possess one of the most remarkable homing instincts of the animal kingdom. During their lifetime, young fish travel from the river of their birth out to sea, where they grow to maturity. When ready to spawn they return, often across hundreds of kilometres of open sea, to locate the exact river they left as a juvenile. Then, with unerring accuracy, they swim upstream to the same tributary where they hatched.

How they perform this feat of navigation is not entirely understood. Some people have postulated that they navigate through the sea by sensing the Earth's magnetic field, or perhaps by responding to the direction of polarised light. Once off the coast of their homeland, however, salmon rely on a gifted sense of smell. They can detect the particular odour of their home river, imparted by the types of rock, soil or vegetation found in the headwaters. It is an extraordinary achievement, considering that the salmon have somehow managed to remember this odour after all their years at sea, and can detect it diluted over a million-fold in salt water.

Of the three salmon species introduced to New Zealand, only quinnat salmon (*Oncorhynchus tshawytscha*) is well established and undertakes a sea migration. Before returning to fresh water, the adult fish cease to feed and their digestive organs degenerate. From now on, their single purpose is to breed. Swimming powerfully upstream and leaping small waterfalls, they follow the water's scent, making the correct turn at each branch in the river to eventually find the home tributary. Here, in the gravelly bed, the female scoops out a hollow, called a redd, where she lays several thousand eggs, which are then fertilised by the male. The salmon are in an appalling state by this stage, their reserves utterly exhausted by the rigours of the journey and the act of spawning. The females struggle to guard their eggs for a while, but in such an emaciated state, with ragged fins and bones often protuding, neither parent lasts long.

The eggs hatch and, after feeding and growing for a while in the spawning area, the young make their way downstream. They may feed in the river for a year before leaving for the sea. The move between fresh and salt water, undertaken by so many river fish, is no small feat in itself. Complex changes of body physiology are required to shift between the two environments.
In salmon this is called smolting, and the main visible change is that the young, called parr, lose their dark transverse markings and become silvery, like the one in the photograph (below left). They then head out to sea to feed on larger plankton and small fish. Many end up as prey themselves, but those that survive the two to four years to reach adulthood return to their birthplace to renew the life cycle.

Trout The brown trout (*Salmo trutta*) (bottom right) is a member of the introduced salmon family now widespread in New Zealand rivers. Some individuals spend most of their life at sea or in estuaries, returning to spawn in freshwater streams, rather like salmon. However, many spend their entire lifetime in fresh water. They migrate upstream to breed, perhaps several times during their life, and make their way back down again, feeding and growing in deep river pools and lakes. The less common rainbow salmon (*Salmo gairdnerii*) has a similar freshwater lifestyle, living primarily in lakes and spawning in tributary streams and rivers.

Young Quinnat salmon (*Oncorhynchus tshawytscha*) (far left)

Rivers and streams

With high mountains and heavy rainfall, most of New Zealand's rivers are fast moving and temperamental. They jostle among the foothills, surging down boulder-strewn courses before sweeping over shingle beds on the plains. Strong currents and regular flash floods scour many riverbeds clear of silts and muds. Large water plants get little chance to establish in the turmoil of tumbling stones and bulldozed gravel bars. Even on the lowlands there are relatively few gently winding, sediment-rich rivers that are sluggish enough for beds of aquatic plants to flourish by their banks and blooms of phytoplankton to tint their surfaces.

A cursory glance at many rivers will therefore reveal clear rippling water and a stony bottom. Signs of life are not at first apparent. Nevertheless, with gumboots, a small net and an inquisitive frame of mind, a large collection of riverine inhabitants can be uncovered. Most lie in hiding, sheltering from the current beneath rocks on the riverbed or in calm shallows by the bank. Here can be found many of the smaller creatures discussed on the following pages.

Freshwater crustacea

Although crustaceans are primarily sea-dwelling creatures, a number have become successful freshwater inhabitants. The largest is the koura, or freshwater crayfish (*Paranephrops*). *Paranephrops planifrons* lives in the North Island and in the north and west of the South Island, while *P. zealandicus* lives in the east and south of the South Island. Both grow to about 10 centimetres long and live in lakes, ponds and streams. They are bottom dwellers, hiding beneath rocks or buried in silt by day and emerging at night to scavenge for food.

Among New Zealand's other freshwater crustaceans is a crab, *Amarinus lacustris*, found in coastal lakes and rivers in the North Island. The same species also lives in Australia and on Lord Howe and Norfolk Islands, which presents biologists with a curious distribution pattern. The explanation appears to be that the crab larvae are occasional hitch-hikers, getting a lift from place to place by clinging to the feet or feathers of migrating waterbirds.

More frequently seen are freshwater shrimps that dart among the waterweeds in most lowland streams. The most common freshwater crustaceans of all, however, are those least noticed. These are the millions of copepods, ostracods and water fleas, often no bigger than pinheads, that are part of the zooplankton in lakes, ponds and quiet backwaters.

Freshwater crayfish *(Paranephrops planifrons)*

Molluscs

Molluscs can be found in almost every stream or river. There are several species of water snail, though the commonest is *Potamopygrus antipodarum*. It has a shell about 10 millimetres high, either smooth or bearing tiny spines. There are also a number of freshwater limpets. One of these, *Latia neritoides*, has a dark shell about 8 millimetres long and is found attached to the underside of rocks.

In quiet rivers and lakes, where the bottom is of fine mud or sand, live two mussel species. The more widespread mussel, *Hyridella menziesi*, has an interesting life cycle. The larvae are reared within the protection of the parent's shell, and later the young disperse by hitching onto fish by means of tiny hooks. There are also some clams that inhabit quiet waters. All are small, being 8 millimetres or less in diameter, and live buried within the sediment.

Spiders

New Zealand has no truly aquatic spiders, though several species may be found near rivers. One that always lives close to water is the water spider (*Dolomedes*). It is rarely noticed, for during the day it hides beneath rocks and is well camouflaged. However, a torchlight search at night will often reveal one by the water's edge, trailing its front legs on the surface, waiting to catch prey that floats by.

If disturbed by your approach the spider will vanish by using one of two unusual escape options. One is to flee across the water, which it does by means of water-repellent legs that do not break through the surface. The other is to cling onto the bank and haul itself underwater, a coat of non-wettable hairs trapping a supply of air around its body allowing it to remain submerged for long periods.

Water spider (*Dolomedes*)
If alarmed, the water spider will sometimes clamber down the shore and hide beneath the water's surface.

FOOD RELATIONSHIPS IN A STREAM

A fast-flowing stream is no place for floating plankton; its inhabitants need to be firmly attached to the rocks or find a crevice in which to escape the current. However, when water flows over a smooth-surfaced rock, there is a boundary zone of water close to the rock and a few millimetres deep, where the water speed is very much reduced. Many aquatic insect larvae have flattened bodies so that they can crouch close to the rock and crawl around in this low-current boundary zone. This effect also allows layers of algae and bacteria to establish on such surfaces.

The majority of stream invertebrates are insects in their immature larval stage. The most common are the larvae of mayflies, caddisflies, midges and simulid flies (sandflies). They feed on plant debris which has fallen into the river. In forested areas dead leaves gather in slack water or fall between rocks on the riverbed, providing a constant supply of food. The microscopic algae and bacteria growing as a film on submerged or splashed rocks and logs are another source of food, particularly for browsing water-snails. Not all of the insect larvae feed on plant matter. Some stoneflies, for instance, eat other insect larvae. The food relationships in the stream end with the fish, which are all predators.

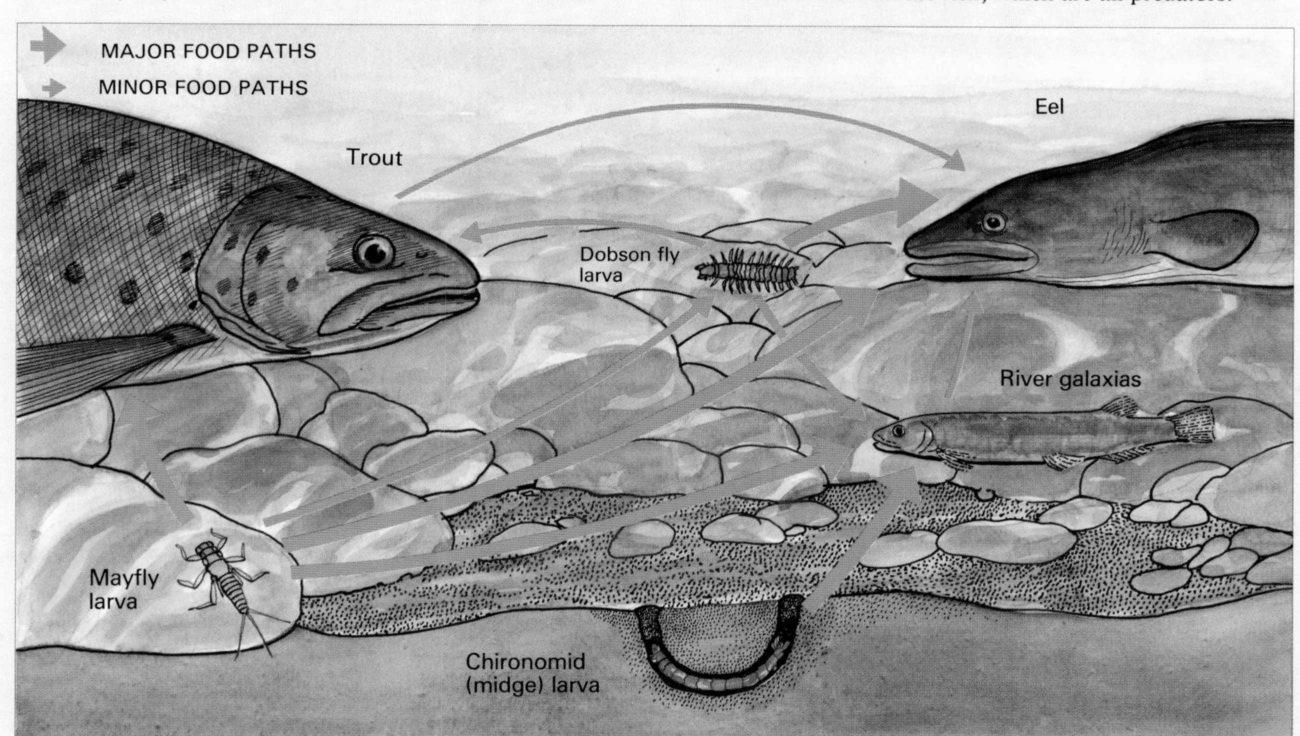

Common bully (*Gobiomorphus cotidianus*) (right)

Bullies

Bullies keep out of fast currents by living on the riverbed among the shelter of rocks. Protruding eyes, strategically placed near the top of their head, offer a good view of the surrounds, while widely splayed pectoral fins act like a car's spoilers in the current to keep the fish firmly placed on the bottom. Bullies are found in both lakes and rivers. There are six species, of which the most frequently encountered is the common bully (*Gobiomorphus cotidianus*). Like other bullies it forages among the rocks and gravels for river invertebrates, particularly chironomid midge larvae and mayfly larvae. During the breeding season males become very territorial and defend a piece of riverbed, about a metre square, from other males. Females are enticed to lay their eggs at spawning sites, which the male prepares in advance by scraping away any covering of algae or other plants from a submerged log or boulder. The eggs are sticky so they adhere to the surface, and as they are being laid the male stays in attendance to ensure no rival sneaks in to fertilise them before he does. Afterwards he drives the female away and dutifully guards the nest, removing small predators and fanning the eggs with his fins to keep them well oxygenated. The hatchlings disperse downstream and enter the sea for their early life before making their way back upstream.

THE BLUE DUCK

The soft, fluty whistle of the whio (*Hymenolaimus malacorhynchos*), or blue duck, is no longer a common sound on New Zealand's rivers. Before settlers cleared large areas of forest the duck was widespread. Now it has retreated to remote mountain areas where its habitat remains intact. Here, within the confines of deep gorges, or along the hidden reaches of forest streams, you may still encounter this bird.

The blue duck maintains an elusive presence, and if it were not for its distinctive call, would rarely be noticed.

Individuals are most active at dusk because the insect larvae on which they feed are nocturnal, and in the half-light their slate-blue colour makes them all but invisible among the river rocks. But if you are fortunate to see one feed, the sight is compelling. The bird moves with a grace that transcends the tumbling turmoil of water, occasionally diving to peck among the rocks of the riverbed for mayfly or caddisfly larvae with its broad, soft-tipped bill. A more riverwise creature is hard to imagine.

If only one bird is seen, the partner is usually not far away. Blue ducks pair for life and establish a territory along a stretch of the river. This the male defends while the female incubates the eggs. The chicks are born with 'oversized' feet to help them keep up with their parents in the surging water. If disturbed, the family has a simple but appropiate means of escape. They swim into the middle of the river and allow the current to take them away — mum, dad and a handful of bobbing chicks. As they get older the young disperse to seek their own territories. It seems, however, that they do not venture far. Most remain within the same catchment, eventually to secure a territory of their own.

Secrecy also surrounds the origins of the blue duck, for it has no close relatives elsewhere. Many of its habits are unusual for a duck. For instance, there are few other ducks in the world that inhabit white water. With rare exceptions, such as the torrent duck of the South American Andes, ducks prefer the calm waters of lakes and wetlands, or coastal seas. The blue duck's territoriality, courtship display and strong pair bonding are also unusual. There are differences in appearance too. The blue duck lacks a speculum, the patch of iridescent feathers found on the wing of many other ducks. All these features add an element of mystery to what must be one of the most enigmatic of the world's waterfowl.

Letting in the sunlight

The clearance of lowland forest has created an aquatic habitat once virtually unknown in New Zealand — the sunlit stream. The native flora, used to shady forested waterways, was not adapted to such open conditions, so there were few candidates among them to invade this new human-made habitat. The area was ripe for exploitation by introduced species. One plant to benefit was watercress, originally introduced as a food plant in the Canterbury area in 1840. By 1857 it was regarded by many as a weed, clogging waterways and impeding the traffic of boats on the River Avon. In a similar way, monkey musk and water speedwell have dominated riversides and wet, swampy areas. Floating plants such as the South American alligator weed have flourished in quiet backwaters and sometimes invaded nearby farmland with their creeping habit.

The success of these plant invaders has brought changes to the animal populations of the waterways they have colonised. Formerly, the main water inhabitants would have been creatures such as mayflies, stoneflies and caddisflies, which favour rocky-bedded forest streams. In the sunlit streams the tangled stems of water-weeds have reduced the water speed to the extent that silts have become deposited among the plants, covering the rocky or shingly bottom. The soft bottom now favours burrowing creatures such as the earthworm-like oligochaetes and amphipod crustaceans.

BIRD OF THE RIVER FLATS AND PASTURES

The native paradise duck (*Tadorna variegata*) has coped relatively well with the changes to its habitat caused by human settlement. Increasing numbers have bred on lowland farmlands in recent years, where they graze grasses and herbs, as well as eat worms and insects. Most New Zealanders, however, will associate these birds with the open tussock riverflats of the high-country. Anyone who has tramped in the mountains will know the paradise duck well, for an encounter with the bird is rarely peaceful. Immediately your presence has been detected, the resident 'parry' will advertise the fact to all and sundry by taking to the air amid a clammering of trumpeting and honking.

The alarm is often raised by a male and female together, since paradise ducks pair for life. They are unusual compared with other ducks in that the female, which has a white head, is more strikingly coloured than the dark-headed male. High-country pairs fly down valley in autumn and winter, and return to the uplands in spring and summer, where they raise the family. Like a number of birds that breed in open areas, the paradise duck employs a distraction technique to protect its young. If you approach too close to its chicks, the parent will hobble off in a pitiful way, limply holding up its wing as if it were broken. This convincing display is sufficient to fool almost any predator, which follows thinking the injured bird is a sure catch. But the parent always manages to keep ahead, despite its apparent handicap. After you have been led a sufficient distance, it will take confidently to the air. Meanwhile, the other parent will have escorted the rest of the family to safety.

River insects

Insects are arguably the most successful inhabitants of the riverbed. Turn over a submerged rock and dozens of mayflies, stoneflies and caddisflies will be seen scurrying for shelter. Like all common riverbed insects, these are immature, wingless larvae. Once they become winged adults they leave the watery world behind and take to the air like other insects.

Aquatic insects originated from land-living ancestors that evolved to spend part, or occasionally all, of their life cycle in water. The move from air to water has required some modifications, the most important being to find a way to breathe. Insects are by nature air-breathing creatures, equipped with a network of fine hollow tubes called tracheae that carry air into their bodies. Since the turbulent waters of fast-flowing streams are so well aerated with dissolved oxygen, many insects have modified their breathing system by adding gills. These are varied and often exquisite structures. Some resemble paddles which beat frantically in the current. Others are like tufts of feathers which trail passively in the water. In all cases they strain oxygen from the water and pass it into the insect's tracheae, or

COMMON INSECTS OF THE RIVER

Mayfly larva

Mayfly (Order Ephemeroptera) Every stream hosts hordes of mayflies. Many have flattened bodies and crawl over rocks on the river bottom rather like stoneflies, though they can be distinguished by having three rather than two tail filaments or cerci. The one pictured is adapted to a more free-swimming lifestyle, so it has a fish-shaped body. This streamlined shape, which is ideally widest about one-third of the way along its length, is called a fusiform body. The mayfly's long tail filaments, acting as a rudder, help keep it facing the current, while hooked feet enable it to grip the bottom when at rest. Its paddle-shaped gills can be clearly seen along the side of the body. They fan like the strokes of an oar, extracting oxygen from the continuous flow of fresh water.

The mayfly has a life cycle unlike that of any other insect. When mature, the nymph rises to the surface and goes through two different winged stages to become the adult. The first, called the dun, has rather opaque wings. Soon afterwards it moults again, casting off its delicate skin, wings and all, to emerge as a winged adult. The adult does not feed. Its mouthparts are useless or absent. Even its legs are too weak for walking. Its only purpose is to mate, for after a year or so spent beneath the water as a larva, it has just a few days, or perhaps hours, to live.

Hundreds of male mayflies gather for their nuptial flight in glistening clouds that undulate above the water's surface. Females which fly into the swarm are seized by a male and carried off for mating. By the following day the mayflies will be dead, sometimes in such numbers as to litter the ground. This poignant scene has been enacted for aeons. Mayflies represent the most primitive of flying insects. Their ancestors appeared in the Carboniferous period, about 300 million years ago.

Caddisfly (Order Trichoptera) Caddisflies often come pattering at lighted windows on sultry summer evenings. They look remarkably like moths, but can be distinguished by their whip-like antennae and the fact that their wings are covered with hairs and not scales. The larvae are common inhabitants of the riverbed, where they usually build a portable case in which to live. This provides physical protection and, since it is usually built of local materials, camouflage too. Cases may be made of sand grains, pieces of leaf or bark, or the discarded shells of smaller animals.

Mayfly adult (right)

Caddisfly (far right)

else directly into the circulating blood. The system works efficiently, for aquatic insects are just as active as airborne ones.

Since they cope so well with aquatic life, one may ask why, as adults, do they leave the water and return to the air? The main reason is to disperse their young. An aquatic larva cannot battle far upstream against the current and it is virtually impossible for it to move from one watershed to another. The adult, however, can do this easily. With wings it can fly upstream if conditions are better for egg laying there. Or it can travel to adjacent rivers and lakes to find new areas to populate.

The life of most aquatic insects can therefore be divided into two parts. The larva is preoccupied with feeding and growing; the adult's mission is to breed and disperse its eggs. For this reason the adult's life is usually ephemeral compared with the larva's. Once it has deposited its eggs it can die. Some adults are literally creatures of a day. Interestingly this is the reverse of the life cycle of seashore invertebrates, such as starfish and molluscs. In the sea it is the larva, not the adult, which is the dispersive stage. The larvae of starfish and sea urchins, cockles and crabs drift like specks in the plankton before settling in suitable habitats to grow into adults. Again, in contrast with the freshwater insects, it is the adult, not the larva, which is the feeding and growing stage. A sea urchin or a paua, for instance, may live for years and move around relatively little.

These materials are bound together by silk secreted by the larva. Sometimes the resulting home can be massive, but thanks to the buoyancy of water and the pieces of wood or twig incorporated like floats into the construction, the larva can amble around with moderate ease. A few species make their cases out of silk secretions alone, and others spin silken tunnels on the river bottom. Most caddisfly larvae are vegetarian, browsing algae or decaying vegetation, though a few are carnivorous. Some inhabiting fast-flowing waters ingeniously use the force of the current to their advantage. They spin tiny silken nets and string them between rocks on the riverbed. Then they just have to wait for the next meal to be swept into the trap.

Sandfly (Simuliidae) No natural history book would be complete without some mention of the blood-sucking sandflies. These persistent insects, with a bite ten times their size, defy disregard by anyone. When besieged by clouds of the hungry creatures, you are led to wonder where they all came from. Equally, given that their bite is so smartly felt and the perpetrators so easily despatched by a sweep of the hand, you wonder how so unsubtle a bloodsucker could be so successful.

The answer is that for most of its life a sandfly does not feed on blood. It lives in streams and rivers as a larva, glued to submerged rocks and vegetation with a sticky secretion and tiny hooks. At the mouth end it has a brush-like apparatus which sifts food particles from the passing water. Later it pupates underwater in a cocoon it spins for itself. When the adult is ready to emerge, a small bubble in the cocoon floats it to the surface like a diving bell, and the sandfly takes wing.

Only the female takes blood, which is used as a high-energy food source to mature its eggs. The male feeds on plant nectar. Blood is therefore a small part of the sandfly's overall diet, but an important part for its reproduction. So while you may swat dozens of the thirsty creatures, each one that manages to gorge itself will lay hundreds of eggs to ensure there are always going to be more sandflies.

Stonefly (Order Plecoptera) The flattened body and broadly spreading legs of the stonefly larva are superbly shaped to crawl within the thin film of relatively still water that exists at the surface of rocks and other objects. Its six hooked feet splayed out at different angles act like the guylines of a tent to hold it against the current. It feeds on rotting vegetation or, in the case of some species, other insects. When mature the nymph leaves the water and crawls onto the bank. Its skin splits and the adult emerges, thence to commence its slow and clumsy flight up and down the stream at dusk in search of a mate.

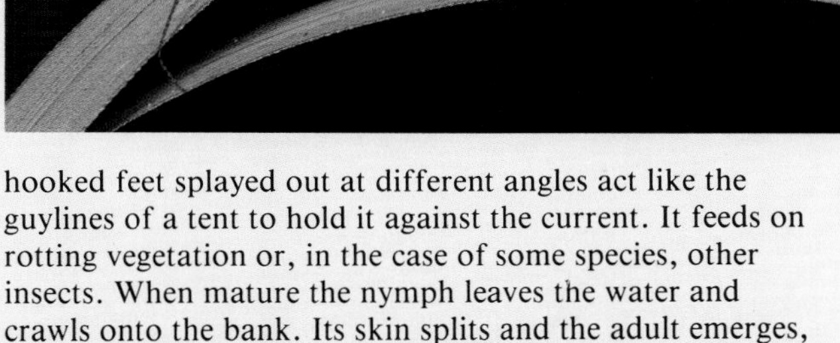

Stonefly larva (above)

Adult stonefly (left)

Dobson fly (*Archichauliodes diversus*) The dobson fly larva emerges from beneath rocks at dusk to crawl over the riverbed and seize insects in its vice-like jaws. The leg-like spikes on the abdomen, which give it the appearance of a centipede, are really gills. After it has pupated, the adult emerges as a robust but surprisingly beautiful insect that flits above the water on large diaphanous wings.

Dobson fly larva

Wetlands

What are wetlands?

While most people will recognise wetlands when they see them, few are so certain about giving a definition. The simplest definition, however, is implied by the name. They are wet land: land that is permanently or temporarily wet. At one extreme, the land must be wet enough to encourage the presence of some plants and animals which are especially adapted to wet conditions. At the other extreme, the land should not be so permanently and deeply submerged as to be considered a lake.

The confusion over identity is hardly helped by the fact that there are many different types of wetland. The term 'wetland' is a collective one for a number of sometimes quite distinct habitats, all of them affected by water in one form or another. On the coast there are wetlands inundated by seawater, such as the estuarine mudflats and salt marshes discussed in chapter 7. This chapter is concerned with freshwater wetlands, and the most common types are bogs and swamps. To this can be added the flooded margins of lakes and rivers.

Wetlands are secretive places. They deter human intrusion with dense thickets of vegetation and the prospect of sinking thigh deep or worse into an evil-smelling mire. Too often, the historical consequence of this has been that wetlands have been condemned as useless wastelands, whose only possible redemption was to be drained, or at least to be used as a rubbish tip. The truth is, however, that wetlands have many values.

INTRODUCED FROGS

As dusk settles on the wetlands, the frogs begin their nightly chorus. It is a sound which was not heard before last century. Native frogs do not croak. Neither do they inhabit large ponds and swamps. The din is entirely due to three species of tree frog introduced from Australia.

The smallest is the whistling frog (*Litoria ewingi*). About 3 centimetres long, it clambers capably among the waterside vegetation after dark to search for insects, even defying gravity by hanging on to the underside of smooth leaves.

Whistling frog (*Litoria ewingi*)

Like other tree frogs, it does this with suction pads on its digits. Each pad is moistened with mucus and can be flexed to gain purchase on different surfaces. The other two introduced frogs look very similar to one another, hence both are often called the green tree frog. One, *Litoria raniformis*, is widespread throughout New Zealand, while the other, *L. aurea*, inhabits only the north of the North Island. Both are about 8 centimetres long, the most visible difference being that *L. aurea* has gold spots rather than a gold stripe down its back.

Tree frogs are prodigious leapers, catapulting themselves from harm's way or pouncing on unwary insects. Sight plays an important part in this activity, as can be seen by the large eyes of the whistling frog. Movement is particularly important in order for a frog to detect its prey. A fly at rest will barely be noticed, but if it even flickers a wing tip, the frog will swivel to gauge its distance with both eyes. It plans its trajectory before it leaps, because at the point of taking off, tree frogs retract the eyes into their sockets and sail through the air blind, probably to protect the eyes from impact.

Green tree frog (*Litoria raniformis*)

They have an important stabilising influence on the region that surrounds them. In times of flood they absorb excess water like a sponge, preventing it from spilling onto adjacent lowlands. In times of drought, water seeps out to keep the rivers from drying out. They also act as a filter trap, reducing erosion by retaining silt and preventing eutrophication by mopping up excess minerals, particularly from agricultural run-off.

Much more than this, wetlands are priceless habitats, catering for an extraordinary diversity of life. This wealth comes from the variety of terrain found in wetlands, from dry land to waterlogged land to open water. The zones of transition from one part to another exhibit an exceptional range of microhabitats, so they provide for an equally exceptional range of plants and animals. Some of these are generalists that can live in a number of other habitats besides wetlands. But many are specialists, found only in wetlands.

Bogs and swamps

Most inland wetlands are either bogs or swamps. The differences between them are that bogs contain stagnant, de-oxygenated water and are infertile, whereas swamps contain moving, relatively well-aerated water and are fertile. Bogs are created wherever drainage is impeded and the main water supply comes directly from rainfall, rather than via rivers. This means that there is little input of mineral nutrients, and since the water sits still for long periods, it becomes depleted of oxygen. Bogs therefore suffer from a shortage of many of life's essentials. Only a few well-adapted plants manage to grow in them, such as bog pine, umbrella fern, sundews and sphagnum moss. As these die, their remains do not decompose very well, since few decay organisms can survive in the stagnant waters either. So the shed leaves and branches accumulate as layers of semi-decayed material known as peat. This in turn compounds the problems that the living plants face, since precious mineral nutrients remain locked up in the dead matter.

Alpine bogs (page 36) and pakihi bogs (page 72) have already been mentioned. Another type of bog is a peat dome, like those at Kopuatai and Whangamarino in the North Island. These owe their existence largely to sphagnum moss, which is one of the success stories of bog vegetation. In some parts of the world it is virtually the only plant to be seen, spreading to the horizons like a green ocean. Sphagnum has two remarkable properties, both of which help domes to form. One is that it holds up to 20 times its own weight of water. The other is that it promotes an acidic, antiseptic environment that inhibits decay organisms and so encourages peat to build up. In the middle of the bog, where drainage is worst, peat steadily gathers beneath a growing blanket of sphagnum. In this way the centre rises, while the prodigious water-holding capacity of sphagnum lifts the water table with it. The result is a raised bog, or peat dome, several metres higher in the middle than at the edges. It is a curious phenomenon, like an island of water amid a sea of dry land.

A swamp forms wherever the flow of a river has become impeded, often by the silt it has deposited. Instead of flowing quickly down a single channel, the water seeps through a maze of waterways, shallow lakes and expanses of soggy ground. But because it is continually fed with water and sediments from its tributaries, the swamp does not become stagnant and mineral nutrients are continually added to it. Swamps are therefore more biologically productive than bogs.

Swamps are never static. Patches of open water are always silting up, while new ones are being created. Likewise the vegetation is constantly changing. When specialist swamp plants colonise shallow water they inevitably build them up into dry land, yielding to a succession of increasingly terrestrial plants. In a typical pattern, native sedges (*Eleocharis*) colonise the submerged margins at the water's edge. As silts gather around their stems and the water becomes shallower, larger plants appear. There may be beds of raupo, and more native sedges such as *Baumea*. Then dense clumps of toetoe grass, flaxes, and cabbage trees take hold on higher ground, in turn giving way to manuka and other swamp-tolerant shrubs and trees. After hundreds, perhaps thousands of years, graceful stands of kahikatea or pukatea will rise as the area turns to forest.

Colonising a lake
Tall stems and leaves of the native sedge, *Eleocharis sphacelata*, emerge from the water by the margins of a sheltered lake. The green stems of this plant contain air-filled cells, and are almost hollow, allowing air to diffuse down to the roots. As dead vegetation and silt accumulate around their submerged stems, the mat of vegetation will spread towards the centre of the lake. On the landward side, gathering silts and organic matter will slowly raise the submerged shoreline, allowing more plants to invade the lake. Eventually shrubs such as manuka will colonise the emerging shoreline, to be followed by kahikatea trees like those already seen on the far side. Thousands of years from now, this lake will be filled with sediments and covered by swamp forest.

MUDFISH

The dark waters of New Zealand's swamps and bogs conceal one of its least known animals, the mudfish (*Neochanna*). Mudfish are members of the Galaxiidae family, which adapted to life in swamps long ago. There are three known species, though given the secluded nature of their habitat, no one can be sure that there are not more.

Living within the murky depths, mudfish have small eyes compared with other galaxiids and probably rely more on the sense of smell to find their food. Their fins have become shaped like those of an eel to help them slither among the submerged stems of swamp plants. Mudfish have also evolved the ability to survive their swamp drying out in summer. As the water drops to critical levels, they burrow into the mud or retreat beneath logs. Here, within a damp refuge, the mudfish enter an inactive state known as aestivation. Their movements are reduced and so, therefore, is their need for oxygen. Much can be absorbed directly through the moist skin. When rain refills the swamp several weeks later, the mudfish stir from slumber and resume active life.

Bird of prey Wherever there are wetlands, the harrier (*Circus approximans*) will not be far away. Like all birds of prey, the harrier has superb eyesight and a beak ideally hooked to rip apart the flesh of animals. During spring, when there are young mouths to feed, it is particularly active. Other wetland birds and animals, which are also raising families, seek cover from its rapacious intent. The harrier often builds its nest in the cover of dense swamp vegetation. Here it lays two to five eggs over a period of successive days, although few chicks usually are raised to fledging. The first hatched are inevitably bigger than those which hatch later. They are able to push their siblings aside at feeding time and thrive while their nest-mates perish. This seemingly cruel state of affairs acts as an insurance policy, enabling the harrier to match the number of chicks it raises to the amount of food available. If it is a good year, then the younger ones will also manage to get their share of food. If it is not, perhaps only one chick will survive.

BIRDS OF THE DENSE SWAMP

The tangled swampland vegetation conceals a number of birds that spend most of their life there. With few exceptions, they are quiet and inconspicuous, with cryptic colours and furtive habits. Many belong to the large family of rails, which includes many wetland birds worldwide. Typically they have heavy bodies, short wings and rarely fly, preferring to take cover from danger.

Pukeko (*Porphyrio porphyrio*) This bird's brightly coloured plumage is not typical of the rail family to which it belongs. It flies but is usually seen clambering jauntily among the swamp vegetation, and can run swiftly on dry land. It is an omnivorous bird, eating insects, worms, frogs and various plants. It also likes to sample the fare offered by nearby agricultural lands, such as crops and grass grubs, so it has benefited from human settlement.

Australasian coot (*Fulica atra*) The long widely spreading toes of this bird is a typical rail feature, allowing it to walk through marshes, stepping on floating vegetation. It also swims strongly and can dive below the water to feed on submerged plants, water snails and insects. Take-off involves much thrashing of wings and pattering of feet over a considerable stretch of open water, but once in the air the coot can cover long distances. It has recently colonised New Zealand by crossing the Tasman.

Spotless crake (*Porzana tabuensis*) Both bird and its nest are virtually impossible to find in the swamp, but the spotless crake can be tricked into revealing its presence by playing a tape recording of its voice, which it will answer. It is a rail and it lives in both fresh and saltwater swamps. Precise details of the nesting habits are not known, but it appears that the male and female build several nests; one in a clump of ferns on land and the others in reeds above the water. Eggs are laid in one of the swamp nests but, very soon after they hatch, the fledglings are taken by their parents to the land nest.

Marsh crake (*Porzana pusilla*) This is the smallest rail in New Zealand, only 18 centimetres long. It is extremely secretive, leaving the dense swamp vegetation after dark.

Australasian brown bittern (*Botaurus stellaris*) If it were not for its characteristic booming call, the bittern would rarely be noticed. When disturbed it has a remarkable way of concealing itself. It raises its head and bill vertically and freezes. The vertical stripes on its breast and the vertical lines of its narrow bill then blend perfectly with the background of reed stalks and leaves. If there is a breeze it may also sway gently back and forth in unison with the surrounding vegetation. Its very sharp bill makes a good dagger, ideal for despatching fish, frogs and small mammals.

Fernbird (*Bowdleria punctata*) This is an endemic member of the warbler family and, as such, is more often heard than seen. It rarely takes wing and its drab colouring hides it well in its habitat, where it feeds on insects. Its tail feathers have a bedraggled appearance, because the barbs do not adhere together as they usually do in quill feathers. Swamp drainage has reduced its numbers in many areas.

Fernbird
Pukeko
Australasian brown bittern
Australasian coot
Marsh crake
Spotless crake

Insects of calm water

Along the sheltered shorelines of lakes, in small pools and quiet backwaters, there is always a commotion of insect life beneath the surface. Without the force of the current to contend with, insects that live here are allowed lifestyle options not possible in the churning water of rivers. Instead of sheltering in crevices or clutching to rocks, they are free to swim. Dytiscid beetles dart through the depths, propelled by hair-fringed back legs that beat frantically at the water. Both adult and larva are carnivorous, often aggressively so, seizing insect larvae and other creatures of similar size. Rowing with more sedate strokes of their back legs are waterboatmen and backswimmers. Both belong to the order Hemiptera, commonly called bugs, which are characterised by having piercing and sucking mouthparts. The backswimmers, which swim upside down, attack other water creatures and suck out their body contents. Waterboatmen are vegetarians, sweeping at sediments with brush-tipped forelegs to sift out particles of organic matter.

Dytiscid beetles, backswimmers and waterboatmen breathe air, which they collect by darting back and forth to the surface. Here they take on a supply of silvery bubbles, trapped beneath wing cases or among

DRAGONFLIES AND DAMSELFLIES

Gray's dragonfly (*Procordulia grayi*)

Dancing on glistening wings, the dragonflies and their more delicate relatives the damselflies, are conspicuous insects found near water. They belong to the order Odonata, which is one of the most primitive groups of winged insects. Their ancestors first appeared during the Carboniferous period about 300 million years ago and some evolved into impressive aerial predators. One species that flew had a wingspan of 75 centimetres. Their modern counterparts, though more humble in proportions, are among the most accomplished of flying insects. They can hover, fly backwards and even sideways, before accelerating away in a blur of wings.

These aerial manoeuvres are guided by a superb sense of sight. Dragonflies and damselflies have large, spherical compound eyes positioned on either side of their head. As in most insects, these consist of bunches of separate light-sensing units called ommatidia. Generally, the more ommatidia, the more acute the vision. A housefly eye has about 4000 ommatidia, while a dragonfly, which probably has the best vision of all insects, has up to 28,000.

No one knows what sort of image a dragonfly perceives with its eyes. Different ommatidia may serve different purposes. Some, for instance, are sensitive to polarised light, which enables a dragonfly to sense the position of the sun and use it to navigate by, even on cloudy days. Perhaps the closest we could imagine a dragonfly's vision to be is a poorly printed newspaper photograph, composed of thousands of individual dots. Certainly the image lacks the definition provided by a human eye, but it makes up for this with an extreme sensitivity to movement. Moving objects will trigger separate ommatidia in succession, so they can be detected instantly, as anyone who tries to net a flying dragonfly will discover.

Acute vision is essential to dragonflies and damselflies since both hunt on the wing. Some species hover among foliage, picking their prey from the surface of leaves and stems. Others pursue flying insects, bearing down on their target with all the manoeuvrability of a mini jump jet, before scooping the victim in their crooked legs.

Like the adults, the underwater nymphs of dragonflies and damselflies are voracious predators, though with a different approach to hunting. Instead of active pursuit they rely on ambush. They wait motionless for their victim to come close. Then with remarkable speed, they clasp it with their 'mask'. The mask is a device peculiar to the dragonflies and damselflies. It is an extension of the lower lip, which has been modified into a hinged 'arm' for grasping prey. A form of hydraulic action extends it in about one-fortieth of a second, leaving no time for escape. The mask then retracts, drawing the prey back to the mouth.

Once a nymph's life is complete it crawls out of the water and sheds its skin. The winged adult that emerges usually spends a period away from water, hunting the surrounding countryside for insects. But once it is sexually mature and has acquired its rich colours, it returns to seek a mate. For many species this means first acquiring a territory. Dragonflies often establish one along the water's edge, which they patrol by flying back and forth. Damselflies may claim the airspace surrounding a clump of rushes, which they defend from a perch.

Any male entering another's territory is immediately challenged, or even knocked into the water. Females are also swiftly intercepted, but with a view to mating. Some species first engage in courtship displays, requesting their pleasures with subtle wing movements and body postures. Others dispense with such pleasantries and rely on rush and grab tactics. In either case the male tries to move in front of the female and grasp her neck with a pair of claspers on the tip of his abdomen. Such a pair are said to be in tandem and often fly together like this on their nuptial flight. Next the female arches her abdomen up to take sperm from the male's mating pouch.

Afterwards the male usually maintains vigil over his partner to ensure no other male mates with her before she has laid her eggs. Sometimes he even stays in tandem to safeguard her fidelity. Such selfish behaviour is genetically motivated. The male is ensuring that it is his genes which are passed on to the next generation and not those of his competitors. Dragonflies have evolved ways to scoop out the sperm from previously mated females, before transferring their own. So only once the female has laid her eggs can her partner be sure that his mating will not be usurped.

body hairs. This keeps them going on their underwater excursions, being periodically replenished by returning to the surface. It is a method that has advantages when the water is so still and stagnant that it does not contain enough dissolved oxygen to be absorbed via gills.

There are other insects of still water that remain connected to the surface virtually all the time, breathing air through a tube, in the same way that a swimmer uses a snorkel. Mosquito larvae obtain air this way as they hang beneath the water's surface in pools and ditches. Better examples are the rat-tailed maggots. These are the larvae of certain flies which, thanks to their breathing tubes, can live in the most fetid oxygen-starved places, even the putrescent fluid of decaying carcases.

Perhaps the most unusual of all aquatic habitats to be exploited by insects is on the surface. Living at the interface of water and air are insects that manage to take advantage of the phenomenon of surface tension. They walk on water. Pond skaters and water striders do this by having water-repellent waxes on their feet, so that they do not break through. Both are carnivorous hemipterans like the backswimmer. They spend their lives treading the vast watery plain in search of small creatures that have fallen in. They are particularly sensitive to surface vibrations, such as caused by a half-drowned, struggling insect, and are quick to home in on the source.

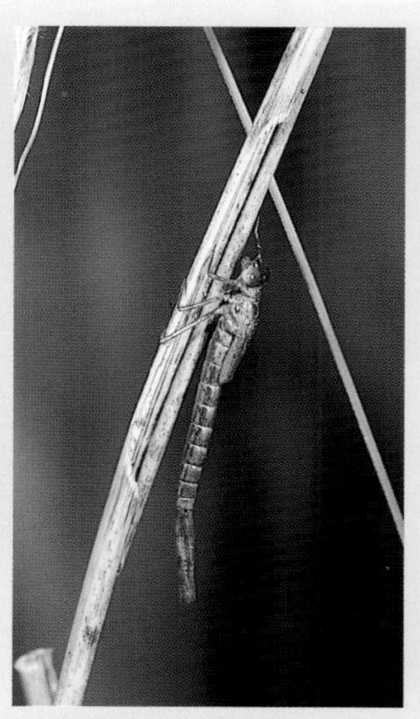

From aquatic larva to winged adult Damselflies spend the first year or so of their lives underwater, as nymphs (above) feeding on aquatic animals. This species, *Austrolestes colensonis*, can be found in most ponds, pools and lakes. During its underwater life it maintains its distance from other nymphs by threat displays, during which it moves its body up and down. After the nymph has completed its aquatic life, it crawls from the water. The nymph then splits its outer cuticle and the adult slowly draws itself out (above right). The adult remains vulnerable, while its soft body and wings expand to their full size, then harden ready for flight. Later, having acquired its vivid blue colour, the damselfly flits above the reeds and rushes in search of food or a mate (right).

Wetland waterfowl

As the early frosts of winter glaze the reeds and rushes, a murmur of excitement spreads across the wetlands. Out on the water's surface, mobs of waterfowl begin their courtship displays. Their numbers will have grown during the autumn months, swollen by arrivals that have flown in from surrounding areas. A shoveller drake in breeding plumage begins his head-bobbing ceremonies, or takes off in breakneck aerial pursuits after a prospective mate. Mallards porpoise through the water or thrash fitfully at the surface with their wings. For many of the ducks, which seek new partners each year, it is a period of intense competition. But for the swans and geese, who pair for life, there is a quieter reaffirmation of nuptial bonds. By spring, the paired

COMMON WATERFOWL OF THE WETLANDS

Grey teal (*Anas gibberifrons*) The grey teal is distinguished by its vivid crimson eye. In its native Australia it is a very mobile bird, travelling long distances as wetlands seasonally dry up. Many of those living in New Zealand are descendants from flocks that have arrived here during particularly bad droughts across the Tasman. Birds nest in clumps of vegetation by the waterside, as well as in crevices and tree holes. The New Zealand population has steadily grown in recent years due to the provision of vermin-proof breeding boxes.

Shoveller (*Anas rhynchotis*) The broad bill of the native shoveller has unusually large lamellae compared with other dabbling ducks, in order to sift small aquatic organisms from the water's surface. During the breeding season, males like those in the photograph (below right) acquire resplendent plumage colours to court females. These are lost in the post-breeding moult, which all waterfowl undergo. This takes about three weeks and since the flight feathers are also moulted the birds are grounded for the duration. Afterwards the male returns to its 'eclipse' plumage of cryptic mottled browns which resembles that of the female.

Mallard (*Anas platyrhynchos*) The quacking of mallards is a familiar sound on urban duck ponds and rural wetlands virtually everywhere. It is widespread in the Northern Hemisphere and has been introduced to Australia and New Zealand. Its long history in the company of mankind has made it very tolerant of human activity. Hence it has colonised the cleared farmlands of New Zealand much better than the shyer native species. It is a typical dabbling duck, often tipping tail-up to sift fallen seed, aquatic plants and small animals from the muddy margins. During the breeding season the drake acquires his distinctive colours of chestnut, grey and bottle green. The nest is disguised among clumps of vegetation and lined with feathers the female plucks from her breast. The mallard is displacing and interbreeding with the closely related native grey duck (*Anas superciliosa*) in many areas. Both male and female grey ducks resemble the female mallard, though grey ducks have whiter stripes above and below the eye.

Scaup (*Aythya novaeseelandiae*) Being a diving duck the scaup can feed in deeper waters. With powerful thrusts of its feet it swims down several metres to search for plants, crustaceans and molluscs. Its rearwards positioned legs are

Grey teal

Scaup

Shoveller

birds disperse to begin nesting. The young are raised during the summer, before the birds gather once more at their wintering grounds.

Swans, geese and ducks belong to the family Anatidae, which has colonised the lakes and wetlands of every continent except Antarctica. The family is divided into groups or tribes, several of which are found in New Zealand. The swans are represented by the Australian black swan and the less common mute swan. The geese are represented by the Canada goose. The ducks themselves comprise a number of tribes. The paradise duck, which frequents pasturelands and high-country riverflats, belongs to the shelducks, a tribe which shares features with both ducks and geese. The scaup belongs to the diving ducks. The brown teal, grey teal, shoveller, grey and mallard are all dabbling ducks. They are surface feeders, dabbling at the water or up-ending to dredge the shallows for small animals and plant matter. These are sifted from the water using a fringe of lamellae along the edge of the beak.

good for diving but clumsy on land, so it is rarely seen on the shore.

Canada goose (*Branta canadensis*) The Canada goose was introduced to New Zealand as a game bird and is particularly well established in the South Island. For some farmers they are perhaps too well established, since like all geese they graze vegetation, sometimes descending on fields and pastures to feed. Their droppings also soil the pasture for grazing livestock. After wintering on lowland wetlands, pairs will often fly inland to nest among the tussocks of high country river flats. The goose incubates the eggs while the gander stands guard. When autumn arrives the family depart for their winter quarters on the lowlands again. The far-off sound of honking geese, flying across the sky in wedge-shaped formation, is one of sheer magic to most nature lovers.

Black swan (*Cygnus atratus*) The black swan has been introduced from Australia and has also managed to fly the Tasman by its own means. It prefers shallow waters, particularly lake margins, flooded ground and tidal flats, where it can reach the bottom with its long neck to graze on vegetation. Birds often nest in colonies close to the waterside. Like most waterfowl they do not venture far for nesting material. Their requirements are usually taken from whatever is within reach, even if it means pilfering some from a neighbour.

Black swan

Mallard

Canada goose

Caves

Nature is forever an opportunist. There are few places on Earth that it has not managed to exploit, or at least to gain a toehold. The web of life even extends into the depths of the Earth. Living within the eternal darkness of caverns are creatures so completely adapted to subterranean life that they would soon perish if brought to the surface.

Most caves are found in limestone. Rainwater absorbs carbon dioxide from the air, which turns it slightly acid. This enables it to dissolve the calcium carbonate of limestone as it seeps into the ground. As millennia pass, flowing water eats into the limestone, hollowing out labyrinths of underground passages. Deep inside, conditions are utterly dark, but they are not otherwise inhospitable.

Caves provide virtually seasonless climates. In a typical lowland cave the temperature will stay at 10–13 degrees Celsius all the year round and the humidity will remain constantly high. Creatures that spend their life here can therefore afford to relax some of the protective measures that they would need to survive the more inclement environment on the surface.

Apart from animals entering caves by misadventure, underground inhabitants can be divided into three groups. Some simply use the cave as a handy shelter, feeding outside but returning to sleep. Bats are a classic example of this. Overseas they roost in thousands within cavern entrances and swarm out at dusk to explore the night for food. But in New Zealand bats are relatively rare cave inhabitants. They appear to prefer to rest in old trees in the forest. Possums and rats are more common examples of cave shelterers. The next group of inhabitants are those that can spend their entire life within caves, but can live in other dark damp places just as readily. Here can be included New Zealand's most famous cave dweller, the glow-worm. Its tiny pin-pricks of light can be found glowing from damp banks in the forest just as easily as in the recesses of a cave. Likewise, creatures such as earthworms and millipedes that inhabit the dark dank world of the leaf litter are equally at home feeding on organic debris in caves.

The most interesting group of all is the troglobites, which are those animals that live only in caves. Long ago, their ancestors were surface dwellers that came to take up permanent residence underground. In doing so they became genetically cut off from their forbears, so evolved in isolation to suit cave life. Many different creatures have become troglobites at various times. In New Zealand caves there are ground beetles, harvestmen, water snails and isopods. Overseas, even

THE GLOW-WORM

The glow-worm (*Arachnocampa luminosa*) is not a worm but the larva of a fungus gnat that emits its blue-green light to attract prey. It spins itself a silken cradle, suspended from the cave roof. From this it lets down a beaded curtain of threads covered in sticky droplets. Then the larva waits, its light shining with an intensity that depends on how hungry it is. Midges and other flying insects are lured upwards by the glow and become snared by the sticky 'fishing lines'. Immediately the glow-worm detects the vibrations of struggling prey, it glides along the cradle and hauls up the appropriate line to devour its catch.

Once it has grown for several months the larva clears away its fishing lines, sheds its skin and develops into the pupa. About 12 days later the pupal case splits open and the adult fly emerges. The metamorphosis from larva to adult is a miracle of transformation, whether it occurs in this humble fly or a beautiful butterfly. During the time the pupa hangs apparently immobile, it undergoes a profound internal reorganisation. Its larval tissues break down to a soup. Meanwhile, other groups of cells that have lain dormant till then suddenly start to multiply rapidly, taking their nourishment from the disintegrating larval cells. Steadily, adult features such as wings and legs take form beneath the enclosing pupal case, until at last it is ready to emerge and take wing for the first time.

During the glow-worm's pupal development its light continues to operate, although intermittently. For the adult

males this acts as a beacon, guiding them through the darkness to the female before she has emerged. A female pupa may have several males in attendance, each waiting in the hope that they can be the one to mate when she hatches. If the emerging female does not find any waiting males she flashes her beacon to summon a partner. Once mated she then flies off to lay her eggs. Her duties then dispensed, she dies.

JOHN PYBUS

Senses in the dark
In the perpetual darkness of a cave, creatures must find their way using senses other than sight. The cave weta (*Gymnoplectron*) (top left) has small eyes and feels its way instead with unusually long legs and antennae, both of which carry sensory organs to detect smell, touch and vibrations. From foot to antenna tip, a mature specimen can measure over 20 centimetres. Like many underground inhabitants, cave wetas are scavengers, feeding as opportunists on virtually anything that good fortune happens to bring into the cave. For much of their food, however, cave wetas probably rely on night-time foraging excursions into the surrounding forest.

An ancient lineage
Spelungula cavernicola (bottom right), resting on its egg sack, lives in the caverns of north-west Nelson. It is New Zealand's largest spider, with a leg span of up to 15 centimetres. Details of its life history are uncertain, but it preys largely on cave wetas, probably catching them by waiting motionless for one to blunder within reach. *Spelungula* is of particular interest to those who study spiders. It belongs to a small group of spiders descended from the earliest of the so-called 'true spiders', which first appeared hundreds of millions of years ago. It is the 'tuatara' of the spider world.

such large animals as salamanders, fish and crayfish have become troglobites. After generations underground, most have become pale coloured, since animals living in total darkness have no need of colourings or markings. Their eyes have shrunk or vanished altogether, while in exchange they have often acquired unusually long antennae or scores of sensory bristles to feel their way and home in quickly on rare morsels of food that get carried to their distant world.

Invariably, becoming a troglobite has been a one-way move. The adaptations evolved underground are so extreme that troglobites can no longer live on the surface. This raises the question of how these creatures manage to disperse between cave systems. The answers are still not entirely clear. Even though no subterranean routes may be apparent to human observers, it seems that caves are often interconnected by tiny fissures suitable for small creatures to crawl through. Underground aquifers and flash floods may help transport some animals over greater distances. Nevertheless, for many troglobites, separate limestone landscapes are as isolated from one another as islands are by the sea. For this reason discrete regions may contain certain unique troglobites that have evolved independently from those elsewhere.

Since plants cannot grow in caves the inhabitants are dependent on food supplied from outside. Possums and rats sheltering in caves will deposit dung and food scraps where they sleep near the entrance. The occasional creature that blunders deep underground and dies will bequeath a windfall for the hungry inhabitants. Most of the food, however, is swept in by rivers. Within any cave system you will sooner or later encounter the cavernous roar of water tumbling through the depths. This continually carries in decomposing leaf litter, fine organic particles, insect larvae and other water creatures. Scores of cave scavengers, such as millipedes, springtails and cave wetas feed on this. In turn, spiders, harvestmen, glow-worm larvae, ground beetles and other cave predators prey on the scavengers. Each of these animals also hosts its share of parasites.

Caves therefore harbour simple communities, which nevertheless depend on the sunlit surface for sustenance. Herein lies the danger for these unique life forms. Any change that humans cause above ground will have unseen consequences for the fragile life beneath. Logging may deluge them with eroded silts. Replanting catchments may change their food supply. For this reason naturalists urge caution about the development of industry or farming within limestone regions, and beg consideration for the hidden inhabitants, whose ways we as yet so little understand.

CHAPTER 6

CITIES AND SETTLEMENTS

Fortunately for New Zealanders, as well as for the wildlife of the country, New Zealand lacks the enormous conurbations found in parts of Europe and North America. Most towns and settlements are small, and well separated from one another. Even the larger cities of New Zealand are not the concrete jungles so often found in the rest of the world. This is a country in which there is room for everyone, and in which householders expect to live in a house surrounded by its own section of land. Its cities and settlements are by no means inimical to wildlife.

New Zealand has been most densely inhabited where there is a harbour, a river or an estuary and that fact alone ensures that the cities are permeated with a network of sanctuaries for wildlife. Roadside verges, uncultivated land beside rivers, railway embankments all provide other habitats on the small scale, as well as routes by which plants and animals can penetrate from surrounding areas.

A city, therefore, presents a complex mosaic of plant and animal communities. It is home to more plant and animal species than one would at first believe to be possible. However, few of these species exist in enormous numbers. Just like their human counterparts, they face the twin problems of finding food and shelter. Neither of these is easy to obtain in a landscape dominated by buildings, concrete and asphalt.

Common wasp

Living in cities

One of the main preoccupations of any city-dwelling animal is to obtain an adequate supply of food. In spite of the activities of parks and gardens departments, it is inevitable that there is a scarcity of plant life in the city centre. A bird such as the tui, which feeds mainly on nectar, fruit and berries, is not able to survive there. These birds also feed on insects, but there are few insects in the city because the insects, too, depend on plants for food.

The lack of plants in cities is partly compensated for by the human habit of putting out food for birds. This favours those animals that are not shy of humans, such as sparrows, finches and mynahs. There are also domestic rubbish bins and refuse from restaurants, which provide a rich source of food for a wide range of animals, including mice, rats, and insects such as wasps and houseflies. Where the housefly flourishes, spiders flourish too.

On the whole, the appreciable amount of waste food materials in urban areas is of most benefit to those animals that are opportunistic in their feeding habits. House sparrows abound in city areas, where they feed on almost anything available, including grain, fruit, food scraps and insects. The blackbird is similar in that it accepts a wide variety of foods and is willing to rest almost anywhere; consequently it is common in most parts of a city. By contrast, its close relative the thrush is much less adaptable in its feeding and resting habits, and is usually found only in parks and gardens. The house mouse and rats eat a diversity of foods and become numerous in cities unless kept under control. The ship rat (*Rattus rattus*) nests in buildings and is an agile climber. The Norway rat (*R. norvegicus*) does not climb well but is a strong swimmer. It frequents the lower parts of buildings, rubbish tips, and the sewers. Other animals that find food almost anywhere are the gulls, particularly the southern black-backed gull and the red-billed gull, which are frequent and abundant visitors to the city rubbish tip.

The passage of wheels and the trampling of feet are a hazard to living organisms. But the constant activity of the city does have a bonus. Motor vehicles produce heat, as do the hundreds of people in the streets. In winter, heated buildings add further to the general warmth. When the sun shines, concrete and brick warm up quickly, releasing the heat stored during the night. As a result, cities are warmer than the surrounding countryside and have fewer frosts. In winter, the centre of a large city is up to 5 degrees Celsius warmer than areas outside. This is of benefit to both plants and animals living in city areas. The warmth is an asset to insects, plants, and many other groups whose rate of growth and development depends upon temperature. In spring, for example, daffodils in city parks bloom several days earlier than those growing wild. The warm-blooded animals, too, gain from the warmth. For instance, starlings have developed the habit of commuting. They may spend the night in the warmth of the city square but by day they flock to suburban gardens and paddocks to take advantage of the more abundant food supply there.

The benefits of city life, however, are only of use to those organisms that can cope with the city's other problems. The masses of motor vehicles emit noxious fumes, particularly sulphur dioxide, which suppress plant growth. Buildings provide precarious nesting sites for birds, and expanses of concrete and asphalt present surfaces that are difficult for plants to colonise. These problems make it hard for the majority of organisms to do well in the city, but there is always a number of specialists that can overcome them. Some plant species are more tolerant of sulphur dioxide than others. Some bird species nest readily on buildings and there are even plants that can colonise concrete and asphalt. For these species that have adopted city life there is the advantage of freedom from competition, allowing an enhanced chance of survival.

The fact that some organisms have adaptations that help them survive in built-up areas does not mean there has been any evolution of city-dwelling species as such. Most of the species come from environments posing similar problems for survival. For instance, plants and animals colonising the sides of buildings and walls usually inhabit cliffs and rocky places in nature, as does the rock pigeon in the photograph. They are pre-adapted to city life.

Pre-adapted to city life
In nature, the rock pigeon (*Columba livia*), as its name implies, nests in rocky sites, especially sea cliffs. City buildings provide an acceptable substitute, often with the bonus of an abundant food supply from the passers-by who love to feed the pigeons in city squares. The rock pigeons in New Zealand are descendants of domesticated breeds that have escaped from captivity and now live wild in settlements and also on cliffs, both on the coast and inland. The mixing together in the wild of the distinctive domestic breeds, originally derived from wild rock pigeons of southern Europe, has given rise to an assortment of plumage colours, most tending toward the wild type.

City microhabitats

Within the broad habitat of the city there are numerous and diverse sites of limited — perhaps very limited — extent that provide living-space for organisms. Examples of such sites are a blocked gutter, a shady bank, or a disused mail-box.

In these sites the environmental conditions differ in some way from those in the city as a whole. They may be damper or drier, warmer or cooler, more exposed or more shaded, or there may be a distinctive environmental feature there not found generally throughout the city. Such a site has its own version of the local climate, its microclimate, and its own combination of environmental factors, its microenvironment. Such a subdivision of the city habitat is known as a microhabitat. It is one of the features of inhabited areas that they contain a very wide variety of microhabitats.

Microhabitat in the making A leaking drain-pipe (left) provides a micro-habitat in the making. The steady drips of water have allowed a thistle to take hold. Blown leaves and dusty soil particles are accumulating around the base of the thistle. These will form a pocket of fertile soil in which other plants can grow, later attracting animals to the microhabitat.

Pavements and pathways

Pavements of asphalt or concrete present an arid microhabitat with a minimum of space for roots. Mosses, many of which are adapted for living on bare rock, can form a carpet on pavements, provided they are not subject to trampling, and are shaded from excessive sunlight. Often we find that mosses grow on pavements only on the north sides of roads that run east-west. There they are sheltered from the drying effects of sunlight by walls and buildings.

The lack of a porous soil is no handicap to mosses. They do not require root space since the fine root-like absorptive structures of mosses are able to obtain nutriments from the thin covering of wind-blown soil that accumulates around them. The soil in a clump of moss soon becomes colonised with self-contained communities of small soil creatures, including bacteria, fungi, roundworms, mites and small soil-inhabiting insects such as springtails.

Soil pathways provide material for larger plants to root in, so long as they can withstand being trampled.

Mosses carpet a pavement.

Daisies and the plantains, with their flattened rosettes of tough leaves, do well in this microhabitat. So does the tough cushion of procumbent pearlwort. The resilient sprawling stems of the wireweeds and their ability to grow in soils with low nutrient content fit these plants to survival on pathways.

Lawns

Well-mown lawns are an open microhabitat in which the grass is prevented from reaching its full height. The grass never grows tall enough to shade out the shorter plants growing among the grass plants. The enthusiastic gardener can do more harm than good by mowing the lawn too short. Raising the cutters of the lawn mower by as little as 1 centimetre allows the grass to grow that much taller and eliminates possibly unwanted species, such as Onehunga weed (*Solvia valdiviana*), which survives only in short turf.
Other weeds favoured by close mowing include the low-growing rosette plants such as hawksbeard, catsear and daisy, as well as the mat-forming plants such as procumbent pearlwort and selfheal, all of which are characteristic of open natural habitats.

Procumbent pearlwort (*Sagina procumbens*)

Red admiral
(*Bassaris gonerilla*)

Lichens

Spur valerian
(*Centranthus ruber*)

Walls

Walls are open and usually arid microhabitats favouring plants that grow in dry or rocky places in nature. There are two main wall-growing plant types. One has a stout rootstock or taproot able to penetrate crevices in the wall. The plant is relatively inactive during dry spells but develops new shoots very rapidly after periods of rain. Examples include spur valerian (*Centranthus ruber*), a very common plant, also found on cliffs and embankments. Another is buddleia, frequently found on walls as well as on banks and roadsides in disturbed areas. Buddleia is sometimes known as the butterfly bush because its flowers produce a rich supply of nectar that attracts butterflies to them. A wall covered with buddleia may make an attractive microhabitat for butterflies such as the red admiral (*Bassaris gonerilla*) shown here feeding on buddleia nectar.

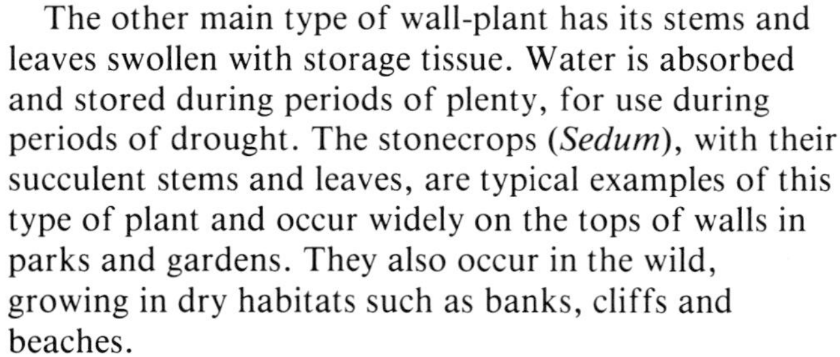

The other main type of wall-plant has its stems and leaves swollen with storage tissue. Water is absorbed and stored during periods of plenty, for use during periods of drought. The stonecrops (*Sedum*), with their succulent stems and leaves, are typical examples of this type of plant and occur widely on the tops of walls in parks and gardens. They also occur in the wild, growing in dry habitats such as banks, cliffs and beaches.

The sedums have an additional technique for survival under arid conditions. This is known as crassulacean acid metabolism (CAM), named after the family Crassulaceae, of which sedum is a member. CAM is now known to occur in several other families too. When a plant opens the stomatal pores on its leaf surface to absorb carbon dioxide for photosynthesis, it inevitably allows water vapour to escape. The CAM plants overcome this disadvantage by opening their

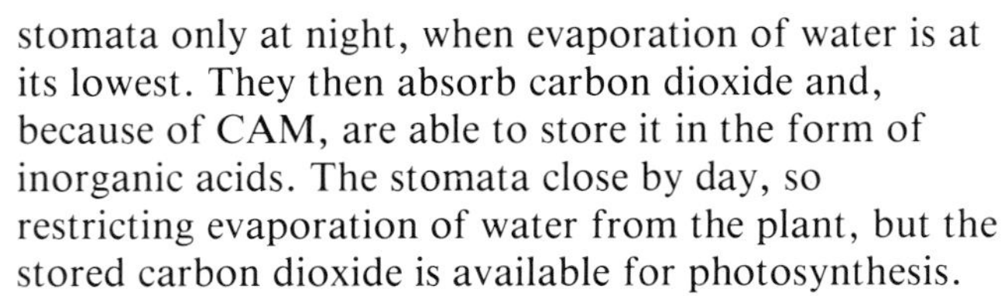

stomata only at night, when evaporation of water is at its lowest. They then absorb carbon dioxide and, because of CAM, are able to store it in the form of inorganic acids. The stomata close by day, so restricting evaporation of water from the plant, but the stored carbon dioxide is available for photosynthesis.

The ivy-leaved toadflax (*Cymbalaria muralis*) is often found growing on walls even in the centre of towns. It shows an unusual adaptation to its microhabitat. Like many other wall species, its leaf-stalks and flower-stalks grow toward the light. This is to ensure that leaves all face in the direction from which maximum light is received and that all flowers are easily visible to pollinating insects. In *Cymbalaria*, when a flower has been pollinated, the response of its flower stalk is reversed and it grows strongly away from light. As a result the elongating flower stalk carries the ripening capsule toward the darkest regions, helping to deposit the seed in a crevice where conditions are ideal for germination.

Old walls and fences are often the home of mosses and lichens. A lichen consists of a fungus living in partnership, called symbiosis, with an alga. It is a characteristic of lichens that they grow very slowly; on dry rock or stone surfaces they extend only a few millimetres each year. This is why they are prominent only on old surfaces. They are very efficient at extracting mineral ions from rainwater as it drains down the surface. This helps them to survive in an environment lacking in dissolved nutrients but also means that lichens are very sensitive to pollutants such as heavy metals and dissolved gases. In city centres the concentration of sulphur dioxide and pollutants (such as lead) from motor vehicle exhausts prevents the growth of most lichens. Environmentalists use the presence or absence of certain lichens as a reliable indicator of the level of atmospheric pollution in a district.

Ivy-leaved toadflax (*Cymbalaria muralis*)

Thrush (*Turdus philomelos*)

Trees

Whether planted in a city street or in a town park, trees are a haven for many kinds of wildlife. The thrush (*Turdus philomelos*) finds security for its young amid the branches of a tree, but it has to leave the tree to find food for the young, so the tree cannot be considered a microhabitat for the thrush. By contrast, many dozens of organisms spend almost their whole lives in or around the tree, which thus constitutes a complex of microhabitats. Some minute animals, such as the larvae of leaf miners, tunnel within the moist tissues of a leaf, feeding on the tissues, hidden from predators and avoiding desiccation. Leaf rollers create their own microhabitat by rolling a leaf into a sheltering tube, fastening it with silken threads. They feed on the leaves and fruits of the tree.

Some insects and related small animals induce a plant to make a microhabitat for them. The leaf and stem galls formed on the woody climber *Muehlenbeckia* are examples. The stem galls are caused by a moth (*Morova subfasciata*) while the pouch galls on the leaves are caused by a mite. The adult moth lays its eggs in the stem. The plant responds by producing a large swelling or gall, consisting mainly of soft, moist tissue. The moth larva hatches inside the gall and there finds an ideal microhabitat where it is hidden from predators, and has ample supplies of food in the form of gall tissue. It grows and pupates within the gall, then hatches and flies away to repeat the life cycle.

Leaf miner tunnels

Muehlenbeckia climber with stem galls induced by the moth *Morova subfasciata* and leaf galls caused by a mite.

The garden wilderness

It is not necessary to visit 'wild' areas to observe nature. Even the most manicured garden will provide micro-habitats for hundreds of animals. Like animals everywhere, they face the trials of finding food, finding a mate and avoiding becoming food for others. Many show interesting ways of solving these problems.

The poisonous butterfly

The monarch butterfly (*Danaus plexippus*) is a native of North America that has crossed the Pacific and become established in New Zealand. With its boldly patterned wings and large (80–100 millimetres) wingspan it is an attractive visitor to our gardens. The bright colours, however, serve as deadly warning to would-be predators that the monarch is poisonous.

In its native America, the monarch caterpillar feeds on species of the milkweed plant, which are rich in cardiac glycosides — powerful poisons affecting the heartbeat of birds and mammals. In New Zealand, people plant the related swan plant to encourage the monarch to visit their gardens. The monarch caterpillar is quite unaffected by the poisons in the plant and this allows it to exploit a food source avoided by most other animals. Not only does it tolerate the poisons, it actually stores them in its body, so inheriting their protection. The caterpillar passes its toxic defence on to the adult butterfly. Even the eggs are toxic.

The effectiveness of the monarch's defence has been well demonstrated in a series of experiments. When birds were, for the first time, offered adult butterflies, they rejected them after a quick taste. From then on they refused any further offerings. They easily learnt to recognise the monarch's very distinctive wing markings and keep away. The caterpillar, with its conspicuous black and yellow stripes, is also clearly 'labelled' dangerous. Its colour scheme is a warning shared with other insects that predators do well to avoid, such as wasps, bees and the magpie moth (page 87). In the second part of the experiment, monarchs were reared, not without difficulty, on cabbages. This time the adult butterflies were perfectly acceptable to birds, although they were still avoided by any birds with prior experience of the toxic monarchs.

The monarch butterfly comes to gardens searching for nectar or, in the case of females, for swan plants. Once the butterfly has found a good source of food, such as a eucalyptus tree in full bloom, it may spend a quarter of an hour or more fluttering from flower to flower, drinking the nectar. Egg-laying is a much more transitory affair. The female hardly seems to have touched down on the swan plant when she is off again,

Monarch butterfly (*Danaus plexippus*)

to find another plant. The egg hatches in a few days to a greyish caterpillar with a shiny black head. The caterpillar feeds on the swan plant and grows rapidly, shedding its skin three times before it displays the characteristic coloration. After the fifth moult, about 3 weeks from hatching, it has grown to full size and is ready to pupate. The caterpillar hangs from a branch and sheds its skin, revealing the lime-green pupa. Over the next 3 weeks, the organs of the adult become visible through the thin pupal skin. At this stage, the adult butterfly is ready to hatch. It swells up, splitting the pupal skin, and crawls out, hanging from the now empty pupal skin. After a few hours, when its wings have dried and hardened, the butterfly is ready to mate and produce another generation of monarchs.

The night hunter

After dusk, the hedgehog (*Erinaceus europaeus*) stirs from its resting place and ambles into the darkness in search of food. Insects, slugs, worms and other invertebrates are all sought after. The hedgehog may wander widely on its nightly hunt, perhaps travelling a couple of kilometres before returning to its nesting site. The hedgehog relies little on sight during these feeding excursions. It depends more on acute hearing and smell to locate its food as it snuffles through the undergrowth. Touch-sensitive hairs around its snout also help by giving a good tactile sense.

The hedgehog has been introduced from Europe and is now well established in New Zealand. The best type of garden to find it in is one with plenty of bushes, unkempt corners and lots of leaf litter. Not only does this offer a good supply of insects among the moist decaying vegetation, it also provides excellent nesting sites for the hedgehog. During the day the hedgehog likes to bury itself in piles of leaves and twigs that it heaps together, usually beneath a hedge or in a quiet corner of the garden. As the autumn months get cooler, the hedgehog seeks an even more sheltered site, perhaps within a wood pile or beneath an old shed, to build its winter nest. Here it goes into hibernation, both its body temperature and pulse falling. It may remain in this state for up to 6 months in cool parts of the South Island, or for just a few weeks in Northland.

A few years ago the distribution of hedgehogs in New Zealand was sampled by the simple expedient of counting their squashed corpses on the roads. The investigators drove along the main highways of both islands, recording the number of hedgehogs along each 100 kilometres of road. This investigation showed that hedgehogs are uncommon in native bush and forest plantations, frequent in grassland, and are most common in suburban areas, including farmsteads. The preference for suburban areas may be because hedgehogs do best in damp areas, where insects are abundant, yet require dry sites for nesting. Most remote rural areas are seasonally dry, especially during the critical period of the summer when the young are being raised. Marshes and rainforests lack dry nesting sites. But suburban areas offer wet areas in proximity to dry sites, providing the ideal combination of microhabitats. The corpse counts also indicated that the hedgehog is now more common in New Zealand than in its native Europe, probably because competitors such as shrews and other small carnivores are absent.

The garden snail
Though sometimes seen on very damp days, the introduced garden snail (*Helix aspersa*) is usually hidden under large stones or in holes in the ground. It prefers to come out at night, when it feeds on vegetation using its rasp-like radula, or tongue. To find its way it depends on its tentacles, which are sensitive to touch and to taste and have an eye at the tip. When danger threatens, the snail withdraws its tentacles into the body, turning them inside-out in the same way as the fingers of a glove.

Snails are hermaphrodites, and when two mate they rear up their bodies and embrace, pressing their undersides together and touching tentacles. At the height of their love-making, each fires a calcareous dart into the flesh of the other. This triggers a mutual exchange of sperm. Each snail then uses the sperm it has received to fertilise its eggs.

Hedgehog
(*Erinaceus europaeus*)

Insect parasites

In summer, ichneumonid wasps are often seen on the wing. Sometimes they fly indoors at dusk, attracted by house lights. They are fragile-looking creatures, with thin waists and glistening wings. The females trail long, needle-like ovipositors which they use to lay eggs.

The larvae of ichneumonid wasps are parasites of other insects. There are many different ichneumonid wasp species and each has particular types of insect that it attacks. One of the more common of these wasps, the white-spotted ichneumon (*Ecthromorpha intricatoria*), lays its eggs inside the pupae of moths and butterflies. Two that it often parasitises are the case moth and the red admiral butterfly. The larvae of the ichneumon hatch inside the host pupa and feed on its living tissues. Eventually the host is killed and the wasp larvae pupate inside its pupal case. Later they emerge from their own pupal cases as adult ichneumons and bite a hole into the pupal case in which they have spent their larval life. It is not an adult moth or butterfly that emerges, but a number of whitespotted ichneumons.

Because the ichneumon larvae eventually kill and eat their host they are correctly termed parasitoids, rather than parasites. The parasitoid habit is also found in some of the two-winged flies, the Diptera. Most insect species are attacked by at least one species of parasitoid and many parasitoids are attacked by other parasitoids, so that what appears to be an unusual life-style is really rather a common one.

A life of disguise

The case moth (*Liothula omnivora*) is a common garden inhabitant, although you would be lucky to notice it concealed among the branches. It is an unusual moth because the larvae and female adults carry a protective covering with them wherever they go. The case is firmly made of fragments of bark held together by silken threads. Not only does this covering offer protection from physical damage and from drying out but it gives an effective camouflage against the bark of the trees on which the case moth lives. The case is built by the young larva immediately after hatching. Using the small hooks on its abdominal false-feet it hangs on to the inside of the case as it moves about, feeding on the foliage of trees and shrubs at night. When fully grown, it fixes the case to a twig and then pupates inside. Once pupated the adult female does not leave her case. It offers such good security that she remains inside. She therefore has no need of wings or legs and develops neither. In fact, she is barely recognisable as a moth, being no more than a sac-like abdomen with a tiny head and thorax. The male, a typical moth in appearance, breaks out of his home and flies to her. He fertilises the female by extending the telescopic tip of his abdomen through the narrow opening at the lower end of the case. Eggs are laid inside the case and the hatched caterpillars later escape via this opening.

White-spotted ichneumon (*Ecthromorpha intricatoria*) (right)

Case moth (*Liothula omnivora*) (far right)

Jumping spider
(Family Salticidae)
(far left)

Praying mantis
(*Orthodera novaezealandiae*)
(left)

Stealth, or ambush

The jumping spider (Family Salticidae) and the praying mantis (*Orthodera novaezealandiae*) both hunt for insects during the daylight hours, although using different tactics. The jumping spider goes in active search of food. On sunny days it will be seen moving briskly across leaves and walls, pausing to study anything that catches its attention. If it sights an insect, perhaps a fly, it stalks within range and with a powerful jump pounces on its prey.

The praying mantis, by contrast, catches food by remaining still. It relies on its green colouring to conceal itself among the foliage while an unwary insect strays within striking distance. When this happens, the mantis's powerful forelegs, which are usually folded like a pocket knife, snap outwards and obtain a lethal grasp on the victim.

Both the jumping spider and the praying mantis rely on sight to make an accurate kill. The jumping spider has the best vision of all hunting spiders. It has eight eyes; four on the front of its head and a pair of smaller eyes on each side. The side eyes give peripheral vision and are very sensitive to movement. Alerted by the motion of a nearby insect, the spider swivels to face its victim for a better look. The spider's two large central front eyes provide the image quality necessary to identify the potential quarry, while the two outer front eyes are thought to act as rangefinders to determine its distance. Informed of the target, the spider can then pounce.

The praying mantis has large, domed eyes that give an enormous field of view, while the central portion of each eye is highly developed for visual acuity and distance finding. Therefore the mantis, like the jumping spider, faces its prey in order to make an accurate strike. This it does with an unnerving ability to swivel its head, intensely studying every nearby movement with a predacious stare. Sensory hairs determine the angle the mantis has turned its head, and this information is used to coordinate the direction of the strike it makes with its forelegs.

Since the instinct of both spider and mantis is to attack other creatures that come close, courtship and mating can be hazardous affairs. A male jumping spider must take pains to identify himself to a female if he is to avoid becoming a meal. He performs elaborate courtship movements, perhaps running on tiptoes while waving his legs and palps in semaphore. If the dance has been performed correctly, the female's killing instinct will be subdued sufficiently for him to come close and insert his sperm-charged palps into her genital pore.

The male mantis approaches his partner with considerable caution, for she is much larger than he is. He frequently hesitates, as if to weigh up his chances of grabbing the female and mating with her before being himself grabbed and eaten. If she seems receptive he will take his chances. Often he will succeed and live to mate again another day. But sometimes, at the last moment, the female will kill and begin eating him. Despite what one might think, this grisly act does not curtail the male's chance of fertilising the female. The nerve cells that control copulation are held within the male's abdomen, so once mating has started, he can continue successfully by reflex action even after he has been decapitated by his partner. In fact, the demise of the male can be construed as offering some benefit. By providing the female with a nourishing meal, the male increases the chances that she will lay the eggs he fertilised.

Protection by pretence
If molested, a honey bee will deliver a very painful sting. Humans soon learn to leave it alone and so do other animals. The drone fly (*Eristalis tenax*) has no sting to defend itself with, but inherits an immunity from predators by masquerading as a honey bee. Its mimicry is so good that even trained entomologists have had second thoughts about handling it. Of course, with a close look it is possible to distinguish one from the other. But it takes a moment to be sure and, during that hesitation, the drone fly can make its escape.

THE LIFE OF BEES

Bees depend on flowers throughout their lives. When a bee visits a flower it not only sips nectar to obtain the energy it needs to fly to the next flower, it also collects nectar and pollen to take back to the nest as food for its larvae.

Bees are related to hunting wasps and are thought to have evolved a vegetarian diet with the evolution of flowering plants. There are many types of bee and the complexity of their life cycles varies. Most people are familiar with the bumble bee (*Bombus*) and the honey bee (*Apis mellifera*), which have been introduced from the Northern Hemisphere, but there are also about 40 species of native bee. Although relatively common, native bees are infrequently noticed since they are often small and do not live in large colonies as the introduced bees do. Instead they lead solitary lives, the female tending only to her own needs and those of her larvae. Typically she builds a nest in an underground tunnel or in some ready-made shelter such as a hollow stem. This she usually lines with a waterproofing substance. Then she constructs a tissue-like bag and stocks it with nectar and pollen, ferrying in supplies a little at a time. When sufficient stores have been accumulated, an egg is deposited on the sticky mixture and the nest is deserted. The larva hatches and feeds on the food until it pupates. Later it emerges as a winged adult.

Bumble bees, of which four species have been introduced to New Zealand, have a more complex breeding behaviour. They are social animals, living in colonies that may number several hundred individuals. Each colony is founded by a lone, fertilised queen. She selects a suitable site, usually in a sheltered cavity, and builds a wax cell filled with honey and pollen. Into this she lays eggs that hatch into larvae and these feed on the food mixture. The queen continues to collect honey and pollen for her brood until they pupate. When they emerge they provide her with her first set of female workers, which then help the queen with the tasks of collecting food and tending other larvae.

Bumble bees are indefatigable workers. They may visit well over a hundred flowers on a single foraging trip, collecting pollen and sucking up nectar to carry back to the nest. If a bee encounters a flower that does not liberate

Bumble bee (*Bombus*)

Native bee (*Leioproctus fulvescens*)

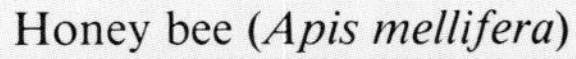

Honey bee (*Apis mellifera*)

pollen in sufficient quantities, it will shake it loose by vibrating its whole body with a loud buzzing sound. The spilt pollen is then gathered up and pressed into two bulging pollen baskets on its back legs. During the height of the season, bumble bees are busy virtually all day and every day. They are even active when the temperature is almost freezing and other insects are comatose. To fly in such conditions they first go through a warm-up procedure of 'shivering'. This involves vigorously exercising the flight muscles till they reach a temperature of about 30 degrees Celsius. Remarkably, there is no visible wing movement during this operation, since bumble bees are somehow able to disengage their wings from their flight muscles.

As the number of workers in the colony increases, so the queen is able to devote herself entirely to laying eggs. Towards the end of the season, broods of male and queen bumble bees are raised. The young queens emerge, mate with male bumble bees and then leave to establish their own colonies. Meanwhile all other members of the old colony, including the parent queen, perish. Over the winter, the young queens may find a place to hibernate, so that they can begin raising larvae in the spring. However, this is not always so. In warmer regions, the mildness of the winter allows bumble bees to pursue their activities throughout the year.

Honey bees differ from bumble bees in that their nests, or hives, are bigger, more complex in structure and last from year to year. There are also much clearer differences in the appearance and duties of different castes of bee in the colony. A honey bee colony has three castes. There is a single large queen, whose only duty is to lay up to 1500 eggs a day, a few hundred male drones, whose duty is to fertilise the queen, and thirdly, there are tens of thousands of infertile female workers. The majority of chores fall on the workers. A worker performs a series of jobs during her busy life. She starts duties as a cleaner and then progresses to being a nurse, feeding larvae. After about 10 days she works as a builder making wax cells and, later, she stocks the combs with honey and pollen collected by other workers. After about 3 weeks she guards the hive entrance and thereafter works in the field collecting food.

The queen bee maintains her control of the hive by producing a chemical pheromone called queen substance. This prevents the female workers' ovaries from developing and also stops the workers from building special large cells in which rival queens are raised on royal jelly. But as she gets older and her powers wane, or when the population of the hive gets very large, there is less queen substance to go round. Then the workers start to build queen cells. When this happens the old queen may leave the colony, accompanied by thousands of workers. They form a swarm that settles in a big writhing cluster, while scout bees go in search of a new nest site. This may be discovered in a hollow tree, or it may be provided for them by a beekeeper. Once a suitable place has been found, the scouts direct the swarm to it and the new colony is started. Meanwhile, back at the old hive, the first of the new queens to emerge kills any others that emerge later. She then mates with a drone and takes over the position held by the original queen.

Butterflies and flowers

When a common copper butterfly (*Lycaena salustius*) alights to feed on the nectar of a flower it fulfils what is a very intimate relationship between insect and plant. A butterfly does not require food in order to grow. Its growing was done while it was a caterpillar devouring the leaves of its food plants, which in the case of the common copper are species of *Muehlenbeckia*. The adult butterfly requires food only to renew the energy consumed in flight as it searches for a mate, or to provide sustenance to mature its eggs. What better source of this, therefore, than the sugar-rich nectar provided by flowers. Without floral 'filling stations' to call at, butterflies would not be able to breed successfully. Likewise, the flower's reproduction is assisted by the butterfly. As the common copper flies between blooms it transfers pollen lodged on its body, so cross-pollinating the plants it feeds on. The relationship could be regarded as a sexual contract, although neither partner knowingly helps the other to reproduce itself. Each is exploiting the situation to its own benefit. As time goes by, plants that evolve flowers more attractive to butterflies are able to set more seed than those that do not. Butterflies that evolve more efficient ways to collect nectar (and so pollinate flowers) are able to raise more young. So by natural selection, both partners become increasingly attuned to their mutual convenience.

Common copper butterfly (*Lycaena salustius*)

Welcome
swallow
♀
♂
Chaffinch
Goldfinch
Blackbird
House
sparrow
♂
♀
Silvereye

BIRDS OF THE GARDEN

House sparrow (*Passer domesticus*) The house sparrow is an introduced species that has spread widely. It often flies in flocks and roosts in city areas at night. It takes a variety of foods, including seeds, fruits, insects, and any edible scraps it can find. Nest sites can be in buildings, tall trees or even in caves by the sea, but seldom far from human habitation.

Song thrush (*Turdus philomelos*) The melodious song of the male, perched high on a rooftop, is a pleasant accompaniment to the summer months, especially in the early morning. The male and female look alike. Thrushes feed on the ground, taking berries, insects and worms. Snails are a favourite food, with one particular rock or area of concrete used as an 'anvil'. This is usually littered with the remains of the shells of snails smashed there for access to their contents.

Blackbird (*Turdus merula*) The male's song resembles that of the song thrush, but is more flute-like and less repetitious. The drawing shows the male; the female is brownish in colour with indistinct mottling on the breast. Blackbirds feed on the ground, eating worms and fruit. Nests are built in trees and shrubs, in woodpiles, and also on or inside buildings.

Chaffinch (*Fringilla coelebs*) The short, stout bill of this bird is typical of finches, which feed mainly on hard, dry seeds. The chaffinch is the commonest finch now living in New Zealand. The drawing shows the male and the female, the latter lacking the red colouring. When not breeding, birds of the same sex flock together. It nests in trees and bushes, low in the fork of a branch near the trunk. The nest is woven of moss, grass and roots and lined with feathers and fine grass.

Goldfinch (*Carduelis carduelis*) This colourful garden bird feeds mainly on seeds, especially from the heads of dandelion, thistle and similar plants. In the breeding season goldfinches are often seen in pairs, the male and female looking alike. They also fly in large flocks or families. Grass roots and cobwebs are used to build nests in trees and shrubs, and these are lined with feathers, wool and thistledown.

Starling (*Sturnus vulgaris*) This very common introduced bird mimicks well the calls of the California quail and the pukeko and both the calls and actions of the fantail. Though starlings may be seen singly in gardens, they feed in flocks in the paddocks in spring, and roost in large flocks in winter. The starling nests in a hole, a building, a tree or a bank.

Silvereye (*Zosterops lateralis*) Large flocks of the silvereye arrived from Australia in 1856 and have been supplemented by further arrivals since. This appealing bird is commonly found in all areas with tree cover up to 1000 metres. After the breeding season, flocks are attracted to gardens where food is put out for them. This can be important to the birds' survival in winter as food shortage as well as cold take a heavy toll. The bird's natural food consists of insects, fruits and nectar.

Welcome swallow (*Hirundo tahitica*) Buildings, bridges, culverts, jetties and similar situations provide favourite nesting sites for this bird. It builds the nest on a convenient ledge, from mud strengthened by grass and lined with feathers. It is not at home on the ground, as it has such short legs, so it is usually found perching on wires and small branches. Swallows may often be seen circling above water feeding on insects.

Colourful invaders

So many flowering plants brought here by European settlers have become naturalised that now there are about as many introduced species in New Zealand as native ones. It is estimated that, in the Auckland City area, one new species becomes naturalised every 88 days. Most of these plants originate from Europe, North Africa and temperate Asia. Often they are regarded as weeds we could well do without, but many, such as buttercups, vipers bugloss and fennel, compensate with showy blooms that brighten the waysides of the land. Native plants typically have rather small, drab flowers and are usually restricted to their natural habitats. The human-made landscapes of cities and cultivated lands would be dull indeed without the introduced flowers.

Conspicuous among the introduced plants are those with particularly large and colourful blooms. Most of these were originally introduced as garden plants and have subsequently escaped. Plants escape from gardens in various ways. Some spread as seeds, some as pieces of plants carried away by animals, some as garden refuse dumped on the roadside or on waste land. Escaping is not just a matter of getting to an uncultivated area. The plant must be able to hold its own in competition with the wild plants already there and reproduce itself. Most garden plants are incapable of surviving when not receiving the devoted care of the gardener. But a few become naturalised successfully and add to the ever-increasing number of naturalised species.

It is a feature of New Zealand that it has so many garden escapes among its wild plants. Maybe this is a result of the mild climate — particularly the mildness of the winters. Maybe it is because so much of lowland New Zealand is constantly being disturbed by cultivation and expansion of settlements that there are repeated opportunities for newcomers to obtain a foothold. Certainly, human activities aid the establishment and spread of many plants. For instance, gardeners tipping their waste by the roadside first help plants to establish. The activities of earth-moving machinery used in land development then help distribute them from place to place. Plants that have spread well this way are those that have a vigorous method of vegetative reproduction. Many of these have creeping underground stems (rhizomes) or produce corms. A piece dug up from one site has sufficient food reserves stored in its tissues to allow it to survive long enough after it has been dumped elsewhere to put down roots. Once rooted, it pushes aside the other plants amongst which it is growing and eventually crowds them out. A typical example is montbretia (*Crocosmia* × *crocosmiiflora*), introduced as a garden plant. This plant is an artificial hybrid between two *Crocosmia* species, bred in France. It produces seeds as well as rhizomes and corms and, since the new leaves are produced before the old leaves have died down, it gives little opportunity to

Montbretia
(*Crocosmia* × *crocosmiiflora*)

competitors. It was first collected in New Zealand growing wild near Thames, in 1929. It is now common throughout the country.

There are numerous other examples of plants that have spread in a similar fashion. The colourful watsonias lining roadsides in warmer parts of the country are one. The wild gingers are another, and are causing alarm to conservationists for their propensity to invade native bush.

Some plants grown in gardens as ground cover also have an invasive habit. They often favour shady situations and may invade reserves. Examples are wandering Jew, Indian strawberry and periwinkle. Wandering Jew creeps over the soil, its stems rooting at intervals. The stems are brittle and pieces that break off are readily able to take root. The stem portions are also spread by streams and in this way the plant is carried into forest reserves.

Climbers, too, have the habit that leads them to become established outside the garden. Blue morning glory does not form seed in New Zealand, but climbs vigorously and may smother trees and shrubs. It spreads along hedges and over shrubby vegetation from areas where it has been planted or dumped. Stems can grow up to 15 centimetres per day. By this means, the plant can soon spread for hundreds of metres. When it has grown beyond the early stages it is difficult to eradicate, for this also involves destroying the plants giving it support.

Finding a place in the natural ecology Many garden escapes and weeds are successful because of their ability to colonise disturbed ground, which is something humans provide continually on a grand scale. In nature, these plants are restricted to sites disturbed naturally, by slips, floods or fire. Introduced plants can enter native habitats in their capacity as colonists. These foxgloves (*Digitalis purpurea*) have found their favoured growing site — an open rocky area — on the terminal moraine of the Tasman Glacier in Mt Cook National Park.

A successful escape
Most of the showy garden escapes are perennials, but a few are annuals, including Himalayan balsam (*Impatiens glandulifera*) (below). This plant shows many of the typical features of a successful weed, such as rapid growth, prolific seed production, explosive pods for efficient seed dispersal, and seeds that are able to lie dormant in soil for many years. Its seed pods are said to be distasteful to animals and the seeds may also be spread by water. As a result of its rapid growth, taking it to a height of 2.5 metres in less than a year, combined with its decorative sprays of large flowers, Himalayan balsam is rated as an asset to the countryside rather than a weed.

Tropical garden escapes
It is interesting to note that, although most of the introduced weeds have come from Europe, the majority of the garden escapes come from South Africa, South America and the tropical regions. One example is *Lantana* (below), the seeds of which are spread by birds. Though the bicoloured inflorescence is decorative, and the plant is still a garden favourite for that reason, this is ranked as one of the most troublesome weeds in the world, particularly in tropical areas. It has escaped from cultivation in New Zealand, but fortunately does not seem to have spread to the same extent as in other countries. This may be due to the climate here being cooler than in tropical America, its native home.

Around the home

We build homes and provision them with food so that we shall have a place to shelter in and feed in all the year round. Our prudence is exploited by many animals.

Some of these animals simply use the house as a convenient place to build their home or nest. Many of the spiders using the walls of the house to attach their webs to are merely making a convenience of this support. The rough bark of a tree does just as well. The mason wasp (*Pison spinolae*) is another example. It lives outdoors but frequently makes use of the house as a site to build its nest. This it constructs of mud, carefully moulded into a number of cells that are often located in the angles between walls, in keyholes, or even in the folds between stored clothing. The wasp then stocks each cell with one or two spiders that it has paralysed, laying eggs in the cell before sealing it. The larvae hatch and feed on the spiders, then form a cocoon of silk and dry mud particles. Later they emerge and break out of the cell.

There are other creatures that go through their entire life cycle in the house. These come from natural habitats for which the home makes an ideal substitute. They can therefore be considered as being pre-adapted to living in the house. Book-lice, for instance, live in the wild by eating bark and damp vegetation with their chewing mouthparts. In the home they turn their attention to fibres of paper and microscopic fungi that grow on book-binding paste under damp conditions. They also often live in cane furniture.

Some timber-boring beetles also spend their entire life cycle indoors, being equally at home in a prized piece of antique furniture as in a dead tree stump. Best known is the house borer, or furniture beetle (*Anobium punctatum*), whose larvae produce the circular tunnel openings that appear on the surface of wooden furniture and house timbers. Wood is a relatively indigestible material and, fortunately for those with wooden houses, few animals are able to digest it. The house borer, like many other wood-boring insects, holds colonies of symbiotic micro-organisms in its gut. These micro-organisms possess wood-digesting enzymes, making the wood available as food for the beetle larva. The nutritional content of wood is low, so it takes 2 to 5 years for the house borer larva to grow to full size and form its pupa. The winged adults emerge during summer and lay their eggs within cracks or irregularities on the wood's surface, and sometimes within the larval burrows.

Another group of timber eaters, the termites, are found only in warmer areas, but the damage they do to buildings can be very serious. They are social insects, living in colonies of several thousands. The native termites excavate tunnels and galleries in dead and

House mouse The house mouse (*Mus musculus*) is common in cities and towns, but also lives elsewhere, even in high mountains. In other locations it is known by other common names, such as field mouse, and bush mouse. It is a nocturnal creature and a good climber. It feeds on a wide range of seeds, insects, household scraps, and stored food, making good use of any suitable foodstuff that is available. House mice living in buildings reproduce on a large scale at any time of year. They have up to eight litters a year, each of five to six young. Almost any cavity in the building that is inaccessible to predators such as the domestic cat can be home to the mouse. The loft is a favourite nesting place. There it lines its nest with paper, cloth or other materials it finds in the house.

rotting tree trunks, but the termites introduced from Australia live underground and burrow into trees, wooden poles (including house piles) and timber buildings. Termites hollow out the timber until only a thin shell a few millimetres thick is left. If the timber is painted, they leave little more than the layer of paint.

Many other 'house guests' are scavengers that can live in various habitats, but find a congenial environment in or near the home. The house mouse and housefly are two examples. The carpet beetle is another example. The adults live outdoors, feeding on pollen, while the larvae are scavengers. However, female beetles commonly enter houses to lay eggs in cracks between floor boards and behind skirting boards. The larvae hatch out and tunnel through carpet, feeding as they go. Wool is not a nutritious food material, so growth is slow. It is usually more than a year before the larvae are ready to pupate and develop into mature adults.

The cockroaches are a better-known group of scavenging insects. Those most likely to be found in the home are the German cockroach (*Blattella germanica*), the American cockroach (*Periplaneta americana*), and the Australian cockroach (*P. australasiae*), although there are several native species that live in the forest. Cockroaches enter buildings because of the warmth, which is better for breeding, and for the food that they may find there. They feed on a wide range of materials and can be a serious household pest, especially as they produce a very unpleasant smell. Cockroaches rely on bacteria living in their gut to assist with the digestion of their food. In the female some of the bacteria migrate into the cockroach eggs and are passed on to the next generation.

Silverfish These are a group of primitive wingless insects. Although they live in the wild in moist situations, such as the seashore, they are more conspicuous in the home. They require a humid environment and a source of food, preferably of a starchy nature. For this reason they are most often found in the kitchen (especially if the house is damp) where there is sure to be enough spilled flour, breadcrumbs and similar sources of food.

Daddy-long-legs
This is the more popular name for the long-legged cellar spider (*Pholcus phalangioides*) found in houses and buildings but not elsewhere. It builds an irregular web in the corner of a room, often sharing the web with others of its kind. The spider does not possess poison glands so it has to rely on catching its prey while trapped in the web. When an insect lands on the web the spider shakes the web violently, entangling the prey before wrapping it in more threads of silk to immobilise it.

Winged menace
Blowflies, such as the golden-haired blowfly (*Calliphora*), seen here flying over some breakfast cereals, often invade homes looking for food or for meat upon which to lay their eggs. This blowfly can drop its maggots from the air, even onto hot meat, the eggs having hatched within the fly's body. With the use of modern refrigeration, the problem of blowflies is less than in olden times.

CHAPTER 7

THE COAST

Change never ceases where land and sea meet. The surge and fall of the waves pare away craggy headlands and crumbling cliffs. Elsewhere the land may gain. Ocean currents deposit smooth sand beaches, while in quiet estuaries, silt sediments gather on mudflats that steadily expand their margins seawards.

Processes such as these manifest themselves in the enormous variety of coastal landforms. To travel the fringe of the land is to encounter seacliffs and sand dunes, muddy inlets and pebble beaches, each of which supports its particular community of plants and animals.

Coastal communities, however, are not communities in the same sense as those of a lake or a forest. Their fate is too linked to the realms of land and sea on either side. Cockles, sandhoppers and seals, for instance, all depend on the sea for their food. Some of these organisms may, in turn, be eaten by animals from further inland.

Nonetheless, the coastal inhabitants have their special identity. For millions of years, they have lived with the confrontation of wave and rock, the interchange of the tides, and the ceaseless transformation of the ground on which they live. These are problems unique to the coast, and the inhabitants have evolved unique solutions to them. Most of the organisms found here live nowhere else.

West Coast, South Island

Between the tides

At the margins of the land there is a habitat quite unlike any other. It is called the intertidal zone. Here, twice each day, a narrow band of coastline is submerged by the incoming tide, then exposed by the falling tide. It is a continually changing habitat, sometimes land, sometimes sea, and this pattern of change has an overbearing influence on the organisms that live there.

When the tide is in, the submerged community becomes a scene of animation. Snails extend undulating black mantles and glide across rocks, grazing upon tiny algae. Barnacles beat at the water with cirral nets, sieving for plankton upon which to feed. Shoals of predatory fish move in, to pick here and there for titbits among the intertidal inhabitants. Then, when the tide retreats, the hustle and bustle abates. Fish depart with the ebbing water. Mobile crabs and starfish retire into small crevices, and shelled animals close up their homes. Everything lies torpid, waiting for the sea to return. The only movements are of shore birds that set down on the exposed fringe of land. Now it is their turn to take the place of the predatory fish, as they probe, pick and pry for any creatures that have not found suitable refuge.

The rise and fall of the tides are caused by the gravitational pull of the moon and, to a smaller extent, the sun. The period between moonrise one day and the next lasts 24.8 hours, and during this time there are two high tides, 12.4 hours apart. The solar cycle by contrast lasts 24 hours, so it is a little out of phase with that of the moon. Consequently the pull of the moon and sun continuously vary with respect to each other. Each fortnight, when there is a full or new moon, both the sun and moon pull together to produce particularly high and low tides called spring tides. Between spring tides, when the moon is in its first or third quarter, the sun and moon pull at right angles to each other to produce much smaller tides, called neap tides.

Where an organism lives, between the highest and lowest levels of the tide, has a profound effect on the living conditions it experiences. Those living at the top may be left high and dry by the sea for several days during the neap tides. They will suffer the longest exposure to the heating and drying effects of the sun. Conversely, those at the bottom will be submerged continuously, except for a brief period each day during the spring tides. Between these extremes different plant and animal species establish themselves in zones according to how long they can tolerate being exposed at low tide. This phenomenon is called zonation and its effects will be seen on every coastline. Even though the types of organism will also vary with the nature of the shore, be it a rocky headland, mudflat or sandy beach, all are subject to the principle of zonation.

Zonation is best seen on a rocky coast. Highest on the shore are usually periwinkles, which can withstand several days beyond reach of the tides, save for a splash or two from the occasional wave. These are remarkably hardy creatures. Once they have retreated into their shells and sealed up the entrance with their lid-like operculum, they can survive being baked at almost 50 degrees Celsius, as well as being left for days in desiccating conditions. Just below the periwinkles on the shore come other shelled creatures, such as barnacles, chitons and limpets, which can also withstand exposure to the sun and wind. Barnacles do so by having hinged plates that shut tight when the tide is out. Chitons and limpets can clamp their shells tightly onto the rock, sealing a precious pocket of moisture within.

Continuing down towards the lowest tide levels, environmental conditions become increasingly benign and the numbers of different organisms proliferate correspondingly. There are swaying beds of seaweeds and racks of mussels and oysters. There are wandering sea urchins and the exuberant colours of soft-bodied, moisture-loving anemones, sea slugs, sea cucumbers and sponges. These seaweed jungles with their teeming communities of animals are a far cry from the handful of species that struggle on the upper shore. But although the environment is certainly more benevolent on the lower shore, the individual species are not necessarily better off. Between the upper and lower shores, organisms have just swapped one form of adversity for another. Those on the upper shore battle with exposure to burning sun and drying winds, but because only a few hardy species can cope, they face

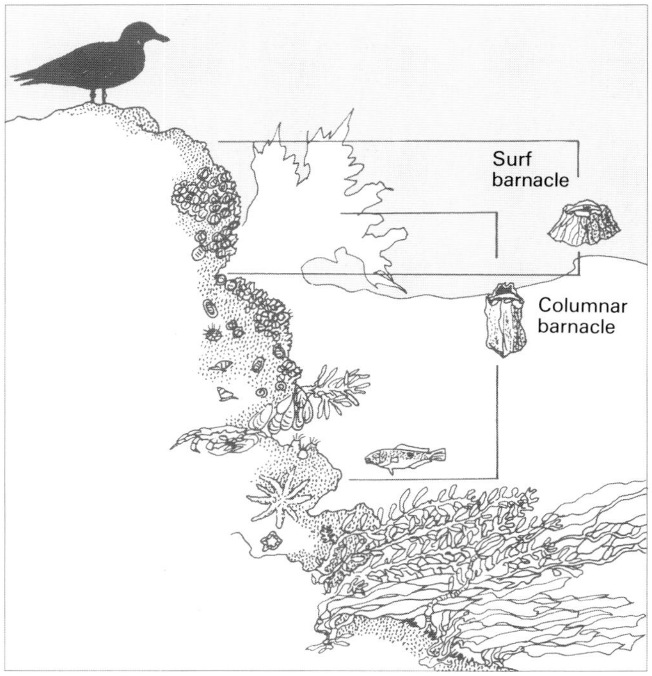

Barnacle zonation
The brown surf barnacle (*Chamaesipho brunnea*) and the columnar barnacle (*C. columna*) are adapted to occupy living zones at different heights on the shore. The brown surf barnacle can survive being left high and dry by the retreating tide better than the smaller columnar barnacle. It can therefore live higher up on the shore. However, if the brown surf barnacle tries to establish itself lower down on the shore, where the columnar barnacle thrives, it is literally overgrown by the smaller more competitive barnacle. It is also increasingly attacked by carnivorous molluscs, which are more numerous lower on the shore. So the brown surf barnacle inhabits a discrete band in the intertidal zone, the top of which is set by its ability to tolerate heat and dryness at low tide and the bottom being set by competitors and predators. The zone inhabited by the columnar barnacle is determined in much the same way. It can tolerate greater extremes of environment than the oysters, mussels and large seaweeds that live below it on the shoreline. But it cannot compete for crowded living space with these other plants and animals if it tries to establish itself in their deeper water territory.

A CLOCK TO READ THE TIDES BY

The routine of the tides prevails in such a repetitive and overwhelming way on the lifestyle of coastal animals that many have become profound creatures of habit. Each time the tide recedes from the mudflats, the common mud crab (*Helice crassa*) returns to be within running distance of its burrow before it is exposed by the falling water level. Even though the timing of the tides varies a little each day, it always manages to predict them and scuttle home to avoid being caught far from the safety of its bolt hole. Then, when the tide floods back, the crab departs once more on feeding forays across the submerged flats. Remarkably, even if it is taken away and observed in a constant environment utterly removed from the sea, the crab persists with this punctual behaviour. It seeks its burrow when the tide would normally be out and becomes active again when the tide would normally be in. It is as if it has a tide-timetable imprinted on its memory.

The timing mechanism that enables the mud crab to predict the tides is called a biological clock. Precisely how it works is not understood, but such mechanisms are common in the biological world. They are found wherever animals are subject to regular and repeated changes in their environment, such as the rhythm of the tides or the alternation between day and night. It enables an animal to organise its routine in anticipation of its changing environment, rather than continually being a victim of it. For instance, cockles buried in sand rely on a 'clock' in order to extend their feeding siphons to the surface to coincide with high tide. Even plants can have biological clocks. Certain microscopic algae that live on tidal flats migrate upwards in the sand just after the tide goes out, so they can photosynthesise on the sunbathed surface. Then, moments before the tide returns, the algae migrate back down to avoid being washed away.

little competition from one another. On the lower shore, where the environment is more favourable to life, each organism must compete with the hordes of others that now flourish. Every square centimetre of rock is disputed as a site to set up home and each small share of sunlight or food is contested. There are also many more predators to contend with, each one of them eager to find its next meal from among the bustling inhabitants.

The zone an organism inhabits on the shore is therefore usually determined by two types of influence. One is physical, such as heat and desiccation, which generally becomes more severe higher up the shore. The other is biological, such as competition and predation by other life forms, which usually becomes more severe lower down the shore.

Rocky shores

Rocky shores are surely the most capricious of coastlines. Within the lee of coves and harbours, the land may be spared all but the lapping of waves, but where it lies open to the sea, storms can erupt with untamed fury. Massive breakers pound against rock, venting their energy in a maelstrom of exploding surf and salt-charged air.

Organisms that live here face particular problems. Clearly they must find ways to withstand the relentless pounding of the waves. A few do so by digging into the rock itself, so long as it is relatively soft. A mollusc called the piddock (*Pholadidea*) uses the sharp end of its shell like a chisel. Pressing against the rock face, it swivels its shell back and forth, slowly gouging out a gallery in which to live. Another mollusc, the date mussel (*Lithophaga*), makes a burrow by a different method. It secretes acids to dissolve the underlying rock. So that its shell is not also dissolved, this is covered by a horny, acid-proof coat, giving the mussel the appearance of a date. Most other tidal organisms resist the action of waves simply by fixing themselves to the rock surface. Barnacles are glued on with natural cements, while mussels spin special byssus threads that tie their shells down. Whelks and many other molluscs rely on suction.

Being fixed to rock means there is a price to pay when the tide retreats. An exposed rock face can soar in temperature by as much as 40 degrees Celsius once it is hit by the sun. Nevertheless, in exchange for such difficulties, rocky shores offer several benefits. The rock itself provides a firm place for creatures to attach themselves, compared with loose material such as sand. The water that bathes the rocky shore inhabitants is always well aerated by the constant churning of waves and it is also usually sparklingly clear. There is very little gritty sediment to clog the delicate filtering mechanisms of creatures that feed from the plankton-rich waters, and seaweeds can photosynthesise readily in the sunlit depths. Even those creatures needing some measure of shelter from the elements can usually find nooks and crannies for refuge. Anemones tuck themselves into shady corners and sea urchins and shellfish cluster in small cracks. Lifting up rocks will uncover enclaves of crabs, brittle stars and sponges but the rocks must be returned as they were found. With so many microhabitats available, rocky shores abound with different types of life. They are by far the most varied of tidal habitats.

AVOIDING WAVE ACTION

The limpet and the periwinkle demonstrate two ways of dealing with wave action. The shell of a limpet fits tightly against the rock surface and is held firmly in place by the powerful and broadly based muscles of the limpet's body.

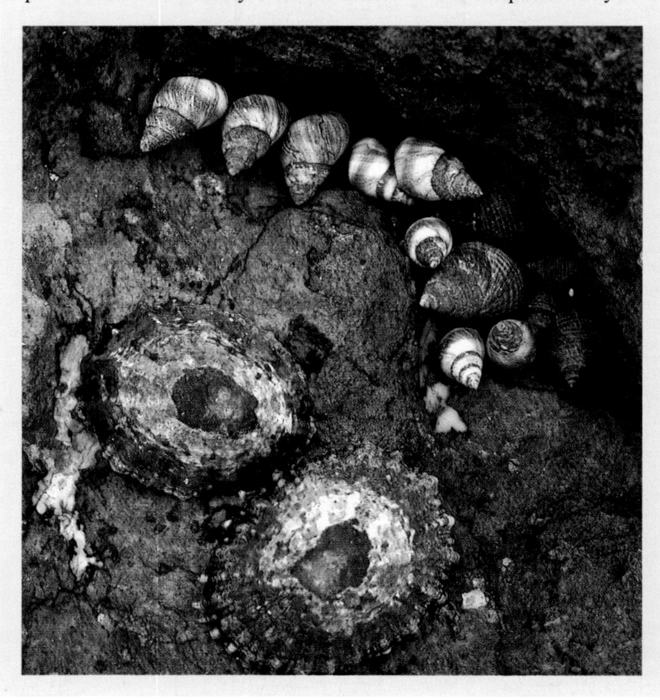

To ensure a good fit, the limpet moves its shell to and fro, grinding away shell or rock, whichever is softer, until the contours of one perfectly match the other. Then the limpet cannot be dislodged by the waves, for the unbroken contours of shell and rock ensure that water currents that flow past the shell meet the least possible resistance. When the tide is out the limpet remains perfectly sealed against the rock, holding a vital supply of water within, until the sea returns once more.

Some limpets display a remarkable homing behaviour. At high tide they wander over the rocks, browsing algae. Yet they always return to their home base and accurately seat themselves down on their custom-fitting site before the tide goes out. How they do this is a mystery. Sight does not seem to be involved since limpets find their way home equally well by day or night. Neither does scent seem clearly involved, unless it is particularly well impregnated into the rock. Vigorously scrubbing a limpet's territory with cleaning agents does not foil its navigation in the least.

The periwinkle shelters from the waves by congregating in cracks. At low tide the animal can withdraw into its shell, sealing itself inside. Unlike the limpet, it makes little attempt to hold fast to the rocks. But if dislodged from a sheltering crevice, its rounded shell affords some protection, allowing the periwinkle to roll freely in the tidal current. Rounded shapes impart great mechanical strength and avoid damage by offering minimal resistance to wave action.

THE HOLDFAST

Bull kelps (*Durvillaea*) thrive on the wildest wave-lashed shores, thanks to their holdfast. This is a clasping pad of leathery tissue glued onto the rock with sticky secretions. The grip is so tenacious that bull kelps can safely extend fronds up to 10 metres long into the surging sea. The writhing mass of tresses is prevented from tangling by being covered with a slippery mucilage, as any unwary person clambering on seaweed-covered rocks discovers.

The success of the holdfast has not gone unnoticed by other shoreline inhabitants. Burrowing animals and other creatures seek refuge within its sturdy base. Among the residents are worms, chitons, limpets and isopods, many of which cannot survive without the plant's shelter. In the end though, too much of a good thing becomes their undoing. The squatters usually undermine the plant so much that a storm rips it off into the sea and the colony perishes.

Although bull kelps and many other seaweeds seem to resemble land plants, their similarities are relatively superficial. The holdfast serves only as an anchor. It has no roots like land plants, even though some may produce small finger-like growths to grip onto rocks. Nor do seaweeds have very elaborate conducting systems to transport sugars, minerals and water back and forth within their tissues, as land plants do. They barely require them, since all surfaces of a seaweed can photosynthesise, as well as absorb water and minerals directly from the seawater.

The rather simple design of seaweeds is so perfectly suited to the marine environment that it has not changed substantially in hundreds of millions of years. Notwithstanding their 'primitiveness' some seaweeds are record breakers of the plant kingdom. The common bladder kelp (*Macrocystis pyrifera*), whose washed-up fronds provide a satisfying 'pop' when trodden on, is the fastest growing plant in the world. It can extend fronds at up to half a metre a day and grow well over 30 metres long.

Spotted shag (*Stictocarbo punctatus*) (left) Rocky coastlines are ideal places to view seabirds. During the breeding season they congregate in raucous mobs to build their nests on cliffside ledges. Among the shags seen here, the spotted shag is one of the most widespread. Shags do not dive into the sea from the air, as most other seabirds do. They alight first on the surface and then slip silently beneath the waves in search of small fish or crustaceans. Their wings are held flush with their body, and they swim with strong strokes of their large feet. In order to make underwater swimming easier, shags have feathers which wet, so losing the buoyancy of air that would otherwise be trapped beneath them. Afterwards the birds have to spend time drying their waterlogged plumage in the sun, striking their characteristic outstretched-wing pose.

Tubeworms (*Pomatoceros*) (right) The spiny tubeworm thrives on exposed rocky shores by secreting a calcareous tube in which to live. Out of this it extends feathery tentacles, which are used not only as gills for breathing, but to filter-feed from the surrounding water as well.

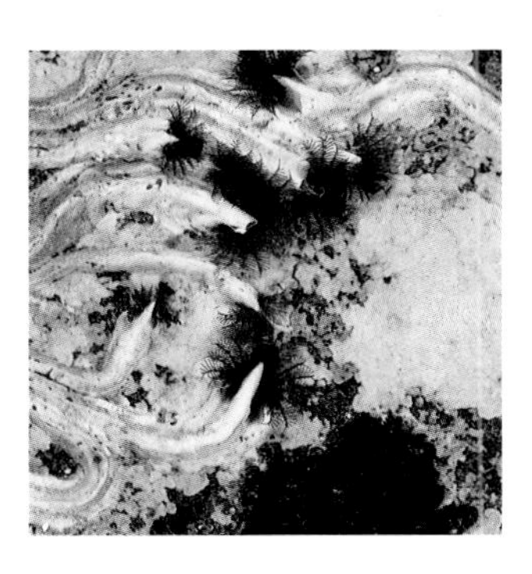

Creatures of the rocky shore

Life began in the sea, so this remains the best place to study the wide array of animal groups that have evolved. Few activities give better insight into this startling variety than a couple of hours spent exploring rock pools at low tide. Many creatures are so unfamiliar to our everyday experience that they appear quite extraordinary — take for example, the sea anemone with its myriad tentacles, or the translucent details of a prawn.

A close look at this collection of creatures will reveal that they can be placed into groups, according to the similarity of their body plans. A prawn has features in common with a crab. Likewise, a paua has similarities to a limpet. Taxonomists have divided all animal life on Earth into basic groups called phyla. The members of a single phylum share fundamental similarities because they all evolved from common ancestors a very long time ago. Some of the most noticeable animal phyla to be found on a visit to the coast are considered here.

Sponges

Encrusted on rocks near the low-tide level are lumpy, but often colourful growths called sponges. These are animals, although it is hard to credit them with being such. They have none of the usual animal features such as eyes, legs or claws. They do not visibly move, or show any response to what goes on around them. They appear utterly inert, glued onto rocks.

This lack of animal attributes caused early taxonomists a headache. Some considered that sponges were plants, perhaps unaware that they were particularly common in underwater caves where there was no light. Other people classified them as plant-animals, or zoophytes.

Sponges have an unusual nature because they are very simple organisms, thought to have appeared very early in the evolution story. They are placed in the phylum Porifera. Sponges possess no muscle or nervous tissue which most animals use to respond to their surroundings and co-ordinate movement. In fact a closer examination reveals that they have no specialised organs at all. What they are is a group of individual cells living together as a colony. There is a division of labour amongst these cells which enables the sponge to co-ordinate one of its main activities in life, which is to filter out microscopic particles of food from the surrounding water. To do this, the body of the sponge is riddled with tiny canals through which sea water moves, wafted along by special cells equipped with beating threads. Other cells have the job of engulfing the food particles as they pass by on their way to a large exit hole at the top of the sponge. Yet another group of cells inside the sponge are specialised for reproduction.

The orange golf-ball sponge (*Tethya auratianum*), about the size of its namesake, is often found in shady places near the low-tide level.

All this activity goes on within a supportive 'skeleton', which gives the sponge its shape. In some it consists of soft, flexible fibres which, once the live cells are removed, provide the sponge we use in the bathroom. In others the supporting material includes needle-like silica spicules, interlocked to form an exquisite scaffolding.

The simple organisational structure of sponges gives them some interesting features. If a piece of a sponge is broken off, it can grow into a new animal. Meanwhile, the damaged sponge can repair itself without ill effect. If two sponges grow alongside each other, they may, as they grow bigger, fuse into a single massive sponge. More remarkable, if certain sponges are passed through a sieve, separating them into their thousands of member cells, the sponge can reconstitute itself, each cell type regaining its correct role within the new animal.

Because sponges live fixed to the seabed they face a problem that most other animals do not. They cannot run away from their various predators, parasites and competitors. Yet a visit to any shoreline will reveal that sponges and other encrusting animals such as sea squirts and bryozoans are rarely eaten. So how do they defend themselves from attack?

One answer to this question has excited science in recent years. It seems that many encrusting animals employ chemical deterrents. These make them unpopular with parasites and predators, as well as the larvae of other creatures that might otherwise consider them a nice surface to colonise and grow on. Equally, these substances may ward off neighbours, as different encrusting animals vie with one another for precious elbow room on crowded rocks. So what often appears to be a passive community of assorted sponges, may be engaged in a subtle form of chemical warfare. While the chemical complexities of these creatures remain incompletely understood, research has already found them a source of very interesting compounds, which may be put to use to overcome some of the diseases that plague humans.

Anemones and their relatives

Anemones belong to the phylum Cnidaria, which also includes jellyfish and corals. They are a primitive animal group, though more complex than sponges. Brush your hand over an anemone and it will contract its tentacles instantly. It has nerves and muscles!

The waving tentacles of the anemone are armed with powerful weapons. Each one is lined with thousands of stinging hairs that inject paralysing fluids into any small animal unfortunate enough to come close. The prey is then pushed through the central mouth into the hollow body of the anemone where it is digested. Being of simple design, the anemone has only one main entrance or exit, so the indigestible remains are later spat back out through the mouth.

Worms

There are many different phyla of marine worms, although few of their members are encountered on a visit to the coast. Most marine worms spend their time buried in sandy or muddy shores, feeding on scraps of debris. The most commonly noticed on rocky shores are the tubeworms that protrude tiny 'chimney-sweep brushes' from their tube homes to filter the surrounding water for food (page 135).

Red anemone (*Actinia tenebrosa*) The red anemone is a common intertidal inhabitant. It might be expected that the soft-bodied anemone would have trouble surviving when the tide is out, but it has a way of dealing with this. It swallows a supply of seawater and then closes its tentacles over the top, waiting like a blob of jelly till the tide returns.

Jewel anemone (*Corynactis haddoni*) The jewel anemone appears in a variety of colour forms. It is not a true anemone. Its clubbed tentacles bear their stinging cells at the tips — a characteristic of many stony corals.

Sea mouse (*Euphione*) One of the bigger free-living worms sometimes found is the sea mouse. It is about as large as its namesake and lives among rocks on the lower part of the shore, burying itself in silt or sand. It is a scavenger, feeding on carrion as it burrows through the silt.

Crabs and other crustacea

Anyone could be confused by the Crustacea, so very varied are their members. Among them are such diverse animals as crabs, lobsters, shrimps, sandhoppers, woodlice and, most unexpectedly, barnacles. Crustaceans are part of the phylum Arthropoda, which also includes insects. The unifying theme of all arthropods is a segmented body covered by an external skeleton of articulated plates, rather like a knight in armour. It is an extraordinarily successful design. There are thought to be three times as many types of arthropod as all other animals put together.

Crabs are the best known of seaside crustaceans. Particularly familiar is the hermit crab, which catches one's attention when what seems a sedate mollusc takes off at exceptional speed. A closer look reveals that the shell is occupied by a hermit crab. The abdomen, or rear end of the crab, is curled to fit into the empty spiral shell of a univalve mollusc. Apart from its front pair of pincers, the crab uses two pairs of legs for walking and its rear two pairs of legs to hold on to its borrowed home. As it gets bigger, the hermit crab faces a housing problem and needs to seek less cramped quarters. Competition for new lodgings can be high among hermit crabs, and a covetous individual may not be beyond evicting one of its relatives from a suitable shell.

MASTER OF DISGUISE

Because of its masterly disguise a decorator crab is rarely noticed. The top of the carapace is equipped with special hooked hairs to which the crab deftly attaches pieces of seaweed and sponge, which it plucks from its habitat. Wandering around with its rooftop garden, the crab becomes almost impossible to detect. A decorator crab will always take pains to match its surroundings. If swept into a new neighbourhood, it will immediately set about renewing its camouflage with local materials. In one experiment, crabs were put in an aquarium with sheets of paper. Soon afterwards, they were busy shredding pieces with which to decorate themselves.

Hermit crab (*Pagurus rubricatus*) This hermit crab comes from subtidal depths. Often it shares its borrowed home with another lodger, a ragworm. Normally the ragworm remains tucked out of sight, within the hermit's shell. But when the crab finds something to eat and begins to shred it with its claws, the ragworm sneaks out and daringly seizes a share of the meal, before retiring with the morsel.

Molluscs

With few exceptions, all the shell-bearing creatures found on the shore belong to the phylum Mollusca. Those most commonly seen can be divided into four groups: chitons, bivalves, cephalopods and gastropods (or univalves). Chitons are easily recognised by their eight overlapping armour plates. Bivalves have two hinged shells that can close over the body of the mollusc inside. They are so numerous that examples can be found on almost any coast. Mussels, oysters, scallops, cockles, tuatuas and pipis are all bivalves. Most are filter feeders, opening their shells when the tide is in to sift out small particles of food from the surrounding water.

The cephalopods include octopuses and squids, which, contrary to their screen roles in monster movies, are harmless, intelligent creatures. They are the most highly evolved of all the molluscs, equipped with an elaborate nervous system and eyes which in some ways are superior to our own. Many have discarded the protection of a shell, relying on their acute senses and quick speed to avoid danger.

The gastropods, or univalves, have just one shell. Usually it is coiled like a turban, such as among periwinkles and whelks. Other gastropods have a more flattened shell, such as limpets and paua. Small paua (*Haliotis*) can sometimes be found when you are exploring the rocks at low tide, but the larger ones have invariably been taken for the cooking pot. This is a sadness, since paua are slow-growing animals. They take several years to reach maturity so, once a coastline has been heavily fished, recovery takes a long time. Paua graze seaweeds, the types of which can sometimes affect the glorious colours laid down in their shells. Although they look sedentary, paua can move with surprising agility when the tide is in, sometimes nimbly seizing a piece of seaweed as it drifts by.

The most beautiful and specialised of the gastropods have forsaken their shells altogether. These are the sea slugs or nudibranchs, which means 'naked gills', on account of the tuft of gills on the animal's back. Nudibranchs are like butterflies of the sea. Their soft, fragile bodies come in a rainbow of beautiful colours, which usually advertise the fact that the sea slugs would make a very unpleasant mouthful. Nudibranchs can exude potent chemicals to ward off their predators. Like butterflies, sea slugs can also have very specific food preferences, eating only one or two types of prey — often organisms such as sponges, corals or sea squirts, which are avoided by most other creatures. Even the stinging cells of anemones are no problem to some sea slugs. Indeed, as they devour the anemone, these sea slugs manage to separate the stinging cells intact and store them in special pouches in their bodies to use as a personal armoury against attack.

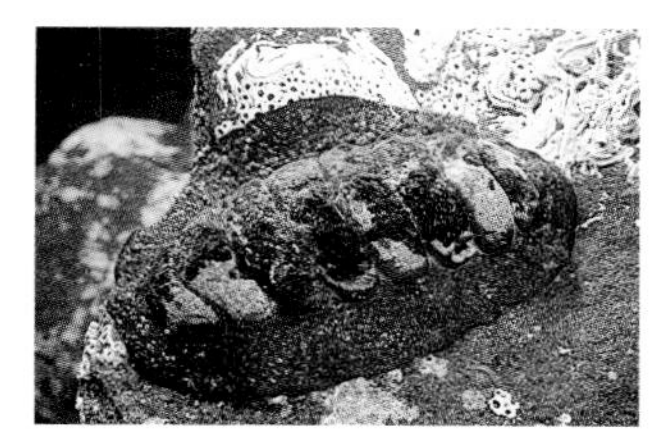

'Primitive' molluscs Chitons, with their overlapping shell plates, are considered to have a long evolutionary history and bear certain resemblances to early molluscs.

Intertidal delicacy Paua (*Haliotis iris*) are collected for food as well as for the rainbow patterns on their shell interior. In many areas, paua are vulnerable to overfishing.

Molluscs without shells The sea slugs are a group of molluscs that have lost their shells. They are beautiful marine inhabitants, often richly coloured, such as this warty sea slug (*Archidoris wellingtonensis*). Their gills, exposed on the animal's back, often resemble a petalled flower.

Animals with spiny skins

These animals include the sea urchins, starfish and sea cucumbers. Most have a skeleton made of calcareous plates with spikes that stick through the skin; hence the name of their phylum, the Echinodermata, meaning spiny skin.

As a sea urchin wanders around, browsing on seaweeds or grazing the organic growth on rocks, it moves in a most unusual way. Each of its numerous spines has a ball and socket joint at the end, allowing it to swivel in any direction. Between the spines are rows of flexible tentacles, bearing small suckers at their tips. These are called tube feet, and they are operated by a hydraulic system that is a speciality of the echinoderms. The tube feet are hollow, and by forcing water in or out, the urchin can move them around. When the urchin 'walks', it uses its hydraulically operated tube feet and swivelling spines in a co-ordinated fashion, travelling along as if on hundreds of prickly stilts. Which way it goes is just as it pleases, since like other echinoderms, the urchin has a body plan with more or less radial symmetry. It has no front or back, left or right; just a top and bottom.

The hollow, egg-like skeleton or 'test' of the urchin, minus its spines, is often washed up on the beach. If you pick one up and take a look you will see that it is made of rows of plates fused together. This gives us a clue as to its relationship with the starfish. In the starfish these rows are not fused together. They are splayed out, rather like a peeled banana skin, to give five arms. Underneath each arm are dozens of tube feet, just like the urchin's, and the starfish uses these to move around.

These thread-like tube feet can clearly be seen in the photograph, extending from one of the arms of the cushion star (*Patiriella regularis*) as it moves over the rock. Many large starfish are voracious carnivores, preying on almost anything they are strong enough to overwhelm. Their long arms are particularly suited to overpowering shellfish. With their tube feet they grip both halves of a bivalve shell and try to pull it open. The tube feet exert a considerable force and they are usually able to maintain the tension long enough to tire the mollusc. The shell may only open a small crack, but this is all that is needed, for the starfish can achieve an extraordinary feat of contortion. It is able to turn its stomach inside out from its body and insert it through this crack into the shell, digesting the mollusc in its home.

Brittle stars have very flexible limbs and are surprisingly agile compared with their ponderous relatives the starfish. A few species live in the intertidal zone, though they are rarely noticed on account of their cryptic coloration and their habit of hiding beneath rocks during the day. They are far more common in the deep sea. Here brittle stars live in such numbers as to be arguably the most successful of all echinoderms. Many are suspension feeders, trapping food particles in mucus secreted by their tube feet. Working in concert, the tube feet then pass small scraps down to the mouth.

Common sea urchin (*Evechinus chloroticus*) (top left) The common sea urchin is one of the most familiar intertidal inhabitants. Individuals can camouflage themselves by picking up stones and bits of seaweed with their tube feet.

Cushion star (*Patiriella regularis*) (bottom left) The cushion star is a common rock-pool inhabitant. It has very short arms and feeds mainly on debris.

Brittle stars The mottled sand star (*Ophionereis fasciata*) (far right) is one of the more commonly found brittle stars on the lower shore. These fragile, spidery creatures can shed a limb to escape the grasp of a predator, in the same way that lizards can shed their tails. The missing limb later regrows.

Chordates

By and large, the phylum Chordata includes those animals we are most familiar with, since it contains the backboned animals such as fish, amphibians, reptiles, birds, and mammals like ourselves. There is a common group of marine chordates, however, that seems to bear no relationship to the backboned animals. These spend most of their lives fixed to one spot, rather like sponges, drawing in sea water and filtering out particles of food. They are called sea squirts because of their tendency to squirt water from one of their two openings when disturbed. The inside of their body is essentially a U-shaped tube, through which water is drawn by beating hairs. The most common types of sea squirt look like blobs of jelly stuck on rocks. One like this can be seen in the photograph of the cushion star (page 140). Other types live in a colonial fashion, with numerous individuals joined together to look like one large organism.

The sea squirt's lifestyle is a curious one for a chordate. Indeed, there would be no reason for calling them chordates at all, but for one thing. During sexual reproduction a free-swimming larva is produced that resembles a tadpole. This has a tail stiffened by a thin rod, which is sufficiently suggestive of a backbone to warrant the sea squirt being considered a chordate. The larva swims around for a while, then makes a once-in-a-lifetime decision and glues its nose to a suitable rock. It then turns into the adult sea squirt, which must stay in the spot chosen by the larva till it dies. Thus the sea squirt would seem to be an extremely early evolutionary offshoot of the chordates that adopted a sedentary, rather than a mobile, lifestyle.

Fish are true backboned animals. They are very much more advanced than sea squirts, having evolved a skeleton, with a complex muscular and nervous system co-ordinated by a well-developed brain. All this makes them agile and alert; ideally suited to their active, mobile lifestyle.

When the tide retreats, few fish remain behind in rock pools. Most of those that do are known as cockabullies. This conveniently broad term comprises dozens of species of small fish, many from different families. Among the commonest are triplefins (*Tripterygion*), which are often seen lying motionless on the bottom or among weeds, darting off either to take cover or seize small prey.

Lower on the shore, hidden among beds of seaweed, you may be fortunate to find the seahorse (*Hippocampus abdominalis*). This is a curiosity among fish, since it swims upright, fanning itself along with its dorsal and pectoral fins. Needless to say, this is a remarkably inefficient method of propulsion, but then the seahorse has little need to swim. Much of its life is spent motionless among seaweeds, waiting for planktonic crustaceans to come close enough for it to suck them into its tubular mouth, as if with a pipette. The seahorse has therefore dispensed with speed and streamlining in favour of camouflage. Its intricate shape breaks up its outline so it can merge with the surrounding seaweeds. At the same time its tail has lost its swimming purpose and has become prehensile, allowing the seahorse to cling to seaweed fronds and not be swept away.

Sea squirts Sea squirts are of considerable interest to taxonomists, since they belong to the phylum Chordata, which also includes backboned animals such as ourselves. This one, the sea tulip (*Pyura pachydermatina*), lives at or below the low-tide level. Most commonly it is found tossed up on the beaches after storms, like bedraggled bunches of flowers.

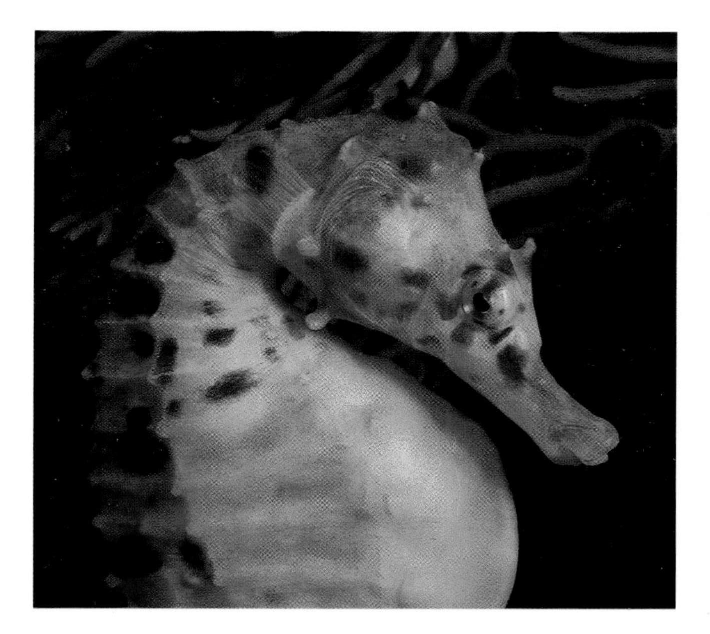

Male pregnancy
The seahorse (*Hippocampus abdominalis*) (left) can sometimes be found among seaweeds at the low-tide level. Apart from its curious shape, the seahorse also has a very unusual method of reproduction, for it is the male that becomes pregnant. When seahorses mate, the female deposits her eggs in a special brooding pouch on the male's lower abdomen. Here the eggs are fertilised by the male's sperm and incubated until they hatch. Then, with muscular contractions, the male gives birth to dozens of miniature seahorses.

Seals and penguins

Seals

Seals belong to the suborder Pinnipedia, which means 'the fin-footed'. They can be divided into three families: eared seals, true seals and the walrus. Only the first two groups occur in New Zealand waters. Eared seals include fur seals and sea lions, and have small but visible external ears. They move on land by turning their back flippers forward and walking on all fours. True seals, which include elephant seals and leopard seals, cannot do this. Their rear flippers stay pointed backwards like a fish-tail and they move in a less elegant fashion, by wriggling caterpillar-style.

Eared seals and true seals evolved in the Northern Hemisphere. They took to the seas over 20 million years ago and evolved from land ancestors that also gave rise to dogs and bears. They are now widely distributed in northern and southern temperate waters.

Seals evoke our wonder, and perhaps envy, because they are at home both on the land and in the sea. As fellow mammals, our own attempts at diving underwater are hopeless. By comparison we are nearsighted, have trouble hearing, get cold and soon run out of breath. Seals have solved all these problems. Their large eyes enable them to see underwater as well as we do above. They are also acutely sensitive to underwater sounds, particularly those of high frequency. The fact that blind seals still manage to catch fish suggests that some can use echo-location to help find their prey, as whales do.

To keep warm, seals have a thick insulating layer of blubber beneath their skin. Fur seals, as their name implies, also rely on a furry coat to keep out the cold when swimming. This has an outer surface of coarse guard hairs, which trap an insulating layer of air and water within soft underfur. If they get too hot, seals simply flush warm blood into their naked flippers and use them like radiators. The flippers are also equipped with sweat glands, so on land they can stay cool by waving their flippers in the air.

It is the diving ability of seals that seems most extraordinary. Most feeding dives that seals make are

Fur seal (*Arctocephalus forsteri*) (top left) The New Zealand fur seal is the most common of New Zealand's seals. It is a coastal species, hauling out on rocky shorelines. It can be found as far north as the Three Kings, but the main populations are around the South Island, Stewart Island, Chatham Islands and nearby subantarctic islands. Like all seals it is carnivorous, feeding on squid and some fish. Females come ashore in spring to give birth at specific breeding colonies. They mate again several days later with dominant bull males, which vie with one another for control of breeding territories and personal harems.

Hooker's sea lion (*Phocarctos hookeri*) (bottom left) Hooker's sea lion breeds on New Zealand's subantarctic islands, although batchelor males are often encountered on the southern South Island coast. Unlike fur seals, which haul out on rocky shores, sea lions come ashore on sandy beaches. They are also larger than fur seals, and the adult male has a distinctively blunt snout compared with the fur seal's. There are only about 6000 Hooker's sea lions in existence, making them one of the rarest sea lions. Like other seals they have their difficulties with humans. Drowning in the nets of squid fishermen is a serious problem. They also have to contend with the ever-increasing amount of human rubbish, such as plastic six-pack can holders and plastic strapping, which become strangulation nooses.

Elephant seal (*Mirounga leonina*) (below) The elephant seal is the largest of pinnipeds, adult males weighing over 3000 kilograms. Elephant seals are widespread in subantarctic islands. They spend a lot of time at sea, making large migrations and often returning to their point of birth. The main colony in New Zealand waters is on the Campbell Islands. Females, however, occasionally pup on the South Island mainland. The most distinctive feature of the elephant seal is the large snout of mature males. This becomes enlarged during the breeding season and is used as a resonating chamber, enabling the male to issue an impressive roar to browbeat other males. Female elephant seals, like seals in general, minimise the time spent ashore suckling their pups by feeding them incredibly rich milk, which has about 10 times the fat content of human milk. The pup can more than double its weight in just 3 weeks, after which time the mother deserts it and returns to the sea.

relatively shallow, less than 100 metres. On occasions, however, they go much deeper. Sea lions can reach depths of about 500 metres. The larger elephant seal has been recorded at staggering depths of 1200 metres, a record only exceeded among mammals by the sperm whale. To achieve these dives, seals have a number of adaptations. To carry a good supply of oxygen they have almost twice as much blood as humans, per unit of body volume. Much of this blood contains the molecule myoglobin, which stores oxygen against demand during dives better than haemoglobin. On deep dives seals conserve oxygen by restricting or stopping blood flow to all but the most critical organs. Their pulse drops at the same time, to about a tenth of normal.

Penguins

Penguins are a distinctly Southern Hemisphere group of birds. They evolved in the cool southern oceans at least 60 million years ago and are not found in the Northern Hemisphere. There are about 18 penguin species worldwide. Fourteen breed in the New Zealand region, including its subantarctic islands. Four types of penguin breed on the New Zealand mainland: the Fiordland crested penguin, the yellow-eyed penguin, the blue penguin and it subspecies, the white-flippered penguin.

Although flightless in the aerial sense, penguins have retained their wings and powerful flight muscles, which they use, quite literally, to fly underwater. Their streamlined body helps them to move through water with minimal resistance, while their feet and tail are used to steer. Because they are generally smaller than seals, penguins cannot dive as far, but they are nonetheless accomplished swimmers. Yellow-eyed penguins can dive up to 100 metres, a remarkable feat for so small a creature.

Less is known about the underwater adaptations of penguins than of seals. It is thought, however, that the two share certain characteristics. These include having a relatively large volume of blood and having the ability to restrict their circulation to all but essential organs, while allowing the pulse to drop. Fat below the skin helps them keep out the cold, though their feathers are probably more important for insulation.

Yellow-eyed penguin (*Megadyptes antipodes*) (bottom left) The yellow-eyed penguin breeds at sites along the South Island coast from Banks Peninsula to Southland and Stewart Island. Other populations occur on the Auckland and Campbell Islands, neither of which interbreed with the mainland population. Its preferred food is small fishes. Yellow-eyed penguins are unusual because they build their nests somewhat isolated from one another, rather than together in the usual communal penguin gathering. Unfortunately, introduced predators and the destruction of nesting habitats have whittled its numbers to the point that it is now probably the rarest penguin in the world.

Fiordland crested penguin (*Eudyptes pachyrhynchus*) (top right) The Fiordland crested penguin is found in coastal regions from South Westland to Stewart Island and feeds on krill, squid and small fish. Like all penguins, males and females form a strong pair bond during breeding. Birds come ashore at specific breeding colonies during the winter. The tasks of incubating the eggs and feeding the young are shared by both partners.

Blue penguin (*Eudyptula minor*) (bottom right) The little blue penguin is represented by a number of subspecies, restricted to Australia and New Zealand. It feeds close to shore on small fish and fish larvae. It is the most commonly encountered penguin in New Zealand and makes its presence particularly well known during the breeding season, when it holds noisy nocturnal gatherings in coastal scrub and sometimes under houses.

Sandy shores

Sandy shores lack the enormous variety of life usually found on rocky shores because there is no firm ground for organisms that need to anchor themselves to the bottom, such as sponges, sea anemones, corals or seaweeds. There are compensations though. Organisms can bury themselves in the soft sand or silt where they are not obliged to resist the constant battering by waves or drying-out at low tides, which they would on a rocky shore.

Beaches, therefore, harbour more life than is at first apparent. Concealed beneath the 'barren' expanse of sand are worms, molluscs and other burrowing animals. How many there are depends on the nature of the beach. Sheltered beaches, where the slope is gentle and drainage therefore slow, are ideal for burrowing animals. This is particularly so at lower levels of the beach, which remain more or less saturated when uncovered by the tide. The shelter also offers a better opportunity for organic food particles, upon which many burrowers depend, to settle out of the overlying water. By contrast, sandy shores that are exposed and steeply sloping are far less habitable. They drain more thoroughly at low tide and receive less organic debris, so fewer buried animals can survive. The coarser sands of exposed beaches also exacerbate living conditions by draining quickly and becoming compact and stiff. Under pressure they lose water and get even stiffer, resembling concrete to a creature trying to dig a home. Finer sand, silt and mud remain much moister and are easier to tunnel into.

Microhabitats on the sandy shore

The sandy shore presents a gradation of drainage conditions at different tidal levels, but there are very few distinctive microhabitats. This is another reason why sandy shores do not support the variety of life found on rocky shores. But there are exceptions. An isolated boulder on a sandy beach may be a microhabitat for a number of species. Small algae

THE BEACHCOMBERS

Each fall of the tides leaves a mixed offering of food scraps on the beach. There are bits of seaweed, bodies of dead fish, drowned insects and stranded jellyfish. This twice-a-day delivery is an important food source for a number of animals. By day the red-billed gull (*Larus novaehollandiae*) often inspects the strand-line, methodically gulping down those items deemed edible.

By night an entirely different scavenger takes over. About an hour after sunset the sand beach isopod (*Scyphax ornatus*) pops out of its burrow near the high-tide level. Barely longer than your fingernail, this small animal makes a lengthy excursion down the beach to search for stranded carrion. Drowned honeybees are a favourite item, and if it comes across one it will spend 10 minutes or so devouring the find. An hour before sunrise, the isopod retreats back up the beach and burrows into the sand again.

Red-billed gull (*Larus novaehollandiae*)

The sand beach isopod's routine is perfectly timed. By coming out after dark, it not only escapes being seen by predators such as the seagull, it also avoids the heat and dryness of the sun. For a creature so small, crossing the same stretch of beach by day would be like traversing the roasting Sahara Desert. It relies on a biological clock (page 133) to tell it when night has fallen for, living within a dark burrow, it would otherwise have no way of knowing without venturing repeatedly to the surface for a look.

The timing mechanism seems to be even more complex than this, for there are nights when the isopod does not come out at all. On some beaches they prefer to feed when the tide is advancing, as then the waves sweep all the debris into a narrow band where it can be located with a minimum of effort. Because the timing of successive tides varies, there are several days in a row each fortnight when this feeding opportunity does not present itself. The isopod's internal clock seems able to predict this and tell it when to remain in its burrow, so saving the wasted energy of fruitless searches. After a few days and nights of rest, when the tides are favourable again, it emerges to feed — appearing as punctual as ever soon after dark.

Sand beach isopod (*Scyphax ornatus*)

attach themselves to it and a community of shrimps and other crustaceans may live in the sand beneath. If the boulder is high on the beach its top will be encrusted with lichens. If it is near the low-tide level it may be smothered with tubeworms, bryozoans, sea urchins and chitons. It is a rocky shore in miniature, though constant abrasion by sand may prevent some organisms establishing themselves.

Another microhabitat, perhaps temporary, is created when a storm throws up piles of seaweed, torn from nearby rocky shores. Turning a piece over will uncover scores of scavenging creatures feeding in the moist shelter of the decaying weed. Leaping for safety are sand hoppers, which belong to the amphipod group of crustaceans. These are segmented creatures, flattened from side to side. Also feeding on the seaweed will be members of another crustacean group, the isopods. Isopods, sometimes known as sea lice or sand lice, have their bodies flattened from top to bottom. Large numbers of the black top shell (*Diloma nigerrima*) may also be found, feeding on the decaying seaweed.

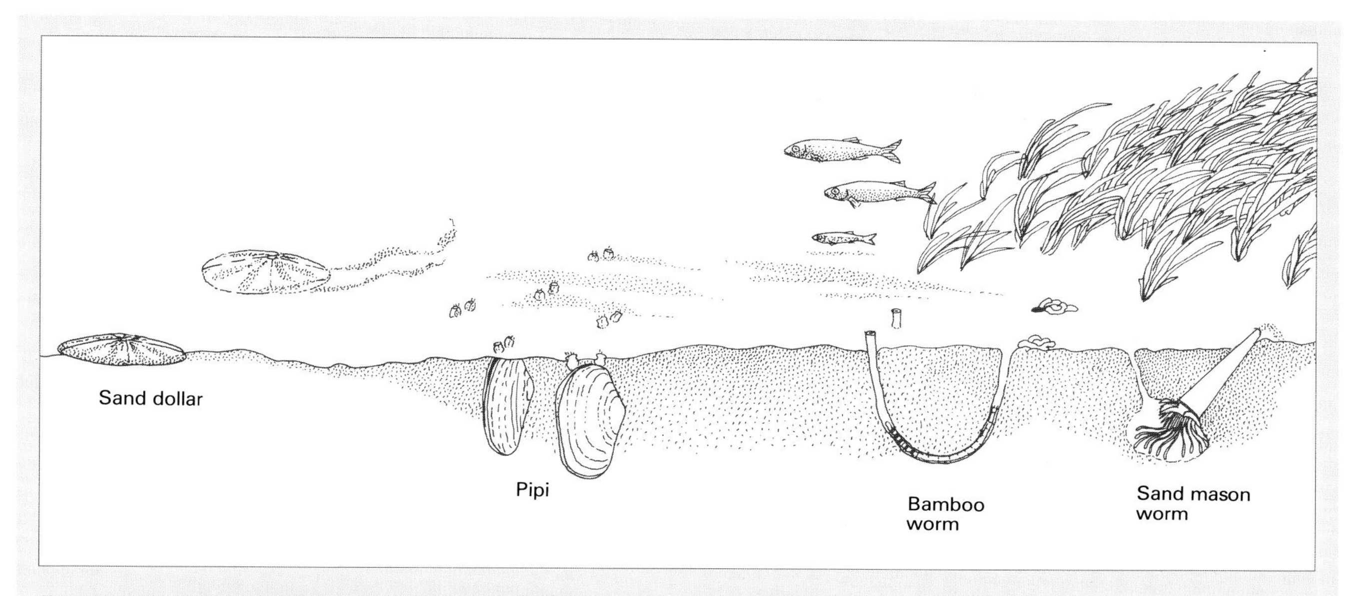

SURFACE DWELLERS, BURROWERS AND TUBE DWELLERS

There are a number of ways that animals live on sandy shores and in estuaries. Some, such as the sand dollar (*Arachnoides novaezelandiae*), remain almost on the surface. This creature, about the size of a biscuit, is related to the sea urchins, although it is less spiny and is flattened to a disc so it does not get wafted around by the current. Since there is no firm seabed to grasp, the sand dollar's tube feet have no suckers. Instead they are modified for sorting out pieces of food from the sand.

Many of the burrowers are bivalve (two-shelled) molluscs. Three of the best known are species of *Paphies*: the pipi, tuatua and toheroa. All these buried shellfish have two siphon tubes that reach to the surface. Water containing suspended food matter and dissolved oxygen is drawn in through one siphon, the oxygen is extracted and the food filtered out, and the water is forced out of the other siphon. Each of the three shellfish live in slightly different habitats. The pipi (*P. australis*) lives on or just under the surface of silty or gritty sand in sheltered estuaries and harbours. The tuatua (*P. subtriangulata* and *P. donacina*) lives on more exposed surfy shores, digging itself in just below the surface near the low-tide mark. The toheroa (*P. ventricosum*) lives higher up on exposed beaches, where it needs to dig deeper to find adequate shelter.

Fate is not always kind to these buried shellfish. Those living on open beaches face the chance of being swept from their sandy refuge by churning waves. The toheroa, living on particularly stormy beaches, is an athletic burrower, perhaps for these reasons. It can rapidly bury itself to a depth of 20-30 centimetres in wet sand. Beds of pipis in sheltered estuaries, on the other hand, are prone to having their delicate filter-feeding systems clogged and overloaded by silts. The erosion caused by inland forest clearance can literally suffocate them with sediments. Even when buried in the sand, bivalves are not safe from attack by predators. Wandering over the surface at high tide may be the arabic volute (*Alcithoe arabica*). This is a large, carnivorous snail-like creature, with a shell about 15 centimetres long. It seeks the protruding siphons of buried bivalves, and when it finds one, it clasps the siphon ends in its foot. With its supply of oxygenated water cut off, the bivalve is suffocated. Then the volute feeds on its victim.

Many burrowing worms keep in contact with the surface by building a tube in which to live. The bamboo worm (*Axiothella serrata*) builds a U-shaped tube made of sand, which is glued together with mucus to avoid it collapsing into a slurry. The worm lives on small pieces of organic debris it finds in the sand. The sand mason worm (*Pectinaria australis*) leads a more mobile existence. It glues together a fragile tube of sand which it carries around, spending life burrowing through the sediment like a miniature dredge, sifting for food with tiny tentacles.

Sand dunes

Sand dunes Constantly shifting sand is one of the most difficult habitats for plant and animal life.

When a beach is exposed to strong winds coming predominantly from one direction, sand from its surface may be winnowed up and deposited on the adjacent land as a dune. It needs only a slight irregularity, such as that caused by a stone or a clump of grass, to begin the formation of a dune. The irregularity causes the wind speed to be reduced slightly, and the blown sand is deposited. The deposited sand increases the size of the irregularity and so the dune gets bigger. It is a self-perpetuating process and the dune may reach an enormous size. Not only does it grow but it moves downwind. The wind lifts sand grains from the windward side and deposits them on the leeward side. Unless it is colonised by vegetation, the dune will gradually move inland, engulfing farmland and anything else in its way.

Sand dunes are so dry and unstable that few plants are able to colonise them. Traditionally, two of the more important colonisers were the native sedge, pingao (*Desmoschoenus spiralis*), and the sand grass (*Spinifex hirsutus*). However, since its introduction from Europe, marram grass (*Ammophila arenaria*) has by and large taken over the role. Marram's vigorous growth habit enables it to keep ahead of the dune's increasing girth. As sand piles up and threatens to bury it, marram produces roots further up its stem. The roots branch in the surface layers of the dune, often moistened by dew at night. They spread rapidly, sending up tufts of leaves as they go. In this way, marram keeps pace with the growing sand cover.

As the dune gets bigger, so marram and other colonisers continually grow towards the surface, leaving a network of roots and stems buried below. This binds

Coastal geckos
The Pacific gecko (*Hoplodactylus pacificus*) (right) is found in a number of habitats, including sandy beaches and dunes. This, and another coastal gecko, *H. maculatus*, are ground dwellers rather than climbers. This puts them at risk from predators such as cats. The fact that many individuals have regenerating tails is evidence of the usefulness of their tail-shedding ability. Both geckos are nocturnal, coming out of their daytime hideout beneath logs or within crevices to feed on insects and berries. The Pacific gecko also visits flowering specimens of pohutukawa, ngaio and flax to lap up nectar, probably pollinating them at the same time.

ANIMAL LIFE ON DUNES

Animal life is scarce on dunes. Some insects and spiders are relatively common, but for most creatures conditions are just too dry and exposed. Even where there are plants, there is precious little leaf litter to offer protection from the extremes of temperature, salty spray, or the blast of wind-borne sand. Consequently animals that live here tend to be burrowers, avoiding the harsh conditions at the surface by sheltering underneath. Some also have complex social and parental behaviour, designed to nurture their young in this unfavourable environment. This is the case for the hunting wasp (*Priocnemis nitidiventris*). The basal segments of its forelegs are lined with small spines to rake out the sand when digging a burrow. Afterwards the wasp goes in search of spiders. It moves in short flights, constantly alighting and running across the sand to seek suitable quarry. Once it has flushed out a spider it gives chase, eventually pouncing on the terrified animal and paralysing it with a sting. With a herculean effort, the wasp then drags the immobile prey back across the undulating sand to its burrow. There it is buried and an egg laid alongside. The wasp larva hatches in the cool shelter of the burrow and then feeds on the spider.

the sand together, eventually stabilising the dune. Once this happens other plants can take hold. These still need to tolerate drought, even if they no longer need to deal with shifting sand. Examples are the native shrub tauhinu (*Cassinia leptophylla*) and the introduced tree lupin (*Lupinus arboreus*). Tauhinu is a salt-tolerant shrub whose dense branches and tiny leaves shield the dune from the wind. Tree lupin is deeply rooted for water uptake and holds colonies of nitrogen-fixing bacteria in root nodules which compensate for deficiencies of nitrogen in the sand.

As the pioneer plants die, their remains add humus to the sand. This builds up the nutrient reserves of the dune, improves its moisture-holding capacity and helps bind the sand particles together. The sandy soil that develops provides a hospitable seed bed for other plants. Slowly but surely an increasingly mixed community appears. If nature is allowed to take its course, what was once bare sand will yield to scrub and eventually forest.

DEALING WITH A DRY ENVIRONMENT

The coastal environment is an arid one for plants. Exposure to sun and wind continually draws moisture from their leaves, while sandy shores drain so rapidly after rain that there is little opportunity to replenish the loss. In addition, things are made more difficult by the pervading presence of salt, continually deposited by spray from the sea. Salt causes an effect known as osmosis; water tends to be drawn out of the plant into the salty water in the soil.

Plants of the coast counter these problems in various ways. One is to have a thick waterproof waxy coat, or cuticle, on their leaves to reduce evaporation. This is what gives coastal plants like shore bindweed, ngaio and mirror leaf coprosma a characteristic sheeny surface.

An unusually high number of shoreline plants have fleshy or succulent leaves. The ice plants (*Carpobrotus* and *Disphyma*) are outstanding examples. Their leaves are triangular in cross section and crammed with bloated water-storage cells. Water is absorbed rapidly and stored there after rain, for use later on. Being succulent may have other advantages too. It helps some coastal plants dilute the harmful levels of salt absorbed from the soil. In some cases succulence also provides a form of temperature control. Plants of dry, open places often suffer from overheating. This is because they are exposed to the full heat of the sun, yet cannot afford to keep cool by evaporating water from their leaves. Succulent plants can partly avoid this by using their stored water as a heat sink. Water warms slowly, so by holding lots of it in their tissues, succulents take longer than normal plants to reach a critically hot temperature. Conversely they also take longer to cool down. It is a simple method to moderate the temperature extremes to which they are subjected.

The long, wiry blades of marram grass have their own ways of avoiding drought. Marram, like most land plants, has tiny open pores on its leaves called stomata, to exchange gases with the atmosphere for photosynthesis. These pores also lose moisture, so marram protects them from the drying effects of the outside air by sheltering them in grooves on the bottom of their leaves. When dry, the leaves curl downwards into tight cylinders with the stomata on the inside, further protecting them. It is exactly the same system that snowgrasses use to deal with dry environments in the mountains (page 25).

Ice plant (*Carpobrotus edulis*)

Marram grass (*Ammophila arenaria*) and purple groundsel (*Senecio elegans*)

Mud snail (*Amphibola crenata*) As the mud snail wanders across the exposed tidal flats, it gulps down great quantities of organically rich sludge. As much as twice its own weight is consumed each hour. It digests small particles of food from this, such as algae and bacteria, excreting the remainder as a continuous faecal trail.

Catching fish The white heron (*Egretta alba*) breeds only in a coastal swamp near Okarito, but disperses to wetlands all over New Zealand. It is often seen in coastal estuaries, where its long legs enable it to feed in fairly deep water. It wades gently, barely raising a ripple. Then, like an uncoiling spring, it will pierce the water and pluck out a fish.

Mudflats

By the time a river reaches the lower part of its course, it has become laden with particles of mud and silt, eroded from inland areas. At its estuary, where the river meets the sea, the flow of water is reduced, halted and reversed twice a day by the tides. When the water speed is reduced, the suspended particles are deposited. Gradually a layer of silt or mud is laid down on the riverbed. In some parts of the estuary, usually near the centre, there are channels that carry the flow of water at reasonable speed. There is little deposition here. In other parts, usually near the river edges, the water stands idle for much longer periods and here deposits build up quickly. Eventually, they become so thick that the receding tide exposes them, leaving broad flats of mud or silt.

Life is not easy on these tidal flats. When the sea is out they may be exposed to the baking heat of the sun by day or to chilling cold at night. Often the underlying mud is so permanently waterlogged that it is stiflingly deficient in oxygen. As the tides ebb and flow, the salinity of the water changes, sometimes tenfold. Another hazard is that suspended particles of mud or silt can clog the feeding and breathing mechanisms of many kinds of water creatures. The effect can be devastating when heavy rains or forest clearances increase the rate of soil erosion inland.

These demands allow only a few well-adapted species to live on tidal flats. On the other hand, each of these species is usually present in enormous numbers. This wealth of life is rarely evident if you walk onto a mudflat at low tide. More apparent are great expanses of black, sticky and sometimes smelly mud. But then you are not likely to notice the thin coating of billions of microscopic algae on the mud's surface. Nor will you be aware of the myriad worms, shellfish and crabs living buried underneath. Neither will you see the fish, such as mullet and flounder, that glide over the flats to feed when the tide is in. All these things do exist, in abundance.

The reason for such immense populations is that an estuary is an open ecosystem. It receives a large proportion of its basic food and mineral requirements from other ecosystems. By contrast, a closed ecosystem, such as a forest, is self contained; its basic requirements come only from the forest soil and from the trees and the smaller plants of the forest itself. The river brings to the estuary, from inland areas, a continuous supply of mineral nutrients, suspended organic matter and plankton. As the tide comes in, there is also an influx of nutrients from the sea, though usually to a lesser extent. The minerals nourish both the simple algae living on the surface of the mud and the plants of the salt marshes and other parts of the flats. These plants, together with plant plankton, provide food for small animals such as crabs, bristle-worms, shrimps and cockles. These in turn, together with animal plankton, provide food for the carnivores such as fish and flocks of wading birds that frequent the flats. It is an enormously productive ecosystem. Measurements have shown that estuaries are at least four times more productive than equivalent areas of agricultural grassland.

Among the few large plants to establish themselves on the mud are eel-grasses (*Zostera*), also known as sea-grass. The eel-grass family has achieved a special ranking among the flowering plants to which it belongs. Flowering plants are usually considered to be land inhabitants, but eel-grasses are the only ones that have managed to adapt to a truly marine lifestyle and return to the sea. They can complete all stages of their life beneath the surface, even flowering. When an eel-grass plant flowers, it releases very long and slender pollen grains. These have the same buoyancy as the surrounding water so that they stay in suspension. As they drift back and forth with the tide, they tangle like small threads with any female stigmas they encounter.

Meadows of eel-grass establish on the seaward borders of the flats. Their roots help stabilise the mud and, because the presence of the grass helps reduce the speed of water flow, more mud or silt settles between them. Gradually a raised bed develops which becomes home to a prospering community of animals, including crabs, shrimps and cockles. There are also a few animals that specialise in feeding on the eel-grass. One is a small limpet, *Notoacmea helmsi*, which has a narrow shell that grows no wider than the eel-grass leaves it feeds on. As time goes by, the sheltered environment created by eel-grass will be colonised by other plants. The flats will develop into a salt marsh or a mangrove swamp as discussed later.

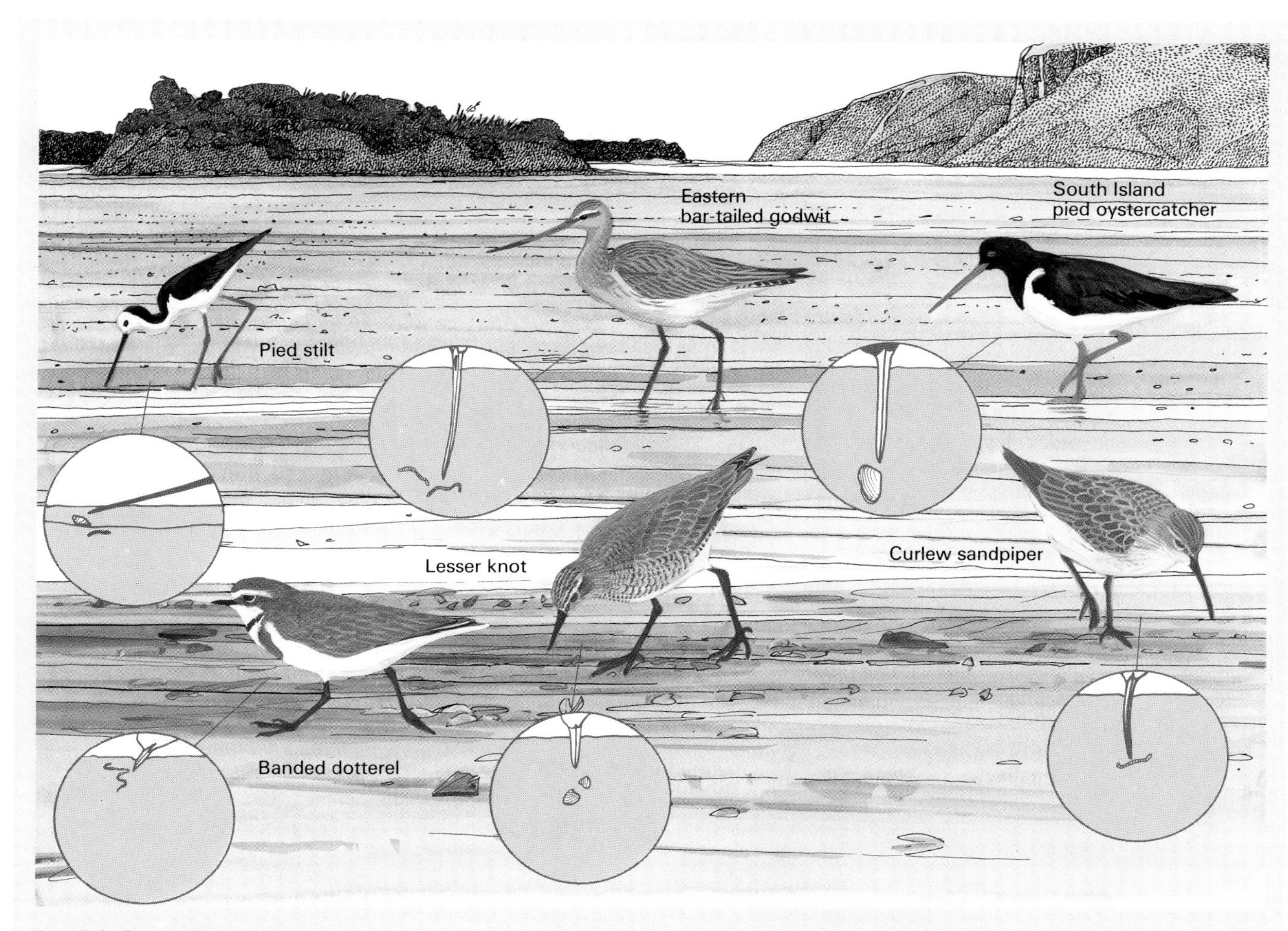

BIRDS OF THE FLATS

The teeming life of tidal mudflats provides an enormously rich feeding ground for wading birds. Large flocks congregate when the tide is out, methodically picking and probing their way over the bare expanses of mud. Each species avoids competing with others by having its own particular feeding habits. These are determined by the characteristic leg and beak length of each species, which allow it to wade and probe for food at a different depth from other birds.

Pied stilt (*Himantopus himantopus*) This bird has three features typical of wading birds. Long legs allow it to wade into shallow water to feed without getting its body wet, while a long beak enables it to probe beneath the mud or water for food. Widely spreading toes are the third feature, helping it to walk on soft muddy surfaces. As it wades it often feeds with a sweeping motion of its bill through the water. In spring and summer, birds breed in wetland areas such as salt marshes, riverbeds and damp paddocks.

Eastern bar-tailed godwit (*Limosa lapponica*) This is a migrant wader from Alaska and north-east Siberia often seen in flocks of hundreds or even thousands. It spends October to March in New Zealand, before heading back to breed in the Northern Hemisphere. Its upwardly curving bill is about 80 millimetres long, which allows it to probe deeply for burrowing tubeworms and molluscs. It also picks small animals and plant material from the mud's surface.

South Island pied oystercatcher (*Haematopus ostralegus*) The strong orange bill of the pied oystercatcher is used to probe deeply in the mud for a diet of bivalve molluscs. In spite of its name, it does not feed on oysters, which live well out of reach below the spring-tide level. Cockles, however, are devoured in huge numbers, perhaps as many as 200 a day. It splits them open with a powerful thrust of its beak. During spring, birds breed inland on riverbeds and open farmland.

Banded dotterel (*Charadrius bicinctus*) This tiny wader often occurs in large flocks on tidal flats, picking for food on the surface. When nesting it scrapes a hollow in the sand or shingle on beaches or inland river flats. As soon as they are hatched, the chicks can run — an advantage in such an exposed habitat.

Lesser knot (*Calidris canutus*) This wader breeds in eastern Siberia and migrates to New Zealand for the summer. It is often seen on the flats with flocks of godwits. Both birds feed amicably together as the knot's shorter bill (35 millimetres) restricts it to items near the surface of the mud.

Curlew sandpiper (*Calidris ferruginea*) Each year the curlew sandpiper migrates from its breeding grounds in northern Siberia. Its long downwardly curving bill, similar to that of the curlew, is used to dig for molluscs and aquatic worms from tidal flats and shallow brackish pools.

Salt marshes

When meadows of eel-grass establish in the tidal waters of the mudflats, they start a chain of events which leads to the creation of a salt marsh. Their roots help bind the underlying muds and silts together, while the sheltered water around their leaves and stems encourages more sediment to settle. At the same time the steady turnover of plant matter adds its rotting remains as humus to the soil. In this way, eel-grass becomes the architect of its own demise. For by helping to raise the flats a little more from the influence of the sea and adding to their fertility, it cultivates conditions suitable for other more terrestrial plants to take over. There follows a succession of different plants, each one raising the surface a little more and then yielding to the next, just as the eel-grass did.

Often the first plant to take over from eel-grass is glasswort (*Sarcocornia quinqueflora*), which covers the young salt marsh with creeping mats of succulent jointed stems. Another pioneer may be sea rush (*Juncus maritimus*), often with jointed rush (*Juncus articulatus*) growing further inland. In estuaries in the northern North Island, the mangrove may become established, as discussed later.

As the tides ebb and flow between the stems of these salt marsh pioneers, more silt accumulates and conditions increasingly favour terrestrial life. The steadily rising salt marsh acquires a changing community of animals. Burrowing marine worms are replaced by burrowing terrestrial creatures such as earthworms. Spiders, beetles and many other insects become more common.

After several decades, the stage is reached when the salt marsh is rarely covered by the tides. Then it is known as a salt meadow. The beds of glasswort will have been completely replaced by later colonists. Flowering carpets of *Selliera radicans* and bachelor's buttons (*Cotula coronopifolia*) scramble between clumps of sedges and rushes. Here and there, the seedlings of shrubs such as saltmarsh ribbonwood (*Plagianthus divaricatus*) start to appear, taking advantage of the declining salinity and improving drainage.

By this stage the soil level has risen so that it is well above the influence of the tides. Where freshwater streams enter the area, there are stands of raupo and flax. Seedling trees appear next and the earlier plants become overgrown by manuka, cabbage trees and other woody plants. Slowly, coastal scrub begins to take over.

This succession of vegetation makes an interesting study when the tide is out. Its regularity may be distorted in places by the passage of a creek, the existence of a strong current, or an outcrop of rock. But with patient exploration the overall sequence will clearly reveal itself. It is important to realise that the sequence is dynamic. As time passes, each zone of vegetation develops into the next stage of the succession. The flats become covered with salt marsh, the salt marsh becomes covered by salt meadow and the salt meadow becomes covered with coastal scrub. Meanwhile, on the seaward margins of the flat, submerged eel-grass meadows continue to expand outwards as more muds and silts are deposited beneath the waves.

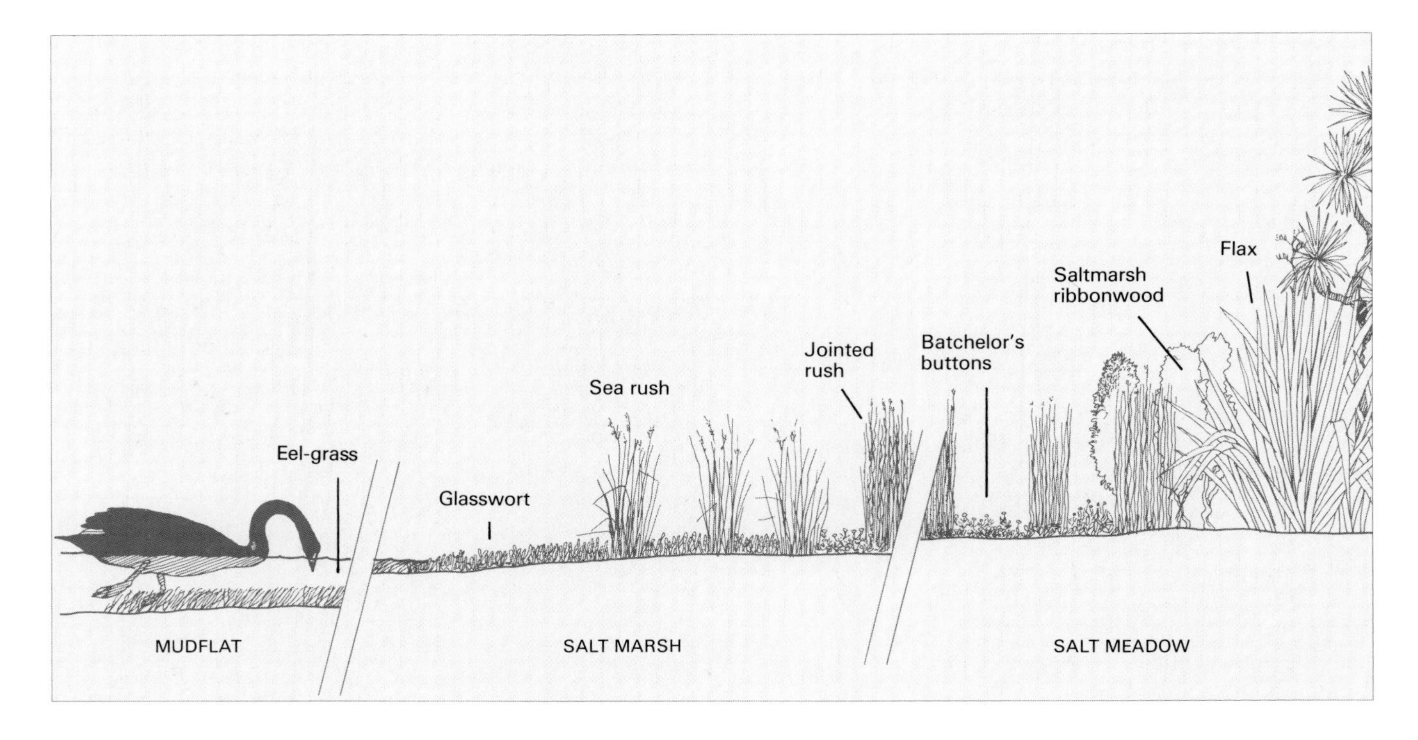

Profile through the vegetation bordering an estuary, showing changes from tidal mudflats to salt meadow.

The paradox of drought Glasswort (*Sarcocornia quinqueflora*) (left) faces a paradox. Even though it may be awash by the tides twice each day, it is not much better off than if it were living in a desert. This is because the water it is immersed in contains salt. It is difficult for plants to take up water from a salty solution. In fact, if the concentration of salt in the surrounding solution is strong enough, water will be drawn back out of the plant. Glasswort therefore suffers from shortage of water. To cope, its leaves have become reduced to tiny scales to slow evaporation and its stems are thick and succulent, like those of a cactus.

Like many plants of salty places, glasswort is also a halophyte. That is, it can grow in soils so salty that they would kill normal plants. Glasswort manages to do so by tolerating high salt levels in its tissues. Accumulating salts is one way that halophytes can alleviate their water problems. It improves the osmotic balance in their favour, so they can absorb water more readily from the saline solution they are rooted in. Glasswort is so good at this that it was once harvested as a source of soda for glass making.

The remarkable mangrove

In some parts of the world, mangroves have become key players of an entire coastal ecosystem, by being able to do what no other trees can — grow in salt water. In tropical regions, mangroves cover vast areas of tidal mudflats and estuaries, providing an enormous living breakwater against the force of the sea.

There are many mangrove species worldwide, belonging to several plant families. One of these, *Avicennia marina*, lives on sheltered shores of the northern North Island. The entire life cycle of the native mangrove is a story of adaptative ingenuity to its unusual habitat, starting with the seeds which germinate while still on the parent plant. These fall off and float away, ready to take root the instant they run aground. Once the seedling has lodged somewhere suitable it grows rapidly, sending out roots to anchor it in the mud. These roots spread out in the surface layers of the surrounding ooze, and at intervals send vertical breathing roots, called pneumatophores, to the air above.

Pneumatophores are a feature of mangrove forests. Low tide exposes them, projecting from the mud like a palisade of spiky stalks. Without them, the roots would not survive, buried in the airless and evil-smelling mire below. Each pneumatophore is filled with air-conducting channels connected by small pores to the atmosphere. When the tide is out, air passes down through these pores and into the roots. When the tide returns, a protective waterproof corky layer around the pneumatophore stops seawater from entering the breathing system.

Mangroves have also evolved to deal with the problems of salt. Most land plants cannot absorb water from the sea, because it usually also means absorbing salt, which quickly accumulates in the foliage in lethal amounts. Mangroves overcome this in a number of ways. They have special cells to pump excess salt onto the upper surface of their leaves, where it can be washed away by the rain. Mangroves are also very conservative in their use of water. They achieve this by having a thick, glossy leaf cuticle to retard evaporation. Underneath each leaf is also a dense layer, or tomentum, of white or buff hairs. This gives protection from the intense glare reflected off the sea, as well as cutting down loss of water vapour in much the same way as the tomentum on the alpine Celmisia leaf discussed on page 25. The mangrove tomentum also fulfils another essential service. It is both porous to air and water repellent, so that the leaf's stomatal pores can absorb the atmospheric carbon dioxide required for photosynthesis, but avoid becoming clogged by salt if splashed or submerged by the sea.

Once established, the mangrove presides over an intensely productive ecosystem. Worms, crabs and snails feed on the organic detritus shed by the trees and brought by the tides. Oysters, barnacles and mussels crowd onto sea-washed branches and roots as they would a rocky shore, filtering food from the planktonic pastures of the surrounding waters. At high tide, fish roam among the latticework of roots, feeding and being fed upon in the food webs of the mangrove swamp. Each turn of the tides also deposits silts in the sheltered waters. A mangrove forest acts as an enormous sediment trap. In time it will build up land where once there was sea. Glassworts, rushes and sedges colonise the emerging ground. Eventually a salt meadow is created, with some of the larger mangroves still growing in it, even though the area is no longer flooded by the tides.

Mangroves The native mangrove, manawa (*Avicennia marina*), is common in tidal estuaries of the northern North Island. Although uninviting to humans because of their tangled stems and sticky mud, mangrove swamps are productive and important natural communities.

KIM WESTERSKOV

CHAPTER 8

THE SEA

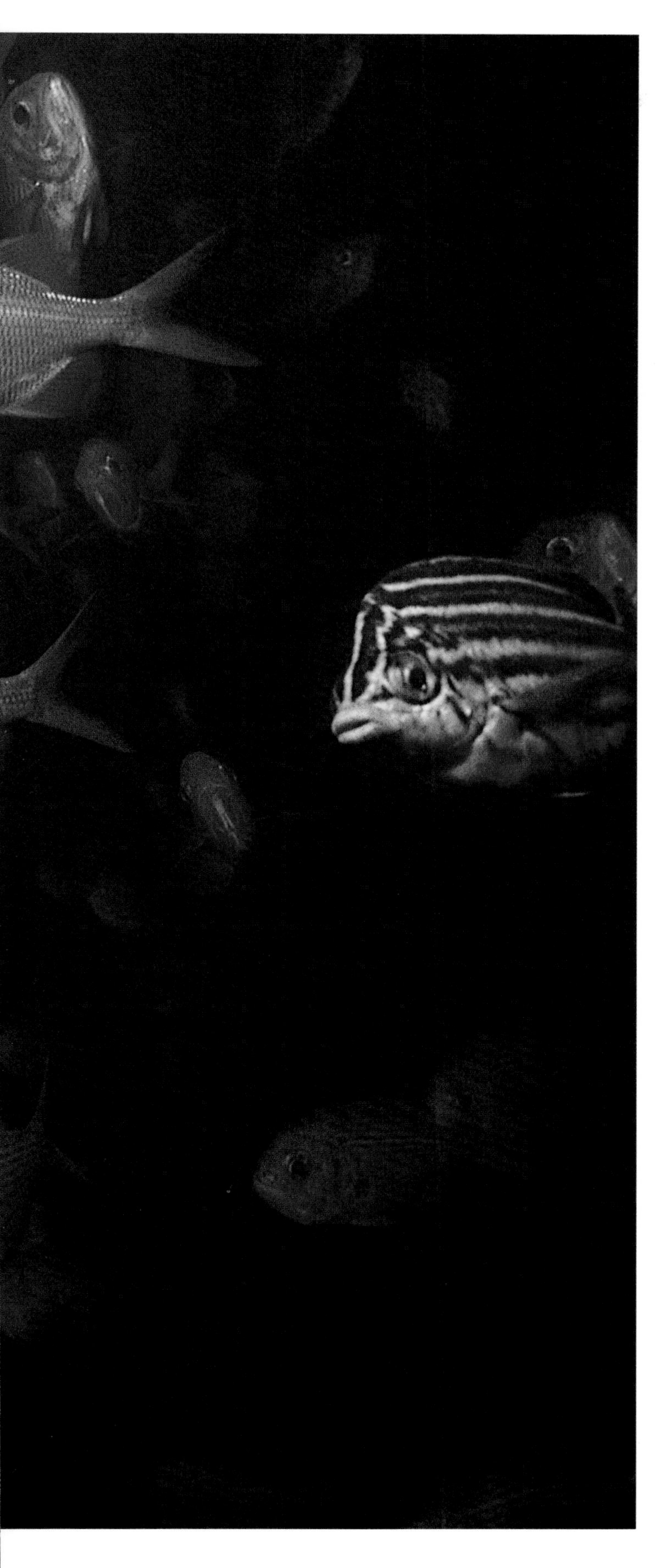

Golden snapper

Beyond the beaches and bays, the headlands and harbours, the broad blue sweep of the sea inherits the horizons. As land-dwelling animals, we often overlook the fact that the Earth is really seven-tenth's sea. Yet even this is an underestimate of its enormous importance as a haven for life. The sea is inhabited to depths of several thousands of metres, whereas on land only the 20–30 metres from the soil to the treetops can truly be considered as living space. Only when this is considered are the true dimensions of the sea apparent. It holds over 99 per cent of all the inhabited space on the planet.

This vast watery realm contains a living world so diverse and complex that we are only beginning to understand its workings. It is an understanding we should foster. The sea does not just provide food, the ways of its life also have much to teach us. There is, too, a dawning realisation that the patterns and processes of the sea are inextricably linked to the forces of climate and atmosphere that affect all living things. The sea may well determine our destiny. Yet it remains the last great wilderness, relatively untouched by humankind.

The seas around New Zealand

Remote from other landmasses and embraced by the world's largest ocean, New Zealand is among the most maritime of countries. The main islands extend across temperate latitudes where prevailing westerly winds blow virtually unhindered and drive a surface current, the West Wind Drift, that encircles the Southern Hemisphere. As New Zealand lies directly in the path of this flow, the general movement of surface currents is clockwise around the northern half of the country and anticlockwise to the south.

Waters of the surface currents immediately surrounding New Zealand are subtropical in origin and comparatively warm. Offshore to the south and south-east is water of subantarctic origin, cooler and with a lower salinity. Abrupt changes in water properties characterise the front, the Subtropical Convergence, where these water masses meet. East of the South Island, the Convergence lies roughly over the Chatham Rise, between Banks Peninsula and the Chatham Islands.

The Convergence is a major feature of the southern oceans, especially for the distribution of offshore plants and animals which, being used to only small variations in temperature and salinity, tend to be restricted to water of either subantarctic or subtropical origin. Inshore water is affected by freshwater runoff from land and is more readily influenced by seasonal differences in air temperature. There thus tends to be distinct coastal water over the continental shelf: more variable in its properties and more turbid. Organisms of coastal waters have to be physiologically adapted to tolerate this more changeable marine climate. Those that penetrate estuaries and shallow inlets need to be especially versatile in this respect.

Beneath the sea, the landscape of the seabed is surprisingly varied. Immediately surrounding the New Zealand landmass there lies an underwater plain, called the continental shelf. It dips gently seawards, generally to a water depth of 130 metres, before giving way to the steeper continental slope. The width of the shelf varies

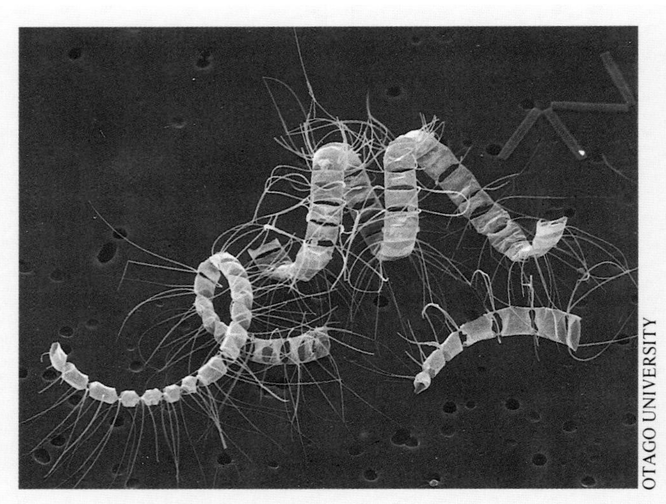
OTAGO UNIVERSITY

Diatoms, magnified 300 times

PLANKTON — DRIFTING LIFE

The surface waters of the sea teem with minute drifting life. There are countless plants, too small to see, and swarms of tiny animals that feed upon them. This, the plankton, is of fundamental importance to the ecology of the oceans. It is the food source upon which almost all marine animals ultimately depend.

Microscopic examination of the plant plankton, or phytoplankton, reveals a myriad forms. Usually predominant are diatoms (opposite above), with their often very ornate silica skeletons, and flagellate forms, some enclosed in calcareous plates, which possess a whip-like flagellum for propulsion. In terms of their abundance and contribution to productivity, some of the smallest plant plankton are the most important, many being less than one-thousandth of a millimetre in length.

Foremost among animal plankton, or zooplankton, are the copepods, micro-crustaceans usually no more than a millimetre in length, but present in vast numbers. The krill are larger shrimp-like crustaceans often 20–30 millimetres in length. They are also known as lantern shrimps, as most have light-producing organs. One highly productive species is *Nyctiphanes australis*, which forms dense breeding swarms that are seasonally important to the diet of many predators, such as squid, fish and seabirds, which converge on them. Other conspicuous members of the animal plankton are arrow worms, gelatinous sea gooseberries (ctenophores) and salps (swimming sea squirts), and amoeba-like protozoans.

Those animals mentioned spend their entire lives in the plankton. There are also, however, many fish and seabed invertebrates that produce a drifting larval or juvenile stage in their life history. The animal plankton of coastal waters in particular contains many temporary members that are the larvae of seabed invertebrates like shellfish, starfish and crabs. These larvae often bear no obvious resemblance to their adult forms until eventually they reach a stage of development where they metamorphose into juveniles and settle on the seabed. Having a planktonic stage enables a seabed animal to disperse more widely and, in doing so, to exploit a different food supply. Many seabed species breed in the spring when there is ample food for their larvae in the plankton. Often the breeding season is short and well defined giving rise to a sudden profusion of larvae.

A striking example is the massive shoals of juvenile red 'krill', or *Munida*, which appear in early summer off the South Island. *Munida* is strictly speaking not a krill but a squat lobster. The adults, which can reach a length of about 40 millimetres, live on the seabed. Juveniles, however, up to markedly. Off Fiordland, it is only 2 kilometres wide in places, whereas off Taranaki and south of Stewart Island, it extends for more than 100 kilometres.

At the edge of the shelf, the seabed drops away as the continental slope, eventually levelling out again at depths of 3000–6000 metres in vast ocean basins such as the Tasman Basin and South-western Pacific Basin. However, the downward plunge of the continental slope is interrupted in places by expansive deepwater plateaus like the Campbell Plateau, Chatham Rise and Challenger Plateau. The deepest parts of the New Zealand sea-floor are the trenches to the north-east and south-west. The Kermadec Trench plummets to a depth of 10,000 metres.

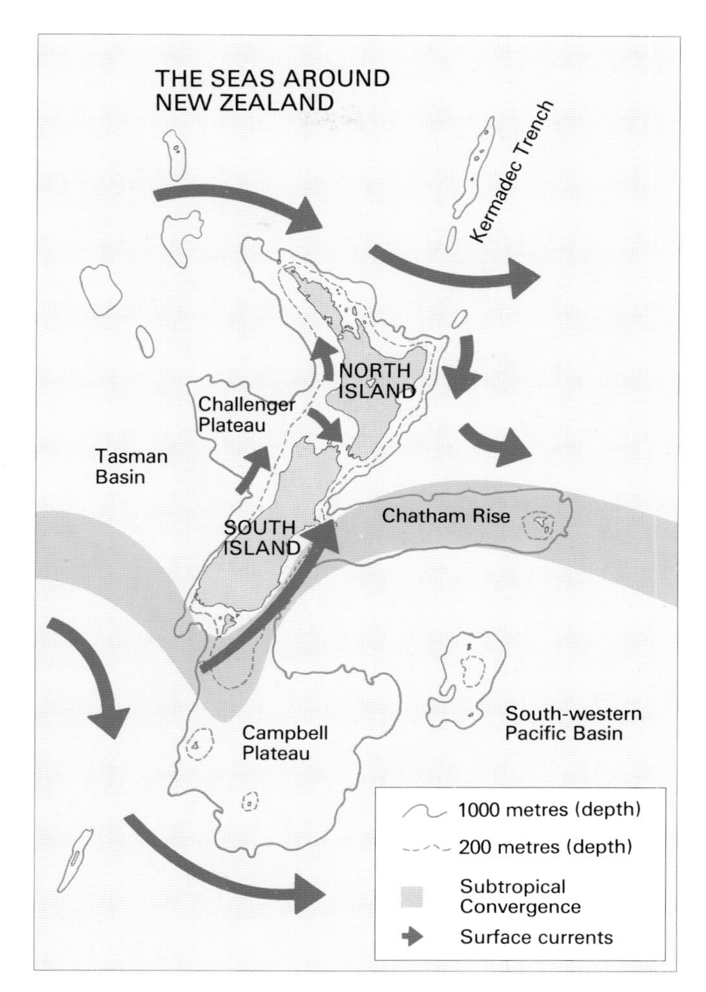

'Krill' (*Munida*)

half this size, congregate in dense shoals before taking up a seabed existence. The shoals, colouring the sea surface bright red, can be kilometres in length. They are seasonally targeted by many predators, including red cod, barracouta, kahawai, arrow squid, gulls and shags. Often a shoal can be detected miles away by the flocks of feeding birds overhead.

The abundance of plant plankton, and hence the amount of animal life it can sustain, depends on the levels of mineral nutrients in the surrounding seawater. This varies in different regions. Where it is high, there is a greater turnover of plants and animals, and ultimately a greater potential harvest for commercial fishing. Coastal waters, fed by nutrients from land and recycled from the shallow seabed, are productive and grey-green, in contrast to the clear, dark blue waters of the oceans, where nutrients are in short supply and life is sparse.

Seasonal replenishment of nutrients occurs during winter when convective mixing brings deep, nutrient-rich water to the surface. Primed with nutrients and in response to the lengthening days after winter, a population explosion is triggered among the plant plankton. Satellite pictures reveal this greening of the planet to be far more dramatic than the coming of spring on land. Gradually, however, nutrients are depleted over the summer, day length shortens again, sea surface temperatures fall, and the production cycle winds down for another year.

Renewal of nutrients can be particularly marked where surface water is displaced by wind, or where circulation is disrupted by bottom topography, thereby drawing deep cold water to the surface. Periodic upwelling of cold, nutrient-rich water is a feature of the South Island west coast, and the water is swept in a plume northwards past Cape Farewell. The resulting boost to productivity appears to be reflected in the aggregations of krill and squid in western Cook Strait.

At times, over-abundance of nutrients can initiate an upsurge of plant plankton, which colours the sea. This could be what Captain Cook saw when he noted a milkiness of the water in Cloudy Bay. A brown discoloration of the sea commonly reported in Karamea Bight is due to blooms of flagellate algae that are probably induced by the upwelling. Blooms of plant plankton can reach harmful proportions and become a potential problem for fish and shellfish farmers and coastal authorities. The soupy conditions can choke many animals whilst the decay of dead algae deoxygenates the water.

The marine food chain

Supporting the food webs of the sea (below) are microscopic plants drifting in the plankton (1). The turnover of millions of these minute plants sustains the living ocean, from bacteria to whales. In the conversion process called photosynthesis, plant plankton use carbon dioxide and nutrients dissolved in seawater to manufacture new organic materials. The reaction is driven by the sun's radiant energy, which plants are able to absorb by means of chlorophyll. This is the pigment that gives green plants their colour, though the chlorophyll may be masked by other pigments, as in the red and brown seaweeds. Photosynthesis can take place only in the upper layers of the ocean where enough sunlight can penetrate. This usually means to depths of tens of metres, depending on the clarity of the water.

Plant plankton represents a pasture upon which planktonic animals graze (2). Among these minute creatures are representatives of almost every major group in the animal kingdom, including protozoans, crustaceans and the larvae of numerous other creatures.

Much of the plant plankton, however, may escape being eaten directly by animal plankton. Nevertheless it contributes to food webs in other ways. Free-living bacteria are abundant in the plankton and are important in breaking down the plankton and its products (3). Dissolved organic materials released by plankton and other marine organisms appear, for instance, to be scavenged by bacteria. Important predators of bacteria are protozoans, which in turn are eaten by the micro-crustaceans in the plankton.

Among the predators of plankton are fish, as well as many of the larger invertebrates (4). Typical among the fish are the members of the herring family, represented in New Zealand by pilchard and sprats. These small inshore species can form densely packed shoals containing vast numbers of individuals.

Squid are important invertebrate members of the food web, both as predator and prey. Arrow squid (*Nototodarus*), for instance, are streamlined and fast moving. Up to 650 millimetres in total length, the body is cylindrical with fins at the tail end, and the animals jet themselves swiftly backwards by forcibly expelling water through the siphon. The tentacles on the head are equipped with suckers for grasping prey. Food is torn apart by beak-like jaws.

Taking the larger plankton and small fish are fast-swimming carnivores (5), such as kahawai, jack mackerel and barracouta. Outstanding for speed and endurance among the carnivorous fish are the tunas. In many species, swimming efficiency is enhanced by their being able to maintain a body temperature slightly higher than that of the surrounding water. These open-ocean fish make extensive migrations from breeding grounds in the tropics. Albacore, skipjack, and southern bluefin tuna are species well known in New Zealand waters and support valuable fisheries.

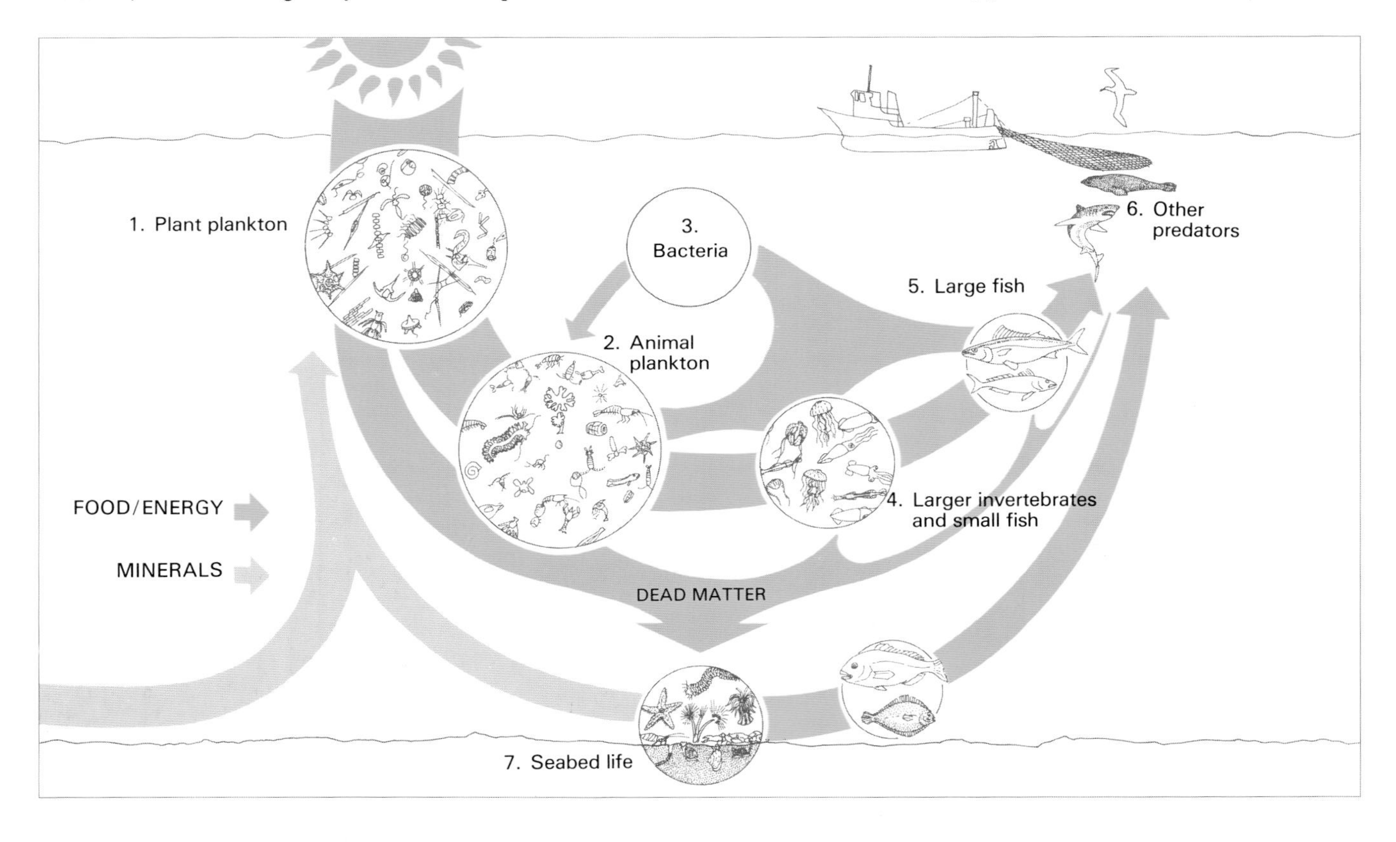

The marine food web

To many people, sharks are the archetypal carnivores of the sea. Among the species seen in our coastal waters are the bronzewhaler and schoolshark, both of which occur mainly around the North Island. Commoner in the south is the great white shark, the species implicated in most attacks on humans. More oceanic in their distribution are the mako, porbeagle, and blue sharks.

Other predators include marine mammals such as seals (6) and dolphins. Also, there are the seabirds, such as albatrosses, petrels, penguins, shags, gannets and seagulls.

Not all plant and animal material gets consumed in surface waters. Much dead and waste matter from the plankton and other organisms sinks to the bottom. Here it sustains bacteria and invertebrates of the seabed and, in turn, bottom-feeding fish (7). Bacteria living on the seabed fulfil an essential role as decomposers. By breaking down organic matter they unlock nutrients, releasing them to the overlying water where they can be re-used by plant plankton.

WHALES AND DOLPHINS

Among marine mammals, the dolphins and whales, or cetaceans as they are collectively known, are masters at fishing. The familiar bottlenose dolphin (*Tursiops truncatus*) takes a wide variety of prey, particularly inshore bottom-dwelling species. The common dolphin (*Delphinus delphis*) frequents coastal waters, but is known also to dive in deep water to take lanternfish and squid. The small Hector's dolphin (*Cephalorhynchus hectori*) is found only in New Zealand waters. Hector's dolphins live close inshore, mainly off the South Island coast, and number fewer than 3000–4000 individuals.

Dolphins are among the smallest representatives of the toothed whales. Larger members of this group include killer whales (*Orcinus orca*) and sperm whales (*Physeter macrocephalus*) both of which frequent New Zealand waters. Killer whales are fast, powerful animals that hunt fish and squid, as well as larger prey such as seals and dolphins. Sperm whales are specialised for hunting the deep sea, diving to depths of at least 1000 metres to feed mainly on large squid.

Among the biggest of the cetaceans are the baleen whales, which do not prey upon other marine vertebrates, but feed directly on members of the animal plankton. They do this by filtering plankton through bristly, bony plates of baleen that hang from their upper jaw. The humpback (*Megaptera novaeangliae*) and smaller minke (*Balaenoptera acutorostrata*) are among the baleen whales found in New Zealand waters.

Life on the continental shelf

The continental shelves surrounding the world's main landmasses support an immense richness of life. Although they account for a mere 7–8 per cent of the world's oceans in area, they support something like 80 per cent of the total weight, or biomass of seabed life. This is sustained because the production of plankton in the overlying water is high, while the shallow sea depth means there is little opportunity for falling organic material to be consumed in the water before it reaches the seabed community. As well as this, there may be important inputs of organic matter from highly productive seaweed beds and estuarine marshes.

The surface nature of the continental shelf strongly influences the types of organism that can live there. Animals such as snails, crabs, octopuses and starfish can roam freely over the seabed. However, animals such as sponges, anemones, hydroids, mussels, barnacles, bryozoans and sea squirts need to live attached to something firm and so are usually most abundant on rocky and gravelly ground. Burrowing animals, on the other hand, are more common where there are fine sediments to dig into. Included among them are many types of worm, clam and other bivalve mollusc, small crustacean, and burrowing echinoderm such as certain brittlestars, sea cucumbers and heart urchins. Even the nature of the soft sediment is crucial to its inhabitants. Oxygenated water, for instance, seeps more readily through clean sand than it does through mud.

Many of these bottom-dwellers feed on the drizzle of organic particles falling from the productive sunlit surface waters, since the seabed itself is often too dark for algae to grow. They have two main feeding methods. One, used by the filter feeders, is to sieve out specks of organic matter from the surrounding water. This method is used by many bivalve molluscs such as the oysters, scallops and mussels, as well as the fan worms, sea squirts, brachiopods and bryozoans. By the concerted beating of cilia, these animals create a flow of water through a filtering device, and trapped particles are carried to the mouth. The other method, used by deposit feeders, is to search for particles and microbes contained in the deposited sediment, a technique employed by many types of burrowing worm and crustacean, sea cucumber and heart urchin. Through their burrowing activities, many have an important role in the reworking of sediments, much like earthworms on land.

Deposit feeders favour muddy bottoms, since the

SIGHT AND SCENT

Scallops are filter-feeding molluscs found on sandy bottoms. Peering out between the two halves of this one's open shell can be seen rows of tiny eyes. These are very simple eyes which are sensitive to sudden changes of light, such as that caused by the shadow of a potential predator. The small tentacles at the edge of the shell's mantle may serve as an even earlier warning device. They are very sensitive to chemicals in the water and can probably detect an approaching starfish well before it gets close. If alarmed, the scallop then escapes with a surprisingly fast turn of speed for a mollusc. It closes its shell with a snap, emitting a jet of water to propel it quickly away. It can actually 'swim' by clapping its shell repeatedly, moving by leaps and starts through the water.

DICK SINGLETON, NZOI

BRACHIOPODS

Brachiopods, or lamp shells, such as these *Terebratella sanguinea*, have a shell of two valves enclosing the body and so resemble bivalve molluscs. But the soft parts inside brachiopods are unlike those of molluscs and the two belong to unrelated groups. Characteristic of brachiopods is a pair of 'arms', usually spirally coiled, that bear ciliated tentacles. These create the feeding current and ensure a supply of oxygenated water. Most brachiopods attach themselves to the seabed by a short, flexible stalk that emerges from a hole at the tip of the larger valve. Brachiopods were common in prehistoric seas, but are now far less common. New Zealand, however, has some 30 species, a number being conspicuous members of shallow-water seabed communities.

quieter water flow also enables light organic detritus to settle. Filter feeders prefer to live on clean, sandy and gravelly sediments, where stronger currents keep food particles in suspension and sweep away the fine muds that would otherwise clog their delicate filtering systems. Thus the structure of seabed communities on the continental shelf roughly parallels the prevailing sediment type. Communities dominated by deposit feeders tend to be well represented on muddy shelves, such as off Westland, Hawkes Bay and Wairarapa, whereas filter feeders are more abundant on the sandy and gravelly shelves off Northland, Otago and Southland.

Seabed communities also have their share of scavenging and carnivorous invertebrates. These include many species of crab and hermit crab, seasnail, octopus, starfish and brittlestar. New Zealand has two species of rock lobster living at shelf depths. The commonest, the red rock lobster (*Jasus edwardsii*), is the basis of the commercial catch. They feed at night and take a wide variety of prey including sea urchins and shellfish, as well as carrion.

Seabed invertebrates are also important in the diet of many species of fish that live on or close to the bottom, such as dogfish, carpet shark, skate, elephant fish, gurnard, tarakihi, snapper and flatfish. Coastal species of bottom-dwelling fish have traditionally dominated the major commercial catch in New Zealand, with snapper (*Pagrus auratus*) being the best known and most important. This inshore species takes a wide range of seabed invertebrates and small fish. Snapper are commoner around northern New Zealand. Here there are major spawning grounds where the fish gather in summer. Exceptionally, adult fish can attain a metre in length and be as much as 50 years old.

DICK SINGLETON, NZOI

Colourful colonisers
Bright clumps of zoanthid polyps are an underwater photographer's delight in the seas off northern New Zealand. Although related to anemones, they differ because most form colonies, whereas true anemones are always solitary. The colony spreads over surrounding ground and often other organisms such as sponges by growing outwards and sprouting new polyps. Each polyp bears a ring of tentacles equipped with stinging cells to paralyse prey, which is then drawn into the central mouth. Zoanthids can be very specific about where they live; some species occur only on shells inhabited by hermit crabs.

Seafloor scavenger
After early life spent swimming near the sea surface (page 154), juvenile *Munida* settle on the seabed to feed as scavengers on carrion, growing into the adult form seen here.

Life in the deep

Deep-sea fish (right) The deep-sea hatchet fish is only about 7 centimetres long. It is a predator and its bulbous upwards-staring eyes may be adapted to help it see the silhouette of its prey against the faint glimmer of light filtering down from above. On its underside it has rows of downwards-shining light organs. Each species has its characteristic light arrangement, suggesting that this is important in allowing the fish to recognise its own kind in the dark depths. The light is produced by colonies of bacteria which the fish cultures in special pouches in its body. Most deep-water fish control the light output by drawing flaps of tissue over each pouch, rather like closing the shutters over a window.

The deep-sea floor
At a depth of 3100 metres, the sea floor south-east of the Chatham Rise appears as barren as the surface of the moon, though even at these depths one may expect a sparse but diverse fauna, mostly of small worms, molluscs and crustaceans burrowing into the fine sediment on the seabed. The curious bouldery shapes are mineral-rich nodules. These have been formed by the precipitation of metals such as manganese, nickel and copper from the surrounding water onto objects that have fallen to the sea floor. Sharks' teeth and other bone fragments are often found at the centre of nodules. The nodules grow at an extremely slow rate. Some gain only a few millimetres diameter every million years.

Food is scarce in the deep sea. Animals living at depth must depend directly or indirectly on food produced by plant plankton in the surface layers. This material is used and reused as it sinks through the water, so that by the time it reaches the deep-sea floor, little of nutritive value may remain. Clumps of organic matter resulting from a seasonal flush of surface production can be relayed to the seabed more quickly than the usual thin rain of organic matter. In a habitat where seasonal changes are otherwise virtually non-existent, this must serve as an important signal to deep-sea inhabitants. The amount of animal life on the seabed normally declines with increasing water depth and distance from land, becoming extremely scant in the deep ocean basins around New Zealand. Because of the very limited supply of food, those animals that do live on the deep-sea floor are mostly of small size with extremely low rates of growth and reproduction.

Fine-grained sediments prevail on the deep-sea floor, and miniature worms, bivalve molluscs and crustaceans are among the more important burrowers in deep-sea sediments. There is commonly little scope for animals that need a hard surface for attachment. Mineral nodules offer opportunities in some areas. A feature of the Chatham Rise at water depths of about 400 metres, for instance, is the presence of phosphate nodules, mostly of 10–40 millimetres in size, which are often festooned with bonsai-like colonies of soft corals and bryozoans.

Photographs of the deep-sea floor show occasional large animals roving the seabed, such as sea cucumbers, sea urchins and starfish. Some deep-sea animals specialise in scavenging large carcasses, such as those of seals, whales and big fish that arrive on the seabed more or less intact. Such rich food sources are, however, few and far between, and carrion feeders need to be highly sensitive to scent and able to home in quickly while stocks last. Large, voracious amphipods, resembling giant sandhoppers, and fish such as rattails are among the more important of these scavengers.

KEN GRANGE, NZOI

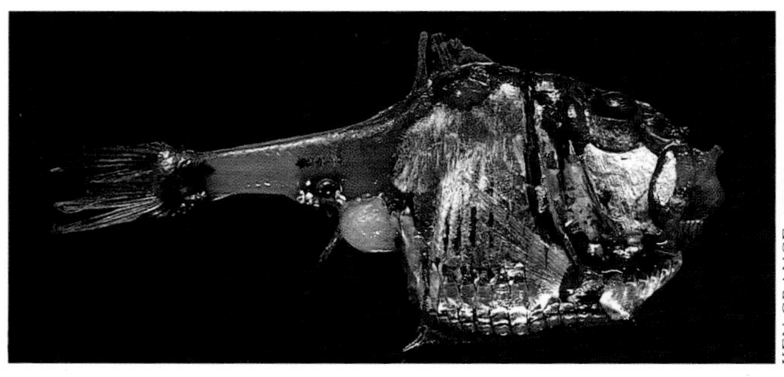

KEN GRANGE, NZOI

Recent discoveries indicate that logs that wash out to sea and eventually sink also represent a sporadic deep-sea food source, with its own specialised fauna. Logs trawled from the Tasman Sea have been found to be colonised by a diverse community that includes many species of snail adapted exclusively for this seemingly unusual habitat.

Compared with coastal waters the deep sea is a constant environment. Seasons come and go with little change. Even the effect of latitude is relatively small, so that whereas many marine organisms of surface waters occur only in the north or south of the country, those of the deep sea are often found throughout the region. To us, however, the deep sea appears hostile. At 500 metres depth, water temperatures can be as much as 10 degrees Celsius, but below 2000 metres temperatures of less than 3 degrees Celsius prevail. The deep sea is also a sunless environment. In clear ocean water, enough sunlight can penetrate to depths of 100–150 metres to enable plants to photosynthesise. Beneath this, darkness prevails save for the luminescence produced by animals themselves.

Between the productive surface waters and the depth where light from the surface is wholly extinguished lies a twilight zone. Many of the animals in this region, especially crustaceans and small fish, make extensive daily migrations by moving up towards the surface after sunset and retreating again to depth before sunrise. One explanation for this behaviour is that food is more available at shallower depths, but is best exploited under cover of darkness to lessen the risk of being spotted by predators.

Many mid-water fish that migrate to the surface at night in pursuit of food live at depths of 1000–2000 metres during the day. Often these species are studded with light organs. These may have a variety of uses, such as to attract and illuminate prey, to confuse predators, and for courtship. Among these are small, delicate fish, many only 5–10 centimetres long, such as lightfish, hatchetfish and lanternfish. Given the vastness of their habitat, included here must be some of the most abundant of all fish in the New Zealand region: species such as the roundmouth lightfish and pearlside. These in turn are important prey for larger mid-water carnivores, such as the viperfish, dragonfishes, and snaggletooths — species that may reach 20–30 centimetres in length. They are typically black or dark brown, have huge jaws with needle-like teeth and, to lure their prey like moths to a candle, a long barbel or ray, tipped with a light organ. Such mid-water species are often found entangled in trawl nets, but as yet none is of commercial importance.

Nevertheless, New Zealand's commercial catch is now dominated by deep-water species, a shift in emphasis following the declaration in 1978 of the country's Exclusive Economic Zone (EEZ). With an area of some 4 million square kilometres it is one of the world's largest EEZs.

Included among species trawled from continental slope depths around New Zealand are oreos, alfonsinos, roughies, rattails, hoki, hake, southern blue whiting and ling. Hoki (*Macruronus novaezelandiae*), one of the leading commercial species, occurs widely around New Zealand. It has a long, tapering body, usually reaching about 1 metre in length. Hoki congregate at spawning grounds in winter, such as off the South Island west coast, an area that has supported a major fishery. Orange roughy (*Hoplostethus atlanticus*) occurs extensively in the world's temperate seas. In New Zealand it is particularly abundant in such areas as the Chatham Rise and Challenger Plateau at water depths of 750–1000 metres, where it has been a major fishery since the early 1980s. It is, however, a very slow-growing species, only becoming mature at about 20 years with a maximum age that may exceed 100 years. This makes it highly vulnerable to overfishing, an important consideration in many deep-water fisheries.

To us, the deep sea appears inhospitable and to have more than its fair share of bizarre organisms. We need to remind ourselves, however, that most of the surface of the globe is covered by deep ocean. This is by far the most typical, if least familiar, habitat of the New Zealand region.

KIM WESTERSKOV

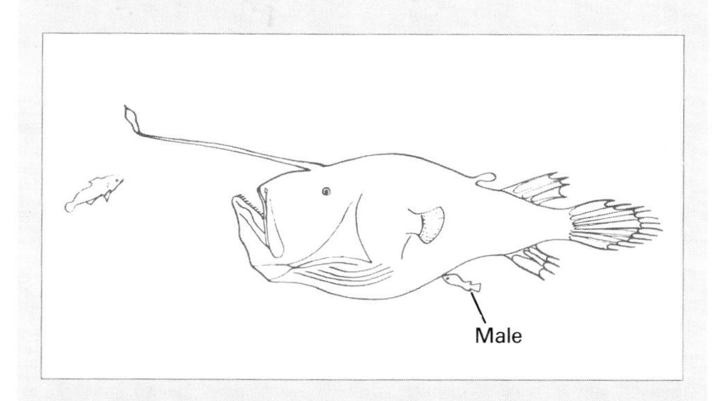

THE DEEP-SEA ANGLER FISH

Since life is sparse in the deep sea, fish living here must contend with two major difficulties. One is to find prey to eat. The other — a more pressing problem in the Stygian gloom — is to find a mate.

Deep-sea angler fish have interesting solutions to both these predicaments. As regards food, they catch their prey by 'fishing'. Their 'tackle' comprises a spine at the front of the dorsal fin that has become greatly elongated to hang in front of the mouth, and a glowing light organ on the tip of the spine. In some species of angler the light organ resembles a worm; in others, it resembles a fish, and to make the deception all the more convincing, the angler may jiggle its lure with swimming movements. Other fish investigate this glowing object waving in the darkness, and when the angler senses their presence, it lunges forward to engulf them in its cavernous mouth. The angler's appetite may, however, be its undoing. It sometimes misjudges the prey's size in the gloom and individuals have been found floating dead on the sea-surface, their jaws choked with a meal many times their own size.

If the angler's fishing technique is unusual, then the breeding of some species is even more bizarre. Details of this came to light when a female fish was trawled from the depths bearing a small growth on her underside. At first this was taken to be a flap of skin, but closer examination revealed it to be a tiny male fish, so profoundly attached to the female that his blood system had fused with hers. It seems that males counteract the difficulties of locating a female in the black vastness of the deep sea by ensuring that when they succeed, they remain fixed to her thereafter. The male initially homes in on the female by using a highly refined sense of scent, or by recognising the glow of her fishing lure. Then he clamps onto her with his jaws, and many of his internal organs degenerate as he becomes dependent on his partner. Having forfeited his freedom, the male becomes an appendage of his gargantuan breeding partner, always on hand to provide the sperm necessary to fertilise her eggs.

Food from the deep
Orange roughy (*Hoplostethus atlanticus*) (left) is one deep-water fish that supports commercial fisheries. Quite a number of creatures trawled up from the deep bear such surprisingly vivid colours of red or orange. Among them are prawns and other crustacea. Since red light rays are rapidly absorbed in the sea, these animals in fact appear black in the ocean depths where they live. They are as well camouflaged as dark-pigmented creatures.

Ocean wanderers

The albatrosses, shearwaters, petrels and prions, or tubenoses as they are collectively called, are so at home with the wind and the waves that most only come back to land to breed. Usually they return faithfully each time to the same partner and the same nesting site on some wild and remote oceanic island. Their nests are built on the ground or within a cosy burrow, and the young are raised on an oily semi-digested liquid regurgitated by their parents. The same sticky fluid is also sometimes spat at enemies as a defence.

There are about 100 species of tubenose divided among four families: the albatrosses and mollymawks (Diomedeidae), the shearwaters, prions and petrels (Procellariidae), the storm petrels (Hydrobatidae) and the diving petrels (Pelecanoididae). Over half are seen in New Zealand waters and many breed on offshore and subantarctic islands.

When not raising young, most tubenoses embark on extraordinary airborne journeys, roaming the world's oceans. Those with large wings, like the albatrosses and shearwaters, are superb gliders, soaring effortlessly over heaving wave crests. The royal and wandering albatrosses (*Diomedea*) will ride the westerly gales of the southern seas to circumnavigate the globe a number of times during their lives (see map). With wingspans of over 3 metres, they glide so efficiently that they burn

Some tubenoses of the New Zealand seas

less than a gram of body weight per kilometre during their travels. At times their flight is so serene that birds have been known to fall asleep on the wing and collide with boats. The sooty shearwater (*Puffinus griseus*), also known as the muttonbird, fulfils an equally remarkable journey (see map). During the southern summer they congregate in their millions to breed off the coast of New Zealand. Then in autumn they depart and are thought to head north to begin a vast clockwise circuit around the Pacific Ocean, following the seasons to enjoy the benefits of summer fishing in both hemispheres.

Tubenoses feed on squid, fish and plankton, the larger bird species taking the larger prey. This they pick off from the sea in various ways. Albatrosses alight on the water to pick squid, krill and fish from the surface. They also follow fishing boats for food, sometimes with disastrous consequences. Large numbers of white-capped albatrosses have been killed after colliding with or becoming entangled in trawling gear. Storm petrels, the smallest of oceanic birds, may hover above the sea as they feed, dabbling its surface with their feet. For the appearance of walking on water, sailors of olden times gave them the name petrel, derived from the Latin for Peter, meaning St Peter's bird. The appearance of storm petrels was also regarded by sailors as a sign that a storm was imminent. Prions have a beak fringed with hair-like lamellae to sieve surface zooplankton from the sea. The small diving petrels, which rarely wander far from shore, are expert divers, using their large feet to swim underwater after prey. They may even 'fly' straight through a wave.

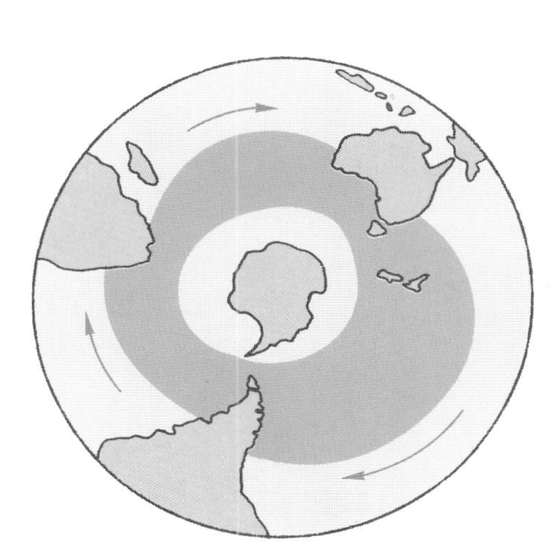

Direction and zone of wandering albatross migration

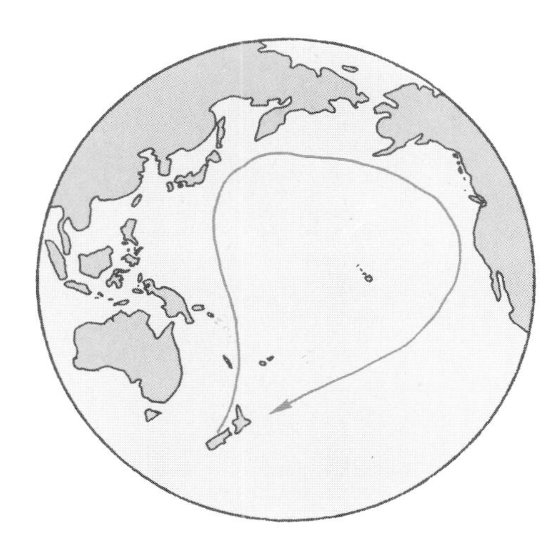

Sooty shearwater migration

CHAPTER 9

THE ISLANDS

To many naturalists, the most exciting places in the world are islands. Surrounded by rich fishing grounds and cut off from the mainstream of evolutionary change, they have an ecology of their own. On islands, seabirds return to nest in numbers that will sometimes darken the sky, and massive seals lumber from the surf in their hundreds to loaf in the sun. On islands live unique land plants and animals that have evolved over millions of years of isolation, and curious relicts whose kind have become extinct elsewhere.

The natural attributes of islands are often expressed in such phrases as 'laboratories of evolution' or 'natural treasure houses'. New Zealand has many examples worthy of these descriptions. More than 700 islands punctuate the surrounding seas, from the Kermadecs in the subtropical north to Campbell Island in the subantarctic south. Some are bleak, tiny outcrops, inhabited by scuttling crabs and encrusting lichens. Others are expansive landscapes of rolling tussockland or verdant forest. Those that have remained virtually untouched give glimpses of life as it was in prehistoric times. In stark contrast, those that have suffered the depredations of fire and introduced animals offer salient lessons on the fragility of island ecosystems.

Elephant seal

The nature of islands

Island isolation — island evolution

Isolation is fundamental to the unique nature of islands. Bereft of breeding contact with mainland populations, island communities are free to pursue their own evolutionary agenda. As generations pass, so species change. Some may get bigger, others smaller, each evolving into unique forms to meet the unique set of needs dictated by island life.

This phenomenon is best observed on outlying islands, such as the Chatham, Kermadec and subantarctic islands, which lie a substantial distance from New Zealand and have been isolated for a very long time. On the Chatham Islands, many plant and animal inhabitants are colonists that have arrived at sporadic intervals from New Zealand, by crossing the intervening 800 kilometres of sea. Those that have been on the islands for thousands, if not millions of years have evolved features distinct from their ancestors. The Chatham Islands pigeon, for instance, is slightly bigger than its close relative, the New Zealand pigeon. Others include island variants of snipe, parakeet, robin, oystercatcher, skink and red admiral butterfly. Likewise the forests, shrublands and bogs contain species of *Coprosma*, *Dracophyllum*, lancewood, *Olearia* and other plants that differ from their closest relatives in New Zealand.

Breeding grounds Islands are important breeding grounds where seals can raise their young, such as this elephant seal pup (*Mirounga leonina*) (right). Huge gatherings of petrels, shearwaters, penguins and other seabirds also congregate on islands during their breeding seasons.

GRAEME TAYLOR

Island evolution Isolated from mainland populations, many island plants and animals have evolved unique forms. The Chatham Islands pigeon (*Hemiphaga novaeseelandiae chathamensis*) is closely related to the New Zealand pigeon, but has a bigger build and a larger bill. Like many island inhabitants, it is also very vulnerable to the changes that human settlement have brought. It was once abundant but now there are just a few individuals left. Its extinction is likely to have a knock-on effect, since several island plants depend on the pigeon to disperse their seeds.

Islands and the sea

Island life overwhelmingly reflects the influence of the surrounding sea. Strong onshore winds and salt spray can determine the types of plant that survive. Also, colonies of seals and seabirds depend on the sea for their food. Often these animals are so numerous that they, in turn, influence the rest of the island, by enriching the soil with their droppings, and burrowing or trampling the ground for their resting sites. For instance, when about half a million fairy prions descend to breed on 150-hectare Stephens Island, they deposit tons of guano. This helps sustain a thriving insect population, on which the island's 50,000-strong tuatara population depends for food.

Island archives

Stepping ashore on some offshore islands is like stepping back to a time before humans reached New Zealand. Such places crawl with lizards, giant land snails, large flightless insects and other life forms, many belonging to species that have become rare or extinct on the mainland.

These 'archive' communities exist on islands lying relatively close inshore, which were attached to the mainland of New Zealand during the Ice Age. Exposed land-bridges allowed them to become populated by plants and animals once found throughout the country. Then, when the Ice Age ended about 12,000 years ago, rising seas isolated the islands, thus protecting their communities from much of the ecological chaos that has befallen the mainland with the arrival of humankind.

In particular, islands have been relatively inaccessible to possums, rats, cats, stoats and other of man's destructive cohorts. Stephens Island, the Hen and

Chickens Islands and Little Barrier Island are three examples that have remained more or less free of introduced pests, but there are many others dotted around the shores of New Zealand. These are now the best places, often the only places, where you can see stitchbirds, saddlebacks and short-tailed bats flying through the canopy, giant wetas scuttling through the undergrowth, and rare lizards such as Duvaucel's gecko, hunting at twilight. Even islands as small as 10 hectares can harbour as many as 11 types of lizard, offering a tantalising glimpse of the diversity of animal life that once thrived on the mainland.

The most familiar of all island survivors are tuatara. Once they lived throughout New Zealand, but since human times they have become restricted to islands, breeding successfully only on those free of rats. The largest tuatara population lives on rat-free Stephens Island in the Marlborough Sounds where, among rocks on higher ground, lives another island refugee — Hamilton's frog.

But for an unfortunate episode in history, Stephens Island might have been home to many more rare species. Until late last century it offered refuge to the kokako, native thrush and saddleback, which were vanishing from the mainland in the wake of European settlement. There was also a flightless wren, the Stephens Island wren. All these were lost when forest was cleared for a lighthouse and cats were introduced. (They have since been removed.) Fortunately for the saddleback, fate was kinder on other islands. The South Island saddleback held out on Big South Cape Island until the 1960s, when it was rescued from an invasion of ship rats. The closely related North Island saddleback survived on the Hen Island of the Hen and Chickens group. A similar story can be told of the stitchbird, a relative of the tui and bellbird, which became extinct on the mainland in the 1880s but fortunately survives on Little Barrier Island.

An island refugee
Many of the unusual plants and animals found on islands are types that have become extinct or rare elsewhere. Giant wetas (*Deinacrida*) were once common on mainland New Zealand, but following the introduction of predators such as rats, they have become more or less banished to islands where these threats are less severe. This species, *D. rugosa*, is about the same size as a mouse and is found only on Mana, Stephens, Middle Trio and Maud Islands.

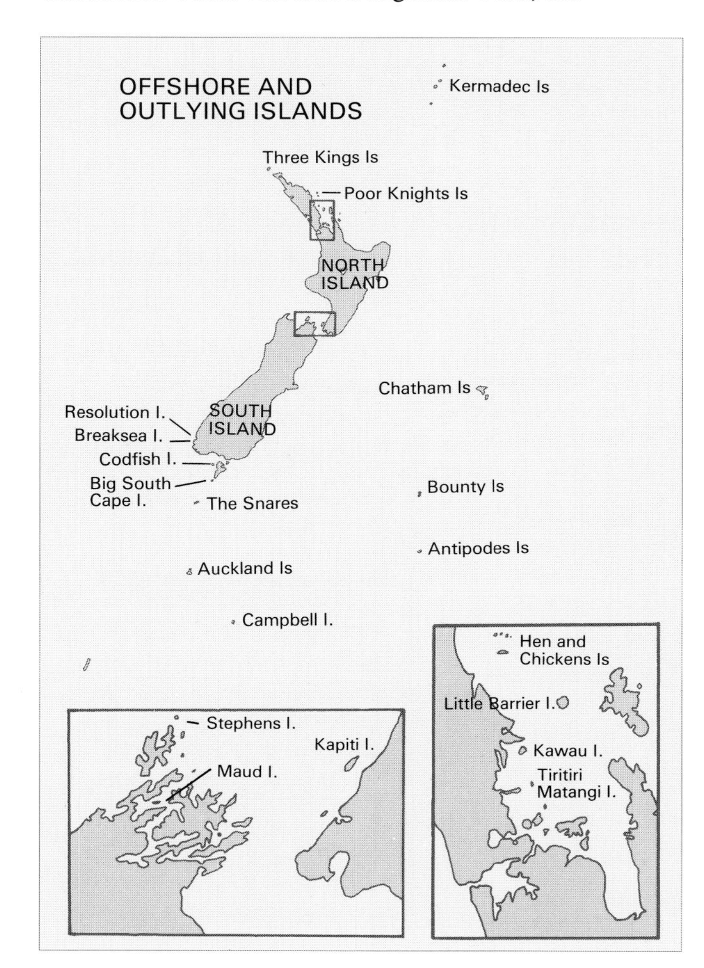

RELICT PLANTS OF NORTHERN ISLANDS

On the Three Kings Islands, off the northern tip of New Zealand, grows what is arguably the world's rarest tree. It is a small tree, named *Pennantia baylisiana*, of which only one wild specimen exists — a female. With no male trees of its kind to breed with, it can set seed only very rarely, by the freak event of self-fertilisation. The species therefore appears doomed to extinction unless artificially cultivated by cuttings.

Goats, which were removed from the islands in 1946, are thought to have contributed to the near demise of *Pennantia*, but its path to extinction may have started much earlier, during the Ice Age which began over 2 million years ago. Before the Ice Age, *Pennantia* and many other plants restricted to the northern offshore islands may have been widespread on mainland New Zealand. As the climate deteriorated, so these warmth-loving plants became restricted to their island refuges, where conditions remained tolerable. Here they have remained in exile to this day.

A similar explanation has been suggested for the phenomenon of many large-leaved plants growing on the northern islands. Kawakawa, ngaio, puka (*Griselinia littoralis*) and several other plants that also occur on the mainland have distinctly bigger leaves on the islands. Large leaves are a feature of plants adapted to warm, moist environments. This, scientists point out, suggests that the island forms are relicts of warm pre-Ice-Age times, while their smaller-leaved mainland relatives are descendants of plants that adapted to the cooler climates prevailing over the rest of the country.

Pennantia baylisiana

Island transfers

Awaiting transfer
Saddlebacks (*Philesturnus carunculatus*) (right) from Stanley Island wait in a holding aviary, prior to being released on Kapiti Island. Special nest and roost boxes have been provided on Kapiti to help the birds establish despite the presence of Norway rats.

Those offshore islands that have remained largely free of rats, stoats, possums and other introduced pests have now assumed special significance as 'safe havens' to place native animals whose existence has become threatened elsewhere. One of the first of such island transfers was made by Richard Henry at the turn of the century. As invading stoats brought havoc to the birdlife of Fiordland, Henry moved hundreds of kiwis and kakapo to the relative safety of Resolution Island. It was a valiant effort, but one that was doomed to fail when stoats eventually managed to swim the kilometre of sea separating the island from the mainland.

Disappointing as this start was, there have since been many successful island transfers. In 1908 the brown kiwi was moved from the mainland to Kapiti Island, where it now thrives. In the 1960s, several North Island saddlebacks were taken from their last refuge on Hen Island, and by a process of successive transfers, were established on several other islands. Similar operations have helped recovery of the South Island saddleback, stitchbird and black robin, to name a few. Even rare lizards, insects and snails have joined the list of transferred species. The method has become the mainstay of

GRAEME TAYLOR

New Zealand's threatened species management.

A successful transfer depends on more than randomly marooning a few individuals on an island. Birds often establish quicker in their new home if they are released with partners and neighbours with which they are already familiar. It is also vital to consider the animals already present on an island. Saddleback transfers, for instance, succeed on islands inhabited by kiore, or Polynesian rats, but normally fail on islands inhabited by Norway and ship rats. Tuatara cannot thrive in the presence of any rats. Even the native inhabitants of an island may jeopardise a successful transfer. Bellbirds drive stitchbirds from preferred food sources, saddlebacks may eat giant wetas, while wekas are

THE KAWAU EXPERIMENT

When Governor George Grey bought Kawau Island in the Hauraki Gulf in 1862, he embarked on a bizarre episode of island modification. Having refurbished his famous mansion, he populated the surrounding land with a taste for the exotic. Brazilian palms, Indian rhododendrons, Mediterranean olives, English oaks, Australian gums, bananas and breadfruits were planted. Then from the corners of the colonies came the animals. Among them were Chinese pheasants, zebras from Africa, antelopes and monkeys. From Australia he imported 12 species of marsupial as well as several types of bird.

Many of these curious liberations failed. The zebras died, while the monkeys became such a pest that they were later shot. Nevertheless, many of the plants still remain to intrigue the visitor, as do the kookaburras, rosellas, deer and possums. Most famous of the surviving animals are the wallabies, of which at least four species breed on the island, each having found a suitable habitat.

From a conservation standpoint, Governor Grey's experiment almost earned itself a reprieve when it was discovered that one of the wallabies was the parma wallaby, a species thought to be near extinction in its native Australia. Individual wallabies were transported back across the Tasman in a bid to reintroduce the species, but later surveys revealed that the parma wallaby was not threatened after all and the reintroduction was abandoned.

TIRITIRI MATANGI — OPEN SANCTUARY

Public visits to most island reserves are restricted in order to protect the rare plants and animals living there. But in recognition of the interest that people have in conservation, several islands have been designated as open sanctuaries, where public access is allowed. Tiritiri Matangi in the Hauraki Gulf is one such island.

When the Hauraki Gulf Maritime Park took responsibility for the island in 1971, much of it was covered in grazed grasslands, yet today rare native birds flourish in healthy stands of regenerating forest. This transformation has been brought about with the aid of public volunteers, who in the years 1984–90 planted over 180,000 native trees on the island. In the same period, rare birds were released on the island, which, despite its long history of human modification, was free of introduced mammals except kiore. Liberations of red-crowned parakeet, saddleback, brown teal, whitehead and other birds took readily to their new home, so much so that some of the establishing birds bred at rates far higher than normal. Tiri is a remarkable example of island restoration. From farmland it has become a prime sanctuary where the public can see some of New Zealand's rarest birds close at hand.

A lizard transfer
One lizard to benefit from island transfer is the endangered Fiordland skink (*Leiolopisma acrinasum*). At one time it lived on the mainland, but predation by introduced rats restricted it to a number of islands off the remote coast of Fiordland, where it remained undiscovered until the 1970s. Most of these islands are no more than tiny rocky islets, but in 1986 some lizards were transferred to establish a sizeable population on bush-clad Hawea Island in Breaksea Sound, which conservationists had first cleared of rats.

partial to the eggs of other bird species, threatened or otherwise.

There is also the question of whether pristine islands should be used to house transferred species. Islands free of predators and human interference are the last examples of natural habitat left on Earth. Introducing new animals, even a threatened native one, compromises this precious status. At worst, it could adversely affect the natural communities already present. Fortunately, this dilemma has largely been solved by improved techniques of island restoration. Rather than using pristine islands, it is now possible to remove many noxious introduced animals from partly modified islands, and revegetate the land to provide a suitable habitat for transferred native animals. Undisturbed islands, thankfully, can now be left in their natural state.

FOUR ISLAND RESERVES

About half of New Zealand's offshore islands are reserves in some form or other. Of these, four deserve special mention.

Covering 3000 hectares, **Little Barrier Island** (Hauturu) in the Hauraki Gulf is an outstanding nature reserve. Not only does the island support one of the largest areas of native forest unmodified by browsing animals, it is now also free of all introduced mammals except kiore. Its native inhabitants include many which are rare or absent elsewhere, among them the short-tailed bat, stitchbird, brown teal, Cook's petrel, black petrel, several species of lizard, snail and earthworm, as well as a giant weta. Breeding populations of kakapo, kokako, brown kiwi and saddleback have all been established.

Like Hauturu, **Kapiti Island** was declared a reserve around the turn of the century. Its beginnings were less auspicious, for parts of the island had been modified by settlers and various animals introduced. Today all introduced mammals except Norway rats and kiore have been removed and the island has been allowed to regenerate. In the undisturbed forest birdlife thrives, including kaka, parakeets and North Island robins. Kapiti is also the main stronghold for the little spotted kiwi, and more recently, stitchbirds and saddlebacks have been introduced.

Maud Island lies in the Marlborough Sounds. Despite a history of farming, the island is free of introduced predators. This led to its being used as an important experimental site for establishing rare animals. Takahe, kakapo, saddlebacks and little spotted kiwis have all been kept on the island. It is also the site of the first successful transfer of an endangered insect, a giant weta (*Deinacrida rugosa*), which was transferred from Mana Island. Maud Island also has a notable indigenous resident, Hamilton's frog, now considered a distinct species from its namesake living on Stephens Island.

Codfish Island, off the coast of Stewart Island, has become centre stage in the fight to save the critically threatened kakapo. Possums and wekas, both originally introduced, have since been eradicated from the island, leaving only the relatively innocuous kiore. This, combined with the island's size of 1200 hectares, has given hope that it will become a stronghold for kakapo transferred from Stewart Island. Apart from kakapo, the island offers refuge to many other rare animals. Among them is the short-tailed bat and an endemic subspecies of fernbird. Large numbers of penguins, prions, shearwaters and petrels nest on the island, including Cook's petrel, elsewhere found only on Little Barrier and Great Barrier Islands.

Island invaders

Isolation shelters island communities from many of the pressures that challenge life on large continents, but it also makes them exceedingly vulnerable to change when that isolation is broken. New Zealand's island plants and animals, which have evolved in the absence of land mammals for millions of years, have few methods of coping with the predators and herbivores recently introduced by humans. Cats, rats and stoats find easy meals among the large island colonies of seabirds, which nest prone on the ground or in burrows. Unusual flightless and partially flightless land birds found on islands are also vulnerable, as are ground-dwelling lizards, snails and large flightless insects. With equal efficiency, goats, sheep and rabbits decimate plants that have never before experienced grazing by mammals. As the palatable plants become scarce, so the vegetation is opened up to invasion by other plants, often introduced ones.

The impact is made all the more acute because island ecosystems are simpler than mainland ones. Islands have fewer species than mainland areas and their rudimentary webs of community interdependence are therefore highly vulnerable. The loss of one species leaves such a 'vacuum' that several other species may follow suit. Once this has happened, it becomes impossible to restore the island's original ecosystem, even if the invaders are removed.

More than 20 species of mammal have been introduced to offshore islands, for a variety of reasons. Goats, pigs and rabbits were released in earlier times as a live food source for sailors in case of shipwreck. Cattle, sheep and cats are often the legacy of failed farming attempts, while stoats, which can cross a kilometre of open water, have sometimes swum from neighbouring land. By far the most ubiquitous and devastating of all invaders, however, are rats. Adaptable, intelligent and prolific, they have spread as stowaways on boats to about 80 per cent of the world's oceanic islands. The kiore, or Polynesian rat, arrived with the first Polynesians to colonise New Zealand. Its noxious influence is apparent when you compare kiore-infested islands with those free of the rodent. In the absence of kiore, smaller seabirds, tuatara, lizards and ground-dwelling invertebrates exist in plenty. Even greater casualties have been caused by the European-introduced ship rat and Norway rat, whose appetites extend to some larger ground animals, as well as a number of perching birds.

Destructive as these animals are, there has been increasing success in eradicating them from islands. Goats and cats have been exterminated by trapping and

Browsed to one plant
Goats, released onto the Kermadec Islands early last century, had a devastating effect on the the native woody plants, several of which were unique to the islands. A casualty was *Hebe breviracemosa*, which for many years was considered to be extinct. But a single surviving specimen was discovered in 1983, soon after the goats had been removed.

TRAGEDY AT BIG SOUTH CAPE ISLAND

The devastating impact that rats can have on island life was graphically illustrated when ship rats invaded Big South Cape Island, off the coast of Stewart Island. Until the early sixties, the island was a naturalist's paradise. Birdsong filled its pristine forest, and by night, the leaf litter rustled with the activities of large flightless insects.

All this came to an abrupt end in 1963, when ship rats were first seen on the island in significant numbers, having probably come ashore from moored boats. By 1965 the island was overrun. A predatory grey tide seethed across the landscape both day and night. For at least three species the result was catastrophic. Big South Cape Island was the last natural refuge for the bush wren, the Stewart Island snipe and the greater short-tailed bat, all of which vanished. The South Island saddleback would have become extinct too, but wildlife workers managed to transfer a few to predator-free islands before it was too late.

A similar toll was exacted upon the once thriving insect population. Of a large flightless weevil, regarded as common in 1955, there was no trace when scientists visited the island in 1968. A large stag beetle had also virtually disappeared. Even some trees had been defoliated and ringbarked, while certain herbs had been chewed to ground level.

shooting programmes, often with dramatic results for the native inhabitants. After a 5-year campaign wiped all trace of cats from Little Barrier Island in 1980, stitchbird numbers soared. Possums, too, have now yielded to control measures. Concerted campaigns, tirelessly executed, rid Codfish and Kapiti Islands of possums in the 1980s. Both were remarkable triumphs. On Kapiti every one of an estimated 20,000 possums was exterminated from the 1970-hectare island. As with most eradication campaigns, the hardest part was removing the last few animals. After several years of trapping, trained dogs with muzzles were needed to locate those possums that were trap-shy.

Rats, the greatest scourge of all, have been the last to succumb to eradication. Indeed, for many years, even removing rats from small islands was considered impossible. But the advent of a new generation of rodent poisons, and ingenious tactics to dispense them, has redressed the situation. An historic achievement came in 1988, when the relatively large Breaksea Island in Fiordland was tackled. Two hundred and sixty-five kilograms of Talon poison bait, dispensed from feeding stations positioned throughout the island, wiped out the entire Norway rat population in less than 4 weeks.

These successes, undreamt of just a few years earlier, have ushered in a new era of optimism for the future of islands. Now it is possible to undo some of the damage that islands have suffered, and to restore their intrinsic value as havens for many of the world's rarest and most unusual life forms.

GRAEME TAYLOR

Impact of grazing
A fence erected on Campbell Island to exclude sheep clearly demonstrates the effect of grazing. On the right, sheep have left a meadow of close-cropped grasses, with the exception of numerous tufts of *Bulbinella*, one of the few large native herbs to be unpalatable. On the left, a healthy community of tussocks and large herbs has recovered.

THE BREAKSEA ISLAND CAMPAIGN

Until recently, the extermination of rats from offshore islands was considered futile. But new rodent poisons and well-planned eradication programmes have changed this. A breakthrough came in 1988, when the relatively large 170-hectare Breaksea Island in Fiordland was cleared of Norway rats with a poison bait called Talon. Talon is slow to act and highly edible, so rats readily consume a lethal dose before they feel any symptoms. Three to 12 days later they are dead.

To administer the Talon so that it was accessible to rats but not birds, special bait stations were made from lengths of pipe. These were then placed about 50 metres apart on a network of tracks that criss-crossed the island. On day one of the poisoning campaign, two bait pellets were placed in each of the 743 bait stations and these were replenished daily thereafter. The objective was to exterminate the whole rat population in one intense campaign, leaving no opportunity for the rodents to recover or become wary of the poison. Even inaccessible rock stacks were supplied with bait by helicopter.

After 3 days, all the bait being put out was taken each day. First takers were the larger, dominant rats. So prized was the new 'food' that they even vigorously defended the bait stations from smaller rats. But as the poison took effect, so the subordinate rats were free to help themselves, equally unaware of the fatal deception. In fact if anything, their eagerness for the bait was enhanced, for when a subordinate rat smells a new food on the breath of its superiors, it learns to seek that food out, even in preference to its traditional diet. In this way Talon worked its deadly way through the ranks. Within a week the number of visits to the bait stations started to decline and by four weeks it was all over. Every rat on the island was dead.

Norway rat (*Rattus norvegicus*) with a poisoned pellet.

ROWLEY TAYLOR

The subantarctic islands

Auckland Islands
A shy albatross (*Diomedea cauta*) stands vigil over its nest on remote South-west Cape, in the Auckland Islands. Beyond lie the indented shores of Carnley Harbour.

KIM WESTERSKOV

In the wild seas to the south of New Zealand, a handful of islands raise their rocky profile above the waves: Bounty, Antipodes, Campbell, Auckland, Snares and the Australian island of Macquarie. These are the only specks of land in a vast and biologically productive amphitheatre of ocean, stretching from the shores of South America in the east to the islands of the Indian Ocean in the west. Little wonder, therefore, that millions of seabirds and seals congregate on them during the breeding season.

The first islands encountered on a clockwise loop from southern New Zealand are the Bounty Islands. Here, 700 kilometres south-east of New Zealand, about 20 granite islets brave the pounding seas. No soil covers the barren rock and there are no plants other than algae and encrusting lichens. The islands are essentially just breeding platforms for huge gatherings of seabirds and seals. Tens of thousands of Salvin's mollymawk and fulmar prion crowd onto the 135 hectares of rocky ground. Erect-crested penguins rub shoulders with one another in raucous colonies, and more than 16,000 fur seals spread out in sublime repose by the shore. Among the few resident land species are a weta and several wingless flies. The evolution of the latter resembles that of flightless species in alpine regions (see page 39). On windswept islands, as on exposed mountain-tops, flying insects tend to get blown away and weeded out of the breeding population. Poorer flyers are more likely to propagate their genes.

One hundred and fifty kilometres further south are the Antipodes Islands. About 2100 hectares in extent and rising 402 metres in height, they are considerably larger than the Bounty Islands. Expanses of tussock grassland and scattered herbs carpet the slopes, and there are 25 species of bird, breeding with a success reflecting the fact that the only introduced mammals are mice. Particularly common are the erect-crested penguin, rockhopper penguin, wandering albatross and light-mantled sooty albatross. The islands are also home to the Antipodes Island parakeet and endemic subspecies of snipe, pipit and red-crowned parakeet.

Situated 700 kilometres south of the South Island and midway between the Subtropical and Antarctic Convergences, the Campbell Islands are lashed by the gales of the 'furious fifties'. Gnarled shrublands of wind-pruned *Dracophyllum* and *Coprosma* grow in sheltered sites, while much of the land is carpeted with tussock grasslands, dotted with large flowering herbs. This wild landscape is famed as a breeding site for the southern royal albatross, of which there are over 7000 pairs. Adding to the wealth of birdlife are large numbers of black-browed mollymawk, grey-headed albatross and rockhopper penguin, with yellow-eyed penguin and erect-crested penguin also present. By the shore, the fur seal, elephant seal and Hooker's sea lion breed, while off the coast, southern right whales congregate to mate. Among the endemic inhabitants are the Campbell Island shag and a small flightless duck, the Campbell Island teal, now virtually extinct as a result of predation by cats and Norway rats.

The Auckland Islands, over 60,000 hectares in extent, are the largest of New Zealand's subantarctic islands.

Their rugged ice-carved relief of seacliffs and inlets has been the site of numerous shipwrecks, sealing ventures and several abortive attempts at human settlement. These visitors left a legacy of introduced animals, particularly cattle, goats and pigs, as well as cats and mice, which have had an impact on the vegetation and wildlife of some islands. Nevertheless, the Auckland Islands' size makes them important for a diversity and abundance of birdlife, particularly albatrosses, prions, petrels and penguins. They are the world's most important breeding grounds for wandering and shy albatrosses. There are also endemic species or subspecies of prion, shag, teal, snipe, rail, banded dotterel, pipit and tomtit. Seals, too, are found in large numbers. The offshore islands of Enderby and Dundas are the world's main breeding grounds for Hooker's sea lion, with a population estimated in 1983 at about 5000. The offshore island of Adams Island, situated at the southern end of the group is one of the largest in the world free of introduced mammals.

The Snares Islands, about 200 kilometres south-west of New Zealand, have also escaped the introduction of any mammals, and are of international significance as a nature reserve. Even the vegetation is pristine, apart from two introduced plant species. The island's scrub-covered slopes are home to almost 6 million sooty shearwaters. Here live a similar number of seabirds as inhabit the entire coast of Britain. Their nesting burrows honeycomb the ground so thickly that it is difficult to set foot without crushing bird or burrow. Remarkably, 22 other breeding species of bird manage to pack themselves onto the 328 hectares of land. Mollymawks, prions and petrels all contribute to the cacophony of sound emanating from the island in the breeding season. Other birds include several found nowhere else: the Snares crested penguin, and subspecies of snipe, fernbird and tomtit. The spectacle of life here almost defies the imagination. It is compelling testimony to the richness of islands untouched by humankind.

PLANTS OF THE SUBANTARCTIC ISLANDS

Forest, in the conventional sense, barely has a foothold on the gale-swept subantarctic islands. A scrub-forest of *Olearia lyalli* and *Senecio stewartiae* clothes the slopes of the Snares. The only true forest is found fringing sheltered shorelines of the Auckland Islands. Here, southern rata grows in twisted stands, providing shelter for other forest plants. Notable among them is *Cyathea smithii*, the world's southernmost representative of the tree fern group.

More common are stunted shrublands, often of *Myrsine divaricata* and *Coprosma*, giving way with altitude to open expanses of tussocks and herbs, for which the subantarctic islands are famous. In places, tussocks rise from the peaty ground in massive shaggy heads over a metre high. Perhaps more striking are the so-called megaherbs. These robust plants, with their immense rhubarb-like leaves and large colourful flowerheads, are a peculiar feature of the subantarctic. Their bold floral displays are remarkable in contrast to the small and often drab offerings of most mainland plants. No satisfactory explanation has been given for the striking difference. One suggestion is that the conspicuous blooms have evolved through intense competition for the few flying insect pollinators found on these cold, windswept islands. Another theory is that the colours are a relic feature, lost from mainland plants that have evolved more simple flowers.

The origin of the subantarctic flora also confronts botanists with some interesting questions. Many plants are shared with New Zealand, having arrived as passengers of the wind, or with passing birds. A few are even shared with southern lands as far away as Tierra del Fuego. But over a quarter of the plants are found only on the islands. Some species, such as those of *Pleurophyllum*, are so distinctive that their links with the subantarctic would seem to be of great antiquity, their ancestors having somehow survived on the islands through the rigours of the Ice Age.

GRAEME TAYLOR

The corrugated leaves of *Pleurophyllum speciosum* (above) are thought to act as 'solar panels', helping the leaf to obtain warmth on sunny days.

ROD MORRIS

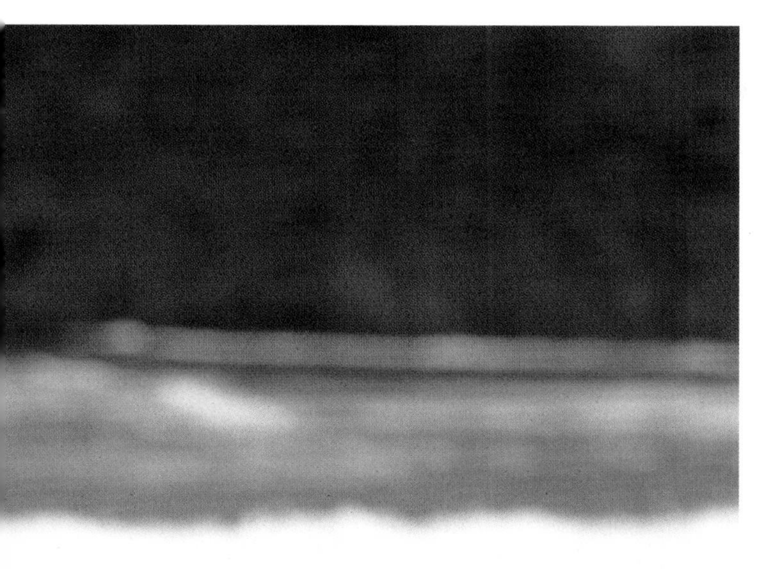

CHAPTER 10

CONSERVATION

We have not inherited the Earth from our parents, we have borrowed it from our children.

— IUCN, World Conservation Strategy

Jamie and the penguin

Why conservation?

When humankind fashioned the first tool, it stepped outside the natural constraints that limit other creatures. By the use of technology — fire, tool making, agriculture and then industry — it colonised new environments and displaced or modified their ecological systems to suit its own purposes. The use of technology characterises the human species. Its success has allowed the human population to spread and grow at an ever-increasing rate. At the same time, technology has created a sense of people being apart from nature.

The unrestrained success of humankind raised concern as early as the eighteenth century. Thomas Malthus (1766–1834) predicted dire consequences as the growing population outstripped its supply of food and resources. For a long time, however, the world could ignore these warnings. Such pessimism was always foiled by humankind's infallible inventiveness. New lands were discovered to increase agricultural output and medical science continued to improve human health. There really seemed no reason to worry. Even early this century, conservationists were regarded as eccentric romantics who wished to preserve the rare and picturesque that had lost any relevance to the modern day, and were anyway destined for extinction by the steamroller of progress.

Our views have changed dramatically since the 1960s. It has become all too clear that to meet the demands of progress, society has consumed large stocks of fossil fuels and vast forests. Agriculture has overtaxed soils and fishing has depleted the seas. Industry has polluted clean air and water. A growing understanding of the importance of ecology has laid the basis for wide concerns, not just for rare plants and animals, but for the continued welfare of this planet's environment. We are now starting to realise that, in effect, we have been consuming the very environment we need to survive.

Some still believe that technology can find a better way, that it can undo the damage and produce an environment more suited to human needs. But as the list of current environmental ills is reviewed, including ozone depletion, the greenhouse effect and pesticide residues, it is apparent that technology is increasingly associated with the problems more than the solutions. There is now an urgent need to review the way that we live. Our goal must be to understand and protect the interdependence of the living and non-living systems that govern the welfare of the environment and hand this on intact to future generations. In the words of an environmental writer, Richard Barnett: 'If we do not see ourselves as trustees of the natural order for something beyond ourselves, there is no answer to the inescapable human question, Why are we here?'

Who pays? It is easy to measure the value of the motor car to our lives, but what is the cost of the pollution it produces, and who is going to pay?

Protecting resources

There is no question of doing away with technology and returning to some previous, more simple lifestyle. Nor can we manage without the resources that nature supplies. But if we are to survive on the planet in the long term, and retain a reasonable quality of life, we need to seek a greater wisdom in the way we deal with the environment. We need to understand that we are inescapably a part of nature and that our demands do have an impact upon the environment and so upon ourselves.

How resources are used is governed predominantly by economics. To make wiser use of these resources in the future, there needs to be a closer alliance between the systems of economics and ecology. The resources most important to our long-term welfare are those that are renewable, such as timber, fibre and food. Included are also things we have often taken for granted, such as clean water, pure air and fertile soils. World stocks of these resources may be regarded as our environmental capital. Properly managed, according to ecological principles, they should last forever. But all too often they have been depleted faster than they can be renewed. To make long-term use of these resources, our demands must be sustainable. For example, pure waters should not be exploited faster than they can be replenished and agriculture should not deplete the fertility of soil faster than it can be restored. In other words, we must use only the interest and not consume the capital.

The economic benefits of developing a resource must also be matched against their ecological costs. For example, it is easy to determine the financial benefit of burning fossil fuels to provide electricity. But what is the cost of the waste produced? Indeed, if the waste pollutes the atmosphere, then who pays? Another country? A future generation? The environmental costs of economic developments, such as pollution, loss of natural habitats, or extinction of a species, are difficult to measure, and often do not show up straight away.

There is a tendency to think of them as being less real, and less important, than the benefits, so they are overlooked. Better consideration must be given to the long-term environmental costs of projects, which in the short term appear to offer benefits.

Protecting natural environments

The call to protect natural environments began in the young colonies of America, Australia and New Zealand. It was here that the impact of humankind on nature was swiftest and most dramatic. Within their lifetimes, settlers witnessed the transformation of nature from a pristine wilderness to a man-made landscape, and it raised concern among some. Those who looked upon the mountains and forests as a natural heritage, called for its protection for future generations. The world's first national park was created in the United States at Yellowstone, in 1872. In 1886, Canada declared Glacier National Park and Australia followed with the Royal Park. Then in 1887, New Zealand created Tongariro National Park, from land gifted to the people of New Zealand by Te Heuheu Tukino, chief of Ngati Tuwharetoa people.

In its early days, landscape protection meant preserving areas of scenic beauty for public enjoyment. Conflicts of conservation versus development were often avoided because many regions set aside were alpine landscapes, which were so remote and rugged as to preclude any economic use such as farming or forestry. More recently, with growing concern for the ecological importance of nature itself, conservation has aimed at preserving prime examples of natural ecosystems and regions of genetic diversity. These include estuaries, wetlands, coastal waters and lowland forest, which are among the most productive and diverse ecosystems, yet traditionally the most sought after for exploitation.

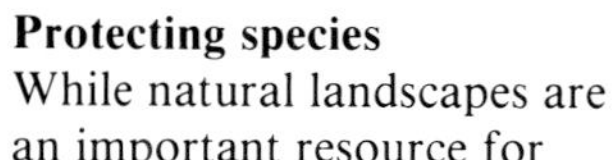

Protecting species
While natural landscapes are an important resource for public enjoyment, they are crucial for the future of many species. There are fewer than 200 takahe living in the wild. If this young bird is to grow to adulthood and raise its own chicks, it will need large areas of suitable habitat protected.

Vulnerable habitats
In recent times, the emphasis for conservation of natural landscapes has shifted from purely scenic considerations to their values as habitats for living organisms. It is now seen as vital to preserve examples of all types of natural habitat, including wetlands, tussocklands, estuaries and marine areas, many of which are vulnerable to exploitation.

Values for nature

Medicinal plants There is increasing interest in the economic value of native plants and animals. Many are known to contain compounds of potential use to medicine, agriculture or industry. The coastal ice-plant (*Disphyma australe*) is one example being examined as a source of anti-bacterial compounds.

Outdoor laboratories (right) Nature offers scientists a challenging field of intellectual enquiry.

Useful species

Our lives depend on plants and animals. They provide us with food, clothing, medicine, fuel, building materials and numerous chemicals. At the moment we utilise the smallest fraction of the world's species for these purposes. We simply do not know how many may hold potential as new sources of food or medicine; even such unlikely organisms as armadillos, foxgloves and sea squirts have been found to benefit medical science. We do know, however, that while less than one tenth of all species on Earth have been described, and less than a tenth of these have been studied for their potential uses, hundreds are becoming extinct each year.

The best way of preserving a large number of different species is to protect the natural habitat they live in. This, after all, is their natural home, and for many it is the only place they can live. Such places can be looked upon as vast storehouses, where genetic resources can be protected and allowed to evolve undisturbed by humankind.

Monitors of change

Natural systems continually change in response to the environment. By monitoring them, we can obtain a sensitive indication of the extent and effect of environmental changes, such as global warming or pollution. For example, the ailing conditions of forests in the Northern Hemisphere have drawn attention to the problems of acid rain.

Pristine landscapes, such as offshore islands, provide an excellent baseline when gauging the impact of human activity on the ecology of modified landscapes.

Tourism

New Zealand's national parks are the central attraction for a tourism industry which earns over one billion dollars annually. The national parks receive 3 million visitors each year.

Tourism Natural regions attract tourists, thereby earning revenue.

Scientific study

Investigation of nature is a major scientific pursuit, the product of which may be beneficial to humankind. The study of how ecological systems work, for example, may help us to improve the efficiency of our own artificial agricultural systems. Understanding nature also helps us to avoid making mistakes that could damage the ecosystem, for example by exploitation or pollution.

Protection

It is well known in New Zealand that forest cover in the mountains reduces erosion and flood damage in the lowlands. Forested watersheds also provide supplies of pure water for drinking. Forests exchange large quantities of carbon dioxide, oxygen and water vapour with the atmosphere. Because of this, major tracts of forests, particularly those of the Amazon Basin, are thought to have a vital stabilising influence on atmospheric quality and climate.

Psychological needs and ethics

To many conservationists, the most important qualities of the environment are those that are hardest to quantify. These cannot be accounted for by conventional economic thinking, and for this reason are all too often overlooked by economists, planners and politicians. There are two aspects. One concerns our psychological need for nature. The other concerns our ethical responsiblity to the rights of other species.

Our psychological need for nature is intrinsic. Humankind evolved as part of nature, and contact with the natural world remains essential to our mental well-being. This is particularly so as society becomes increasingly urbanised. Nature offers a retreat from the unnatural pressures and stresses of modern life.
It renews us with a sense of wonder, and the feeling of being part of a greater whole. In it we experience beauty, exhilaration and awe, all responses to an environment to which our senses have been naturally tuned. It is part of our roots. Not to have experienced nature is to not have shared the experiences of our ancestors.

For these reasons, millions of people take their recreation in the outdoors. Nature also forms a basis for human culture, art, and music. In New Zealand's case, the country's native flora and fauna are largely unique, and are therefore an essential part of the national identity. There is, too, a deep beauty to be found in nature — one that grows with acquaintance of its intriguing life histories, subtle relationships and curious forms and functions.

Humans have an ethical responsibility toward nature. All living things, including ourselves, are part of nature. We share a precious bond of coexistence in this large and possibly lifeless Universe. Along with our power over other life forms, we must respect their right to exist. Human compassion for wild animals can at times be very great. The plight of the great whales has raised concern among millions of people around the world, despite the fact that few would ever expect to see one.

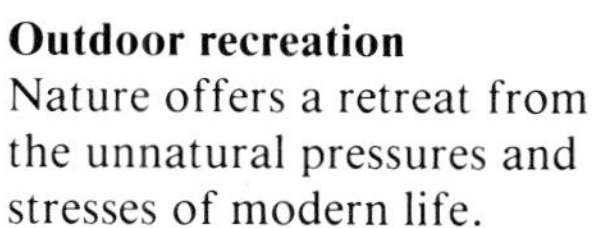

Outdoor recreation
Nature offers a retreat from the unnatural pressures and stresses of modern life.

The right to existence
Humans share a precious bond of coexistence with other living things. We have an ethical responsibility towards their continued existence.

Parks and reserves

New Zealand has a system of protected areas which is the envy of much of the world. Approximately 30 per cent of the country is afforded protection of varying status under the administration of the Department of Conservation. The jewels in the conservation crown are the national parks. These preserve areas of ecological significance or outstanding beauty in perpetuity, for their intrinsic natural value and the enjoyment of the public. Their status can only be revoked by Act of Parliament. There are 12 national parks in New Zealand, covering almost 9 per cent of the country. A further 7 per cent of the country is included in 21 conservation parks. These are less highly protected than national parks, but are nonetheless very important. North-west Nelson Conservation Park, covering almost half a million hectares, is the largest, and contains an extraordinary geological and ecological diversity. Other conservation parks are important for human recreation, particularly those near urban areas, for instance Tararua, Rimutaka and Coromandel Conservation Parks.

Smaller areas of significance are protected by reserves. There are over 1000 of these throughout the country. They are allocated to protect historic sites (historic reserves), scenery (scenic reserves), areas of scientific interest (scientific reserves), marine life (marine reserves) and important natural areas (nature reserves). Sometimes a series of coastal and island reserves have been consolidated under the umbrella of a maritime park. There are three maritime parks: the Hauraki Gulf, Marlborough Sounds and Bay of Islands. The rest of the land administered by the Department of Conservation consists of lands of the Crown that have natural values, collectively called stewardship areas. These are the least protected category of land and their status can be reviewed.

Planning a nature reserve

Planning a nature reserve might seem a straightforward task. But there is more to it than fencing off an area and leaving it to nature. A useful network of reserves

THE WORLD HERITAGE

The pyramids of Egypt, the Grand Canyon, the Taj Mahal and South-west New Zealand (left) share one thing in common. They are all recognised as World Heritage Sites.

This status has been conferred by the World Heritage Convention, an organisation uniting over 100 nations in an effort to identify and protect the world's most precious cultural and natural sites. Stringent criteria are applied before accepting a site for World Heritage status. A cultural site, for instance, must be authentic and represent a unique human achievement or have exerted a great influence over cultural development. A natural site must either contain outstanding examples of the Earth's evolutionary history, represent ongoing examples of biological or geological processes, contain major habitats for rare species or be of exceptional beauty. The South-west New Zealand World Heritage Site qualifies for World Heritage status according to many of these criteria. Encompassing the national parks of Mt Cook, Westland, Aspiring and Fiordland, as well as the forests of South Westland, it is one of the world's most diverse and magnificent landscapes. It contains outstanding examples of past geological events preserved in the ice-carved relief of Fiordland, ongoing geological processes along the active Alpine Fault, ongoing biological processes associated with its dynamic landscape, habitats for rare species such as the takahe, and spectacular scenery.

Conferral of World Heritage status means international recognition, and assistance in the form of help and advice for conservation projects if required. Each country, however, retains sovereign rights over its own sites. The World Heritage List now contains over 200 sites, from Stonehenge to the Vatican and the Great Barrier Reef to Mount Everest.

should represent a cross section of ecological areas. Included should be samples of alpine habitats, forests, tussocklands, wetlands, and coastal habitats, in both the moist and the dry parts of the country. Each site selected then needs to be able to maintain its natural values. There is no point, for instance, in siting a reserve downstream from a factory which discharges pollutants. It also must be large enough to contain genetically diverse breeding populations of the species it is designed to protect. If there are too few breeding individuals, then the total pool of genes may not sustain a vigorous and adaptable population and the tendency for local extinction will be increased. This possibilty raises another important point. There should always be several separate breeding populations of a rare species. Another consideration is that many animals may migrate seasonally outside the reserve for food or to breed, and they may be under threat in other areas. One way around some of these problems is to have several reserves interconnected by natural corridors, which allow for migration and the mixing of breeding populations.

Once an area has been selected for protection, it can rarely be left to its own devices. All too often the ability of nature to get along as it did before has been compromised in one way or another. Most reserves therefore need some form of management. Introduced predators and weeds often need controlling. Assistance may be needed to ensure there are adequate food plants available, or breeding sites for protected animals. In a few instances, seemingly radical management procedures might be required. For instance, tussocklands which were originally created by forest fires might need periodic burning if they are not to regenerate to forest.

Marine reserves

The thin ribbon of coastal water between the land and the deep ocean is the sea's most productive and diverse living zone. Not surprisingly, it is also the zone most exploited by humankind.

As demands upon coastal waters increase, for fishing, aquaculture and waste disposal, there is an increasing need to set aside biologically rich areas as marine reserves, which are free from exploitation. The benefits are many. Not only are marine reserves places where people can study unspoilt marine environments, they also help safeguard the perpetuity of species, as well as the important ecological role that coastal habitats play in processes such as the global carbon cycle. Even commercial fishing can benefit from marine reserves. When the first marine reserve was set up in 1977, near Leigh in the North Island, it met with opposition from local fishermen. Today all are in favour of it.
The reserve acts as a breeding sanctuary from which commercial species such as crayfish and snapper can repopulate surrounding depleted waters.

KIM WESTERSKOV

Marine reserves
Protection for habitats beneath the sea has lagged far behind that for their counterparts on land. For many years, it has been a case of out of sight, out of mind. Now, environmentalists are calling for the allocation of more marine reserves to preserve the abundance and diversity of underwater life.

Saving New Zealand's threatened species

Because of its unusual evolutionary past, New Zealand holds stock of one of the world's most unusual assemblages of plants and animals. Lamentably it has also lost proportionally more of its species in recent times than most other countries. Neither is the prognosis a happy one. One in two of New Zealand's endemic birds and one in ten of its native plants are currently under threat of extinction in the wild. To this can be added several reptiles, amphibians and fish, as well as numerous invertebrates.

If this seems a dismal record, then it must be added that there have recently been some remarkable success stories in the bid to help threatened species. The South Island saddleback was snatched from extinction in 1964 when rats invaded its last stronghold on Big South Cape Island. Several birds were captured and released on nearby predator-free islands. By a process of successive transfers there are now about ten healthy populations on offshore islands. The stitchbird, North Island saddleback, black robin, takahe, little spotted kiwi, Chatham Island snipe and Forbe's parakeet have all shown similarly heartening responses to conservation efforts. Even a small scarab beetle, the Cromwell chafer, has been allocated a reserve for its protection.

An ever-growing field of expertise is being developed in the quest to protect threatened species. Techniques such as transferring threatened species to predator-free offshore islands and improved eradication methods for introduced animals have played an important part in many successes (see Chapter 9). Equally, a better understanding of the behaviour and needs of threatened animals has helped scientists to see ways to manage their recovery. About 30 different types of threatened animal, from kiwis to giant wetas, are being held in captivity. For many of these it is hoped that captive breeding programmes will one day become a way to restore wild populations. For each success story, however, there remain many more species on the sidelines, their cases waiting to be judged by a limited conservation budget. Too often, help for the threatened depends on their finding a place in the human conscience. It has been difficult to raise adequate funds to help the more popularly appealing species, such as kakapo and takahe. For many of the less 'charismatic' ones, such as the threatened Canterbury mudfish, it may be impossible.

WHAT IS EXTINCTION?

In the story of life, which stretches back over 3000 million years, extinction is instantaneous and forever. Extinction has always occurred in nature. Perhaps over 99 per cent of species have become extinct since life began. It is the inevitable consequence of a changing world. Sometimes a species 'disappears' because it evolves into a new species, adapted to the changes in its environment. This is called false extinction. At other times it vanishes because it cannot adapt to the changes of its environment, which is called true extinction. In recent times the rate of true extinction has risen alarmingly worldwide. Estimates are that at least one mammal or bird is vanishing each year, along with hundreds of plants and probably thousands of insects — more than at any other time in the history of life. This is almost entirely due to human activities.

Less widely appreciated is that even by reducing the population of a species to low numbers, we destroy forever a part of the pool of genes held amongst all its individuals. This pool of genes, endlessly shuffled through sexual reproduction, enables a species to produce variation amongst its offspring, and so survive the long-term changes of its environment. The smaller the population the less genetically flexible it becomes and the more prone it is to extinction. This same genetic variation has been enormously useful to humans. From it we have bred such diverse varieties as cauliflowers and kohlrabi from the wild cabbage, or dachshunds and St Bernards from the wild dog. Among many biologists the loss of both genetic and species diversity, because it is irreplaceable, is seen as the greatest ecological catastrophe that we are facing.

GRAEME TAYLOR

Conservation triumph
The rescue of the black robin (*Petroica traversi*) from a population low of five individuals in 1979 was one of the greatest achievements of threatened-species management.

The black robin story

When Europeans first arrived on the Chatham Islands the black robin (*Petroica traversi*) was relatively widespread. But in the all too familiar pattern, its numbers dwindled as European settlement progressed. By late last century it had become restricted to a bleak pocket-handkerchief of stunted forest on top of Little Mangere Island. Here it struggled with its impoverished habitat, until by 1972 there were only 18 individuals left. Just three years later the numbers had dropped to nine. The black robin, it seemed, was facing certain extinction.

In 1976 a team from the Wildlife Service led by Don Merton launched a daring and remarkable rescue attempt. Because the scrubby forest atop Little Mangere was deteriorating it was first decided to move the birds to nearby Mangere Island. It was a risky decision, since the bird's numbers then stood at seven, of which only two were female. Any mistake would finish the species.

The difficult transfer was a success and the birds settled in to breed in their new home. Births, however, did not keep pace with deaths and by 1979 the population was down to five. In a final desperate bid to boost numbers it was decided to try cross fostering, a technique never before attempted in an endangered passerine population in the wild. This involved taking eggs from the robins and putting them into the nest of another species that would serve as a foster parent. The robins, having lost their first clutch, lay a second one, hence doubling the number of young produced each year.

The first foster parent tried, the friendly Chatham Island warbler, managed to raise the black robin chicks with only limited success. Therefore it was resolved to try the more closely related tomtit instead. This meant transferring the eggs 15 kilometres by sea to South East Island, where the nearest tomtits lived — yet another hazardous journey. This idea proved the breakthrough that had been hoped for. The tomtits were model foster parents and in 1983 a second population of black robins was established on South East Island. Breeding success was so good that within three seasons there were 38 black robins. By late 1988 numbers had topped the hundred. The black robin was at last out of danger.

It was a remarkable achievement. A bird had been brought back from the brink of extinction, and may soon be established as a third population on nearby Pitt Island. Even more remakable was that during the critical early years the success of the species rested on just one female bird called Old Blue. Old Blue was one of the two original females taken from Little Mangere in 1976. From 1979 to 1983 she was effectively the only breeding female. When she died in 1984 she had lived an incredible 13 years or so, more than twice as long as normal. If she had enjoyed only the normal life expectancy, the black robin story may well have had another ending.

A turnaround for takahe

In 1987 the founder members of a new population of takahe (*Porphyrio mantelli*) were successfully established in the Stuart Mountains of Fiordland. For the first time in perhaps 100 years the takahe had increased its range beyond the alpine valley it had become restricted to last century in the nearby Murchison Mountains.

This turnaround in fortunes for the takahe was made possible by an ongoing programme to release birds that have been raised in captivity. In the programme, clutches of eggs are first collected from wild takahe in the Murchison Mountains and transferred to a special rearing unit near Te Anau. By taking the eggs early in the season the parents are able to lay a second clutch. At the rearing unit the eggs are put in an incubator and after hatching placed with a fibreglass 'parent', wired to provide warmth. Tape recordings of encouraging brooding calls are also played at hatching and during feeding. Food, which may include tussock, chopped apples and baby food is administered using a takahe-like glove puppet. After a number of weeks the birds are allowed out into a large fenced enclosure where they can feed on tussocks until old enough to be released in the wild.

Successful re-establishment of the young takahe in the wild depends on two critical aspects of the programme. First, the rearing process is carefully carried out so the birds retain wild instincts and are correctly imprinted and socialised upon their own kind. One-way mirrors are used throughout rearing to prevent the young birds from seeing the humans observing them, and their diet is monitored to encourage them to recognise foodstuffs they will find in their natural habitat. Second, deer are heavily controlled in the takahe's wild habitat. Deer browse and often kill the very plants takahe need for food, so there can be no success if they go unchecked. The results of the effort have lived up to all hopes. About ten birds have been released into the Stuart Mountains each year since 1987 and the first breeding attempt was recorded in spring 1989.

Rearing takahe Takahe chicks (*Porphyrio mantelli*) with their fibreglass surrogate mother.

Where now the kakapo?

The kakapo (*Strigops habroptilus*), a native parrot, undoubtedly qualifies as one of the world's most unusual birds. During the millions of years since it flew to New Zealand it has evolved a nocturnal, flightless lifestyle and has become by far the heaviest of all parrots. As if that was not enough, it has also evolved a remarkably complex courtship, known as a 'lek'. The kakapo is the only flightless bird, the only parrot and the only New Zealand bird to have this type of breeding behaviour.

The kakapo's unusual courtship begins when males, intent on breeding, congregate in special courtship areas often measuring several hectares. Here they mock-fight and squabble amongst themselves to establish small territories, called 'courts'. Once a bird has staked out a court he excavates a series of depressions, called booming bowls, which are interconnected by small tracks. Next he sets about soliciting the attention of receptive females. He inflates special air sacs in his chest. Then, puffed out like a balloon, he emits a series of extraordinary deep booming calls that travel for kilometres on the night air to summon potential mates. If a female approaches, the male switches his call to a higher-pitched nasal 'ching' which is more directional and enables her to home in on his presence. In the final stages of courtship it is thought he does a display dance to the female and if she is impressed by his behaviour, mating occurs. After this the female is left to raise the young alone.

Males boom nightly for about three months, after which they are somewhat thinner than when they started. Perhaps not surprisingly then, booming years are infrequent events. They happen about every four years in association with a heavy cropping season of the kakapo's food plants that is needed to bring the males into breeding condition. Unfortunately, this sporadic breeding regime, along with the kakapo's flightlessness, placid temperament and the fact that only the female guards the chick, have conspired to make the bird an easy target for introduced predators. Kakapo numbers became depleted in Maori times, but it was the rats, dogs, cats and stoats introduced by Europeans which pushed the species to the edge of extinction.

The impending demise of the kakapo sparked the first conservation attempt late last century. It was an extraordinary effort, mostly by one man, Richard Henry. Under difficult and isolated conditions at Dusky Sound in Fiordland, he transferred hundreds of birds by boat from the mainland onto predator-free Resolution Island. One could hardly imagine the crushing disappointment when he discovered after several years that stoats had managed to swim to the island. After that the kakapo slowly faded away. But hopes returned in the 1960s and 70s, when a few individuals were discovered still holding out in remote corners of Fiordland. Even more promising, a second, larger group was discovered on Stewart Island. Both populations were in decline. Even the Stewart Island birds, which were spared predation by stoats, were slowly losing the battle against cats and rats.

Efforts to help these birds had a bad start. Attempts to keep them captive failed. The transfer of birds to predator-safe Maud Island in the Marlborough Sounds from 1974 onwards seemed promising, until stoats reached the island seven years later. The next home for kakapo was Little Barrier Island in the Hauraki Gulf. In 1980, with a monumental effort, wild cats were eradicated from the island leaving the more innocuous Polynesian rat, kiore, as the only potential predator. In 1982, 22 kakapo were released and males were reported to be booming a few years later. The first real breakthrough came in 1990 when a chick was hatched.

The remainder of Stewart Island's kakapo were moved to nearby Codfish Island between 1987 and 1990. As on Little Barrier, introduced animals had to be removed first. Wekas, which had originally been introduced from Stewart Island and were potential predators of chicks and eggs, were cleared by 1985. Next to go were the possums, which compete directly with kakapo for food. After an intensive campaign which meant setting over 2000 traps each day the last one was eradicated in 1987.

The next step rests with the kakapo. Conservationists hold their breath in the hope that they will breed in their new homes. Unfortunately time is running out. Of the 43 or so individuals alive in 1990, only 14 were female. Given normal mortality, we may expect only four or five of these females to be alive in the year 2000. More may need to be done for the embattled bird. One possibility is to provide feeding stations where kakapo can get access to protein-rich food, allowing them to come into breeding condition every two instead of four years. Captive-management techniques are being developed using birds that have been reinstalled on Maud Island, now ringed by predator traps. With dedication and, above all, funds borne by the public will, the kakapo's eerie booming calls will continue to haunt the night.

ROD MORRIS

Facing extinction
We could choose to accept extinction as inevitable for the kakapo (*Strigops habroptilus*). After all, is it not doomed by its own inability to cope with a changing world? However, if we do accept this, then might we not accept the same fate for the next plant or animal that falls awry of our impact upon the natural order? And the next? The plight of the kakapo, like that of the giant panda and the whales, is symbolic of the plight of tens of thousands of species whose tenure on Earth is now under threat.

Threatened plants in cultivation

One way to protect threatened plants from extinction is to grow them in cultivation. About 10 per cent of native plants are threatened in the wild, and perhaps 70 per cent of these are grown in cultivation. This, however, should not be seen as an end in itself. There is no joy in envisaging the botanic gardens of the future as 'museums' for species that long ago became extinct in the wild. Cultivation must be looked upon as a way of safeguarding plants so that they can be re-established in the wild. It is vital, therefore, to also reserve samples of natural habitat that can be made safe from threats, whether they be introduced grazers, competing weeds or land development.

Reserves designed specifically to protect threatened plants are as yet scarce. Nevertheless, where possible, programmes of cultivation and re-establishment have been started. For instance, cultivated cuttings of *Hebe armstrongii* have been used to restore wild populations at the Castle Hill Reserve in the Southern Alps. Cuttings have also been grown of the endemic Raoul Island hebe (*Hebe breviracemosa*), which by 1983 had been reduced to one plant by introduced goats. Now that the goats have been removed the hebe can be safely restored to the wild.

Growing threatened plants in the garden
A few of New Zealand's threatened plants are garden favourites on account of their colourful flowers.

Fuchsia procumbens (left), a coastal plant of northern New Zealand, has suffered from stock as well as shoreline development projects.

Kaka beak (*Clianthus puniceus*) (bottom left) is grown in gardens throughout the country, although it has been reduced to about 150 plants in the wild by habitat loss and grazing by introduced animals.

The Chatham Island forget-me-not (*Myosotidium hortensia*) (bottom right) abounded on the coastlines of the Chatham Islands, until grazing and trampling by farm stock put it in the threatened category.

The environmental movement

Today, Kapiti Island off the Wellington coast is one of the few areas relatively accessible from the mainland where people can catch a glimpse of what New Zealand was like prior to European settlement. Native birds, seldom seen on mainland New Zealand, and others now confined to offshore islands, find sanctuary on one of the country's most important nature reserves.

But Kapiti is more than a nature reserve; it is also the birthplace of the modern conservation movement. In 1914, shocked by the condition of the goat- and sheep-ravaged 'reserve', activists lobbied the government to rid the island of the introduced animals. By 1923 they had formed the Native Bird Protection Society of New Zealand, with former Prime Minister Sir Thomas McKenzie as its first president. Thus began New Zealand's first national citizens' conservation group.

Prior to this, conservation had been championed by prescient individuals such as Christchurch politician Harry Ell, and ecologist Leonard Cockayne. Legislation to reserve areas had been introduced in 1874 with the Forests Act, and Tongariro, Egmont and Fiordland National Parks had been created by 1905. A government body, the Scenery Preservation Board — the precursor of today's New Zealand Conservation Authority but without citizen input — set aside a number of areas, often small, as reserves. Some beautifying societies also played a role. The Christchurch Beautifying Society, for example, pushed for the reservation of the headwaters of the Waimakariri River, later to become part of Arthur's Pass National Park.

The second major national conservation group to appear was Federated Mountain Clubs (FMC). In 1931, A. P. Harper, well-known explorer and later a president of the Royal Forest and Bird Protection Society, argued that the proliferation of small tramping, climbing and skiing clubs should form a federation to act on their behalf. FMC became a strong force in the formation of national parks, as well as contributing towards back-country surveying and mountain safety.

Despite conservation gains in the years that followed, including the steady expansion of the parks and reserves system, natural New Zealand was still fast disappearing. The conflict between conservation and development reached a head in the 1960s, when it was planned to raise the level of Fiordland's beautiful Lake Manapouri for power generation. The battle that was fought and won for its protection became the watershed for a new generation of activists, concerned that the environment must not be sacrificed for what was increasingly viewed as the mirage of a better quality of life.

Helping the brown teal
Private organisations play a vital role in many aspects of conservation. One example is the work being done by Ducks Unlimited to restore wild populations of the threatened brown teal (*Anas aucklandica*). Brown teal were widespread when Europeans arrived, but like the wetlands they inhabit, they have been in decline ever since.

Ducks Unlimited are committed to reversing this trend. One of their aims is to preserve, restore and create wetlands to increase wildlife habitat. The other is captive breeding and release of rare waterfowl. Members breed about 100 brown teal for release at selected sites in the wild each year.

THE TASMAN ACCORD

Once considered irreconcilable opponents, industry and environmentalists have increasingly met on common ground. In 1989, Tasman Forestry Limited, one of New Zealand's largest private forest owners, signed a landmark agreement with the Minister of Conservation, the Royal Forest and Bird Society, Federated Mountain Clubs and the Maruia Society.

Called the 'Tasman Accord', this agreement included legally protecting 38,599 hectares of Tasman Forestry's native forest holdings contained within its plantations throughout New Zealand from Coromandel to Otago. A further 3500 hectares of prime kokako habitat were sold by Tasman Forestry to the Department of Conservation and a grant made available by the company for research and management to help ensure the bird's survival. In addition to the important forest stands and wildlife habitats set aside under the Accord, Tasman Forestry confirmed that their New Zealand native forest clearance operations would cease in 1990.

Tasman Accord projects are advanced each year. In 1990, three projects were implemented to contribute to New Zealand's sesquicentennial celebrations. A 90 metre-long footbridge now spans the Arnold River mouth at Lake Brunner to allow access to Tasman Forestry's Aratika Forest Reserve. One of Maoridom's most illustrious warriors was commemorated with the unveiling of a plaque to Te Kooti at the confluence of the Mohaka and Te Hoe Rivers where it overlooks the historic Ngatapa fortress. In the Bay of Plenty, a walking track between Kawerau and Lake Rotoiti was established; the 30-kilometre track passes through Accord reserves and part of the Tarawera Forest.

In total, the Accord represented the largest commitment ever made by a New Zealand company to protecting natural forest habitats. For Tasman Forestry, it was a decision in keeping with the company's new environmental code of practice. In the words of Bryce Heard, managing director of Tasman Forestry, 'We are committed to the best possible use of New Zealand's resources — and sometimes that means to leave them in their natural state.'

The Tasman Forestry footbridge gives public access to their Aratika Forest Reserve at Lake Brunner in the South Island.

GORDON ROBERTS

In the ensuing years the meaning of environmental protection widened from saving forests and wilderness areas to a host of other issues — mining, water quality, energy, pesticides, Antarctica. Environmental groups proliferated correspondingly, as the number of concerns grew. Some of these, such as Ecology Action, Coalition for Open Government and Campaign Power Poll have since faded away. Others, such as the Beech Forest Action Committee and the Pacific Institute for Resource Management, have recently appeared. International organisations have also set up in New Zealand. Among them are Earthtrust, Friends of the Earth, Greenpeace, and the World Wide Fund for Nature. Greenpeace has enjoyed the most spectacular growth of any conservation group in recent years with extensive membership campaigns in all media. As a consequence, they are starting to campaign more on domestic issues, although international issues remain their focus.

Significant indigenous groups today include the Royal Forest and Bird Protection Society, the Maruia Society, Peninsula Watchdog, and the Pacific Institute for Resource Management. Recreation groups are important conservation allies. Acclimatisation Societies, FMC, the New Zealand Federation of Freshwater Anglers and Ducks Unlimited play a valuable role with such questions as public access, lobbying for wilderness areas and protection of wildlife.

Since 1972 Environment and Conservation Organisations (ECO) have acted as an umbrella organisation for all New Zealand groups. By 1990 there were 93 member groups of ECO — a measure of the diversity of community interest in the environment.

THE ROYAL FOREST AND BIRD PROTECTION SOCIETY

Formed in 1923, the Royal Forest and Bird Protection Society remains New Zealand's largest indigenous conservation organisation, with a membership of 60,000 in 55 branches. Originally set up to campaign on behalf of native forest and birds, the society has kept apace with the issues of the day. In the 1930s, 40s and 50s, its main focus was bird protection, erosion control, and weed and pest control. The 1960s saw it embroiled in the Lake Manapouri debate, in which developers proposed to raise the lake level for hydro-electric generation.

By the 1970s Forest and Bird was viewed as too conservative for some organisations, especially the Native Forests Action Council (NFAC), which introduced a much needed brand of environmental activism into the country. Ironically, by 1990 the positions of the groups had reversed; Forest and Bird was regarded as a group less likely to compromise than the Maruia Society (formerly NFAC and the Environmental Defence Society).

Under the 1980s directorship of Dr Gerry McSweeney, Forest and Bird played a key role in the creation of the Department of Conservation (DOC) and the Ministry of the Environment, as well as ending wetland drainage subsidies, forestry encouragement grants and land development loans. Following the formation of DOC, the society successfully fought to rescue 600,000 hectares of conservation land from being allocated to new corporations.

The 1990s see the society involved in a wide range of issues, from climate change and ozone protection to Pacific rainforests, pollution and waste management. Not forgotten, however, are its traditional interests: in 1990 it vigorously and successfully campaigned for an end to native forest woodchipping and is working with Comalco to save the endangered kakapo. One of the society's key initiatives for the nineties is promoting the creation of marine reserves and protecting the seas from overfishing.

The society publishes a full-colour natural history and conservation magazine, *Forest and Bird*, as well as a topical newsletter, *Conservation News.* It has recently started the Kiwi Conservation Club for children aged five to 12.

The Royal Forest and Bird Protection Society actively lobbies government and industry on behalf of the environment. For many of its members, though, the society is a way of sharing an interest in the outdoors with like-minded people — and perhaps giving nature a helping hand with projects such as the one below, to remove weed pines from native tussock grassland.

Society members removing wilding pines.

SUGGESTED READING

Anderson, A., *Prodigious Birds: moas and moa-hunting in prehistoric New Zealand,* Cambridge University Press, 1989.

Ayling, T. and Cox, G., *Collins Guide to the Sea Fishes of New Zealand,* Collins, Auckland, 1982.

Barnett, S. (ed.), *New Zealand in the Wild: an illustrated A–Z of native and introduced birds, mammals, reptiles and amphibians,* Collins, Auckland, 1985.

Bellamy, D. J., Springett, B. and Hayden, P., *Moa's Ark: the voyage of New Zealand,* Viking, Auckland, 1990.

Bishop, O. N. and Bishop, N. G., *Wild Flowers of New Zealand,* Hodder and Stoughton, Auckland, 1990.

Bradstock, M. C., *Between the Tides: New Zealand shore and estuary life,* David Bateman, revised edn., Auckland, 1989.

Brazier, R., Keyes, I. and Stevens, G., *The Great New Zealand Fossil Book: pictures of ancient life in an evolving land,* DSIR Geology and Geophysics, Lower Hutt, 1990.

Brewster, B., *Te Moa: the life and death of New Zealand's unique bird,* Nikau Press, Nelson, 1987.

Brownsey, P. J. and Smith-Dodsworth, J. C., *New Zealand Ferns and Allied Plants,* David Bateman, Auckland, 1989.

Butler, D., *Quest for the Kakapo,* Heinemann Reed, Auckland, 1989.

Chapman, M. A. and Lewis, M. H., *An Introduction to the Freshwater Crustacea of New Zealand,* Collins, Auckland, 1976.

Cometti, R. and Morton, J., *Margins of the Sea: exploring New Zealand's coastline,* Hodder and Stoughton, Auckland, 1985.

Cox, G., *Whale Watch: a guide to New Zealand's whales and dolphins,* Collins, Auckland, 1990.

Cox, G., *Prehistoric Animals of New Zealand,* Collins, Auckland, 1991.

Crisp, P., *New Zealand's Offshore and Outlying Islands,* Nature Conservation Council, Wellington, 1985.

Crisp, P., *Coastal Wetlands,* Nature Conservation Council, Wellington, 1986.

Crisp, P., Daniel, L. and Tortell, P., *Mangroves in New Zealand: trees in the tide,* GP Books, Wellington, 1990.

Dawson, J., *Forest Vines to Snow Tussocks: the story of New Zealand plants,* Victoria University Press, 1988.

Donoghue, M. and Wheeler, A., *Save the Dolphins,* David Bateman, Auckland, 1990.

Druett, J., *Exotic Intruders: the introduction of plants and animals into New Zealand,* Heinemann, Auckland, 1983.

Falla, R. A., Sibson, R. B. and Turbott, E. G., *Collins Guide to the Birds of New Zealand,* Collins, revised edn., Auckland, 1978.

Fleet, H., *The Concise Natural History of New Zealand,* Heinemann, Auckland, 1986.

Forest and Bird, quarterly magazine of the Royal Forest and Bird Protection Society of New Zealand, Wellington.

Forsyth, D. J. and Howard-Williams, C., (eds.), *Lake Taupo: ecology of a New Zealand lake,* Science Information Publishing Centre, New Zealand Department of Scientific and Industrial Research, Wellington, 1983.

Fraser, C., *Beyond the Roaring Forties: New Zealand's Subantarctic Islands,* Government Printing Office Publishing, Wellington, 1986.

Gaskin, C., Peat, N. and Westerskov, K., *The World of Albatrosses,* Hodder and Stoughton, Auckland, 1991.

Gaskin, C., Peat, N. and Westerskov, K., *The World of Penguins,* Hodder and Stoughton, Auckland, 1991.

Gibb, B., *Collins Handguide to the Frogs and Reptiles of New Zealand,* Collins, Auckland, 1986.

Gibbs, G. W., *New Zealand Butterflies: identification and natural history,* Collins, Auckland, 1980.

Johns, J. and Molloy, B., *Native Orchids of New Zealand,* Reed, Wellington, 1983.

Johnson, P. N. and Brooke, P. A., *Wetland Plants in New Zealand,* DSIR Publishing, Wellington, 1989.

Jolly, V. H. and Brown, J. M. A. (eds.), *New Zealand Lakes,* Auckland University Press, 1975.

King, C. M. (ed.), *The Handbook of New Zealand Mammals,* Oxford University Press in association with the Mammal Society, New Zealand Branch, Auckland, 1990.

Knox, R. (ed.), *New Zealand's Nature Heritage* (series), Hamlyn, Auckland, 1974–76.

Malcolm, B. and Malcolm, J., *The Forest Carpet,* Craig Potton Publishing, Nelson, 1989.

Mark, A. F. and Adams, N. M., *New Zealand Alpine Plants,* Reed Methuen, Revised edn., Auckland, 1986.

McDowall, R. M., *New Zealand Freshwater Fishes,* Octopus, Auckland, 1990.

Miller, D., *Common Insects in New Zealand,* Reed, Revised edn., Auckland, 1984.

Morris, R. and Smith, H., *Wild South: saving New Zealand's endangered birds,* TVNZ in association with Century Hutchinson, Auckland, 1988.

Morton, J., Hughes, T. and Macdonald, I., *To Save a Forest: Whirinaki,* David Bateman, Auckland, 1984.

O'Brien, C., *AA Book of New Zealand Wildlife: a guide to the native and introduced animals of New Zealand,* Lansdowne Press, Auckland, 1981.

Parkinson, B. and Cox, G., *A Field Guide to New Zealand's Lakes and Rivers,* Random Century, Auckland, 1990.

Peat, N. P., *The Incredible Kiwi,* Random Century in association with TVNZ, Auckland, 1990.
Poole, A. L., *Southern Beeches,* Science Information Publishing Centre, DSIR, Wellington, 1987.
Poole, A. L. and Adams, N. M., *Trees and Shrubs of New Zealand,* DSIR Publishing, Revised edn., Wellington, 1990.
Reader's Digest, *Reader's Digest Complete Book of New Zealand Birds,* Reed Methuen, Auckland, 1985.
Robb, J., *New Zealand Amphibians and Reptiles,* Collins, revised edn., Auckland, 1986.
Rowe, R. J., *The Dragonflies of New Zealand,* Auckland University Press, 1987.
Rudge, M. R. (ed.), *Moas, Mammals and Climate in the Ecological History of New Zealand,* New Zealand Journal of Ecology, No. 12 (supplement), New Zealand Ecological Society, Christchurch, 1989.
Salmon, J. T., *The Native Trees of New Zealand,* Heinemann Reed, Revised edn., Auckland, 1986.
Stephenson, G., *Wetlands: discovering New Zealand's shy places,* Government Printing Office Publishers, Wellington, 1986.
Stevens, G., McGlone, M. and McCullough, B., *Prehistoric New Zealand,* Heinemann Reed, Auckland, 1988.
Taylor, M., *Mushrooms and Toadstools,* Reed, Wellington, 1981.
Towns, D. R., Daugherty, C. H. and Atkinson, I. A. E. (eds.), *The Ecological Restoration of New Zealand Islands,* Conservation sciences publication no. 2, Dept. of Conservation, Wellington, 1990.
Walsby, J., *Nature Watching at the Beach,* Wilson and Horton, Auckland, 1990.
Wardle, J. A., *The New Zealand Beeches: ecology, utilisation and management,* New Zealand Forest Service, Wellington, 1984.
Webb, C. J., Johnson, P. N. and Sykes, B., *Flowering Plants of New Zealand,* DSIR Botany, Christchurch, 1990.
Westerskov, K. and Probert, K., *The Seas around New Zealand,* Reed, Wellington, 1981.
Wilson, C. M. and Given, D. R., *Threatened Plants of New Zealand,* DSIR Publishing, Wellington, 1989.
Winterbourn, M. J. and Gregson, K. L., *Guide to the Aquatic Insects of New Zealand,* Entomological Society of New Zealand, Auckland, 1989.
Viner, A. B. (ed.), *Inland Waters of New Zealand,* Science Information Publishing Centre, DSIR, Wellington, 1987.

PHOTOGRAPHIC NOTES

The author's photographs were taken using Olympus OM2 and OM4 camera bodies, fitted predominantly with one of three lenses, these being 50 mm (macro), 80 mm (macro) amd 100 mm. Flash lighting was used for many of the smaller and more active subjects, to overcome the dual problems of limited depth of field and subject movement. Kodachrome 64 or 25 films were used almost exclusively, because of their faithful and high-quality rendition. Fujichrome Velvia film was used for the high-speed photography of flying insects.

The photography of flying insects required solving a number of technical hurdles, which took about 2 years to master. Among the various complexities involved was a flight-tunnel, wired with a network of light beams and photo-cell detectors. These light beams, each sensitive enough to be triggered by a falling pin, operated the shutter and flash systems at the precise moment the insect entered the field of view. The shutter was modified to open rapidly and mounted externally on the camera, the conventional SLR shutter having been locked open. Lighting was provided by a series of specially built flash guns, capable of producing a powerful but extremely short light pulse of about 1/40,000 second duration — about 40 times shorter than that provided by conventional flash equipment. This light pulse was sufficiently brief to freeze wing movement of the insect, yet bright enough to expose 50 ASA film at f16. Despite all the elaborate electronics, success was still not assured. As with all nature photography, good results came only from endless patience and many rolls of film — not to mention a supply of replacement flash tubes, which were expected to perform well beyond specifications.

GLOSSARY

Algae: Members of a large group of simple plants, mainly aquatic, which include seaweeds and many single-celled members of the phytoplankton.

Amphipod: Member of the Amphipoda, an order of animals belonging to the Crustacea. Example: sandhopper.

Annual: A plant which completes its life cycle and dies within 1 year.

Arthropod: A member of the Arthropoda, the largest phylum in the animal kingdom. Includes crabs, spiders, insects, millipedes, etc., which are characterised by having a hard, jointed exoskeleton.

Bacteria: Microscopic, typically single-celled organisms, of relatively simple internal organisation. Are very important in the process of decay. A few are renowned as agents of disease.

Blue-green algae: A group of micro-organisms related to bacteria but which are able to photosynthesise. Also called cyanobacteria.

Brachiopod: A member of the Brachiopoda, a phylum of marine animals. They have a two-valved shell, giving them a superficial resemblance to bivalve molluscs, although the groups are not closely related.

Bract: A small, often modified leaf at the base of a flower.

Broadleaved: Term referring to a member of the flowering trees, for example, rata, beech or tawa.

Bryozoans: Members of the phylum Ectoprocta (formerly Bryozoa), a group of small aquatic animals that often grow as colonies attached to rocks and other surfaces.

Canopy: The upper foliage layer of a particular plant community.

Carapace: The shield of exoskeleton covering part of the body of certain animals, such as crabs.

Carnivore: An animal that eats other animals.

Cilia: Fine microscopic threads that project from the cells of certain organisms. By lashing at surrounding fluid, cilia provide a means of propulsion.

Coevolution: Process whereby different organisms that interact with one another also tend to adapt to one another. For example, the coevolution of certain flowers and their pollinating insects.

Community: A group of different plants and animals that inhabit a shared environment and interact with one another.

Cone: Reproductive structure of a conifer, for example, a pine cone.

Conifer: A cone-bearing tree; a member of the Gymnophyta (formerly Gymnospermae).

Convergent evolution: Process whereby unrelated organisms evolve increasing similarities in certain characteristics. Often occurring in organisms that live in similar environments. The similar body shapes of fish and dolphins is an example.

Copepod: A member of the Copepoda, a group of crustaceans often important as members of the zooplankton.

Crustacean: A member of the Crustacea, a class of arthropods including crabs, crayfish, barnacles, etc.

Crustal plate: One of the semi-rigid plates of which the Earth's crust is believed to consist of. These plates move with respect to one another, providing the means for continental drift.

Cuticle: The outer covering of some plants and animals. In plants the cuticle is a waxy layer that reduces water loss. In arthropods the cuticle provides a hard protective exoskeleton that is shed periodically.

Cyanobacteria: See blue-green algae.

Diatoms: A group of microscopic algae abundant in the phytoplankton. They possess finely sculptured cell walls of silica or lime.

Divaricate: An unusual growth habit whereby plants branch freely and at wide angles, to produce a sometimes interlacing mass of stems, with leaves held protectively within the interior.

DNA: Deoxyribonucleic acid, a complex chemical that functions as a blue-print for the synthesis of proteins and is capable of replication. The chemical forms the genetic material of organisms.

Ecology: The study of the relationship between organisms and their environment.

Ecosystem: Inclusive term for a community of organisms and the non-living environment (soil, climate, etc.) with which it interacts, for example, a forest or a pond.

Embryo: An early developmental stage of an organism, produced from a fertilised egg.

Endemic: Found only in a given region or country. The takahe, for instance, is endemic to New Zealand, as it lives nowhere else.

Enzyme: A protein produced by organisms to speed up the rate of a chemical reaction. Enzymes, for example, often assist the break-down of organic compounds so they can be utilised for food.

Epiphyte: A non-parasitic plant that grows on another plant.

Eutrophication: Pollution of water resulting from an abundant supply of mineral nutrients. Permits excessive plant growth which can disrupt the natural community.

Evolution: The process of genetic change, occurring in successive generations, which results largely from natural selection. It has led to the present diversity of living things.

Exoskeleton: Skeleton covering the outside of the body, for example, the hard jointed casing of insects.

Exotic: Not native, having originated from a foreign country, for example salmon and blackbirds in New Zealand.

Family: A unit of classification, consisting of related genera.
Fauna: The total set of animal species found in a particular area.
Flagella: Fine threads projecting from the cells of certain organisms, longer than cilia, which by lashing at the surroundings aids movement.
Flora: The total set of plant species in a particular area.
Flowering plant: A seed-bearing plant, whose reproductive structures are flowers.
Food chain: A metaphorical chain of organisms, existing in a community, such that each link (organism) in the chain feeds on the one preceding it and is fed upon by the one following it. Grass–rabbit–stoat is a simple food chain.
Gall: An abnormal plant growth caused by certain parasitic insects, fungi or bacteria.
Gene: The basic unit of heredity, which is a particular portion of DNA of a chromosome.
Genus: A unit of classification, consisting of closely related species. For example, the black-billed gull (*Larus bulleri*) and red-billed gull (*Larus novaehollandiae*) are closely related species because they belong to the same genus, *Larus.*
Gondwana: The primaeval supercontinent which, over 140 million years ago, consisted of South America, South Africa, Australia, India, Antarctica, New Zealand and several other smaller landmasses joined together.
Gymnosperm: Member of the Gymnophyta, a group of seed plants, including the conifers, with seeds not enclosed in an ovary.
Habitat: Place in which specified organisms live — for example, a beach, or river.
Haemoglobin: Iron-containing red pigment, responsible for carrying oxygen in the blood.
Herb: A non-woody seed plant.
Herbivore: An animal that eats plants.
Host: An organism on or in which a different organism lives.
Hybrid: The offspring from a cross between parents of different genetic backgrounds, usually different species.
Indigenous: An organism which is native to a particular area or country, not introduced. For example, the kiwi is indigenous to New Zealand.
Inflorescence: A flowering shoot, bearing a cluster of flowers.
Insectivore: An animal that eats insects.
Introduced: An organism which is not native to an area and has been introduced. For example, the hedgehog has been introduced to New Zealand.
Invertebrate: A collective term for animals lacking a true backbone. Includes sea squirts, snails, crabs, starfish, anemones, insects, etc.
Larva: The pre-adult stage in the life cycle of some animals. Examples include a tadpole and a caterpillar.
Marsupial: A group of mammals, native to Australia, North and South America, which give birth to young in a very undeveloped state. The young usually continue their development within a pouch where they are fed milk.
Microclimate: The environment close enough to an object to be influenced by it.
Microhabitat: A habitat of restricted size.
Mollusc: A member of the Mollusca, a large phylum of animals which includes slugs, snails, shellfish, etc.
Mycorrhiza: An association of a plant root and a fungus, considered to often be of mutual benefit.
Natural selection: The principal causal mechanism of evolutionary change, whereby those individuals most suited to an environment survive and breed most successfully. This favours the transmission to the next generation of those genes most compatible with the prevailing environment.
Nectar: A sugary liquid secreted by many plants.
Niche: The structural and functional role of a species in its natural community.
Nocturnal: Active at night.
Nut: A dry, one-seeded fruit.
Omnivore: An animal that eats both plants and animals.
Nymph: Larval stage of insects such as dragonflies, mayflies and stick insects, which do not form a pupa (as do butterflies and flies). The nymph often resembles the adult but is sexually immature and has undeveloped wings.
Ovipositor: Egg-laying organ of insects, often a slender tube.
Ovule: The plant structure which contains female sex cells and develops into a seed after fertilisation.
Parasite: An organism living on or in another organism, from which it draws nourishment.
Pedipalps: Second head appendage of an arachnid. In spiders the male uses them for fertilisation.
Perennial: Plants that live for more than 2 years.
Pheromone: Chemical substances which some animals release into the air to influence the behaviour of others of the same species. Insects often release pheromones as sexual attractants.
Photosynthesis: The process in plants whereby solar energy is absorbed by the green pigment chlorophyll and used to build organic compounds from carbon dioxide and water.
Phylum: (plural phyla) A major unit of classification. Examples of phyla are Arthropoda, Echinodermata, Mollusca, etc.
Physiology: The study of the processes that go on within living organisms.
Phytoplankton: The plant members of plankton.

Plank buttress: The radial plank-like outgrowths found at the base of the trunks of some tree species. They help to support the trunk, particularly on swampy ground.

Plankton: The small, often microscopic plants and animals that float or drift in water.

Pollen: Minute grains shed by plants, each one of which is capable of giving rise to a male sex cell.

Pollination: The transfer of pollen from male to female reproductive organs of a plant. Afterwards, the male sex cell produced by the pollen fertilises the female sex cell.

Predator: A free-living organism that attacks and eats other organisms.

Pupa: In insects the stage between larva and adult, during which locomotion and feeding cease, but larval tissues break down and adult features develop.

Quiescent: An inactive state.

Refuge area: An area rich in types of plants and animals. Thought to have arisen because such areas escaped the full impact of the Ice Age.

Rhizome: A horizontal underground stem, producing buds that can give rise to roots and leafy shoots.

Saprophyte: An organism that feeds on the dead tissues of plants or animals.

Species: A basic unit of classification, referring to a group of very similar organisms that are capable of interbreeding.

Stamen: Male part of a flower which produces pollen.

Stigma: Female part of a flower which receives pollen.

Stomata: (singular stoma) The microscopic pores on the leaves and stems of plants that allow the exchange of gases.

Subspecies: A unit of classification below species. The subspecies of a species differ from one another and are often geographically separate, but interbreed readily if brought together.

Succession: The progressive and orderly change in composition of a community of organisms over time.

Succulent: Describing the thick and fleshy water-storing tissues of some plants.

Symbiosis: A close relationship between two different types of living organism.

Tendril: A slender, often coiling structure, developed from a leaf or stem, which some plants use for attachment to a support.

Treeline: The altitude limit on a mountain, above which trees do not grow.

Tribe: Unit of classification, comprising several related genera within a family.

Vascular system: Specialised plant tissue, consisting of tubular structures called xylem and phloem, which conducts water and nutrients between parts of the plant.

Vegetative reproduction: Propagation by asexual means. For example, the production of new plants from buds rather than seeds. Offspring are usually identical to the parent.

Vertebrate: Animals which possess a backbone and a skeleton of cartilage or bone. Includes the fishes, amphibians, reptiles, birds and mammals.

Waterfowl: A member of the family Anatidae, which includes duck, geese and swans.

Zooplankton: Animal members of the plankton.

INDEX

FIGURES IN BOLD REFER TO ILLUSTRATIONS.